The Silence of the Langford

Essays
(and some stories)
by
Dave Langford

with
an introduction by
Teresa Nielsen Hayden

NESFA Press
Post Office Box 809
Framingham, Massachusetts
01701-0809

ISBN: 0-915368-62-5   Library of Congress Catalog Card Number 96-69346
First Edition: September 1996
First printing: September 1996
Second printing (slighlty revised and corrected): December 1997

Less than 50% of the material in this book appeared in the Hugo-nominated *Let's Hear It for the Deaf Man*, NESFA Press, February 1992, 0-915368-50-1, a mimeographed chapbook. This current book reprints all the material from that book with the exception of "Stops and Starts," withdrawn by the author, and some very short 'filler' items.

First Appearance

Ansible Obituary, *Sglodion 1* ed. David Langford, 1989.

Ansible Hyperlink, *Interzone 94* ed. Charles Platt, 1995.

Ansible Review of the Year, speech at Conspiracy '87; *Pulp 6* ed. Avedon Carol, Rob Hansen, John Harvey & Vincent Clarke, 1987.[1]

Ansible Review of the Year: 1992, *Helicon Programme Book*, 1993.

Ansible Moose of the Year: 1994, *Confabulation Programme Book*, 1994.

The Arts of the Enemy, *Villains!* "created by" Mary Gentle & Neil Gaiman, ed. Mary Gentle & Roz Kaveney, 1992.

Best Foot Forward, *8000 Plus*, 1988; (revised) *Interzone 35* ed. David Pringle, 1990.[1]

Bio-Bibliography, *The Silence of the Langford*, NESFA Press, 1996.

Contrivances, *Contrivance Programme Book*, 1989.[1]

The Dragonhiker's Guide ... speech at Seacon '84; *Xyster 5* ed. Dave Wood, 1984.[1]

Endless Loops, *Pulp 12*, 1989.[1]

Fizz! Buzz!, *Trapdoor 6* ed. Robert Lichtman, 1986.[1]

Follies of '88, *Pulp 11*, 1989.[2]

Foodies of the Gods, speech at Helicon; *New York Review of Science Fiction 58* ed. Donald G. Keller and others, 1993.

Fun With Senseless Violence, speech at Orycon 11; *Diolch Yn Fawr* ed. David Langford, 1989.[1]

The Great Con, *The Caprician 3* ed. Lilian Edwards & Christina Lake, 1988.

Highballs!, *New York Review of Science Fiction 8*, 1989; (slightly revised) *Vector*, 1989.

Meanwhile, an Australian fanzine got hold of and published an entire poem by Stephen Donaldson Himself, cut for unspecified but guessable reasons from *White Gold Wielder*. Two lines of this describe the life of a reviewer:

> *Dead fishes could not him affright:*
> *He flailed at whales all the night.*

It was also Donaldson who, trying to do an archaic style in one of his short stories, accurately summarized the feelings of many reviewers who ventured into the labyrinth of the Covenant books without a fat dictionary: "Mayhap all unknowing I ate the mushroom of madness." I certainly get a craving for a quick snack of the mushroom of madness whenever I remember the most unforgettable (and oft-reprinted here) lines from *White Gold Wielder*:

> They were featureless and telic, like lambent gangrene. They looked horribly like children.

Another favourite line of rich, ripe poetry comes at the end of *Dragons of Autumn Twilight* by Margaret Weis, Tracy Hickman and a supporting cast of thousands: *Through his doomed veins the horizon burst....*

William McGonagall could hardly do better. Speaking of Williams, William Morris's fantasies were written a bit before the 1980s, but I read *The Water of the Wondrous Isles* quite recently and thought you might like to know how a real master handled the antique style. The story so far: our heroine has just repossessed a frock which had been swiped by a witch. She speaks to it thus:

> Nay, ye have been in ill company, I will wear you not, though ye be goodly, at least not till ye have been fumigated....

SOCIAL AWARENESS

Fantasy fans will have been interested to watch the gradual spread of equal rights in Piers Anthony's Xanth series. As the books went by, civil rights were extended to centaurs, to ogres, to nightmares and—dramatically—even to women. The seventh book, *Dragon on a Pedestal*, goes further to admit a zombie, though this does look like tokenism since the zombie in question is a fairly fresh one who hardly smells at all. I'm now waiting for the Xanth book in which a gay character successfully emerges from the closet. I'm trying not to imagine its wittily relevant, punning title....

Equally heart-warming is the military loyalty which inspires those crack mercenaries Hammer's Slammers, as already mentioned. They're so determined to do the job, and so fearful that seeming chicken-heartedness will prejudice their future contracts, that they nobly disobey their own horrified *employers'* orders to stop slaughtering people and detonating irreplaceable shrines. There's dedication for you.

Of course sexism has long been a sensitive issue in SF and fantasy: Greg Benford and David Brin are fearlessly prepared to expand our consciousness in *Heart of the Comet*, where women are innovatively characterized as "deliciously unpredictable" with "breasts hard and high."

In *Code of the Lifemaker*, James P. Hogan goes further still! This book features an evolved robot civilization with genders just like ours, and scores another first for science fiction with its bold prediction of robot sexism. Not only do all the female humans occupy subordinate roles, no female robot even gets a speaking part. This is, I *hope*, a bold stroke of satire....

Political differences are best treated with caution: one doesn't want to go round slagging every author who veers from the One True Politically Correct Way (i.e., mine). But I do jump up and down a bit on meeting a truly dishonestly loaded argument, as in the first and readable half of Heinlein's *The Cat Who Crapped Through Walls*. What happens is, this minor character gets all upset at the Moon's ideal libertarian society, and says wimpy things like "It's not fair" on discovering that if you can't pay the air charges you automatically die. The hero and Heinlein clearly disagree with this wishy-washy position: one grits one's teeth and allows as how they're entitled to their opinions. What makes me cringe is the way in which our aforementioned wimp, the only character in the entire book who thinks a few social services might be a good thing, is painstakingly established as obnoxious, sponging, a criminal and— ultimately—a traitor. More or less what you'd expect of the token Jew in an SF novel by Adolf Hitler.

Finally, Isaac Asimov's *Robots and Empire* makes the mistake of adding a sequel to a trilogy which had seemed perfectly complete and self-contained for about 40 years ... the trilogy being the Three Laws of Robotics. The new Zeroth Law is a dazzling step forward, allowing robots to get away with more than ever before, since it translates roughly as: "Whatever the other laws may say, stuff them: the end justifies the means." Oddly enough, Asimov doesn't seem worried about this.

GREAT MOMENTS IN CHARACTERIZATION

Piers Anthony, in *Blue Adept*, offers my all-time favourite doubletake as the hero threads his way down remote underground passages to confront the monstrous Worm (or Slug, or whatever it was) which has slain all previous applicants. Well, gosh, he thinks, here comes the big struggle, I'd better have my sword at the ready. Oops, I seem to have forgotten it. Well, too late to turn back now.

I'm sure you'll be relieved to hear that he wins anyway.

One of my pet theories is that Anthony's characters, with their world-famous slowness to understand things, are based on the creations of the great Lionel Fanthorpe:

> What the devil could it be? he asked himself over and over again. He drew closer, and closer still. Then he recognized the peculiar gleaming object for what it was—a door handle!

Picky reviewers keep demanding that SF characters should not only be subtly drawn but should also be capable of changing as a result of the story they live through. Messrs Niven and Pournelle have a sensitive example of this in (again) *Footfall*, where in the aftermath of alien attack an ecologist loudly repents his foolish opposition to Star Wars (SDI) weapon systems. My God, he says, what a cretin I was, how lacking in elementary foresight, we were *bound* to need them to fight off invading aliens some day! And he very soon gets a chance to demonstrate his new commitment by drowning a less committed journalist in a handy toilet.

GREAT SCIENTIFIC INSIGHTS

It's usually easy to find some apparent cock-up in the average hard SF novel, but for a long time I had a theory that authors, being wholly godlike beings, probably knew something I didn't. I had the chance to put this to the test when on a panel with William Gibson: to subtly draw him out, I asked about a passage in *Count Zero* that had bothered me. Since it takes sixteen whole seconds for the dreaded "black ice" computer defence to eat into an unfortunate hacker's nervous system and fibrillate him to death, it doesn't sound all that lethal: surely some sort of dead-man switch would give complete protection? Mr Gibson turned on me, and quick as a flash he snapped back: "Uh, I don't know, I hadn't thought of that." Then he went all silent and broody for the panel's remaining forty minutes.

There's a much dafter notion in a recent book of supposedly serious futurology, *The 2024 Report* by Norman Macrae. He says that the threat of nuclear war will be ended by "telecommuted computer messages" which you beam at approaching ballistic missiles, whereupon they turn around and head back for their launch silos. As you know, all the best missiles have radio receivers, easy-to-crack command languages, and lots of spare fuel in case they need to make a return trip.

Colin Wilson has probably read J. B. S. Haldane's 1927 essay explaining why giant insects don't make scientific sense, but this didn't prevent him from writing the deeply silly *Spider World*, in which oppressed humanity groans under the lash of giant death spiders. "The spider," writes Wilson, "is the only living creature that spends its life lying in wait, hoping that victims will walk into its trap." It would be a mite pedantic to complain that several beasties including ant lions do just the same ... at least, it would be pedantic if it weren't that Wilson has apparently forgotten writing about an ant lion doing its stuff just eight pages previously.

Alfred Bester's perhaps never been the most rigorously scientific of authors, and in *The Deceivers* he gave us the interesting idea of an electric fence charged up to 1500 million volts: all I can say is, to hold a potential like that it must be a damn' well insulated electric fence. The book's other scientific innovation is crystallized helium.

John Brunner's *Interstellar Empire* (admittedly an early work) contains a subtle bit of environmental adaptation:

> A slave with the hot brown skin of a Marzon and the twitch-
> ing eyes of a man born under a variable star.

You know the way those pesky variable stars hurt your eyes, as they flicker like celestial strobe lights.

Walter Tevis, in *The Steps of the Sun*, improved on safe sex by giving us "safe uranium" ... which lies around on this far planet in mountain-sized chunks and doesn't become radioactive until you magnetize it. I think Tevis must have got this from one of the different periodic tables used by the aliens in *Battlefield Earth*—which novel probably sets some kind of record for lousy science, but I've been over that ground in another and even more boring talk.

Science fiction, however, can never quite equal the real thing. In that famous textbook *The Gold of the Gods*, the coldly logical Erich von Däniken points to a photograph of a human skeleton carved in stone ... and asks incredulously how, without instruction courses from ancient astronauts, stupid "heathens" could possibly have known what a human skeleton looked like? "As we know, Roentgen did not discover X rays until 1895!"

CREAKY PLOTS

Some sort of record in plotting is set by Robert Vardeman's and Victor Milan's six-book sequence *The War of Powers*. After finishing it I felt I'd spent a week at Butlin's listening to Muzak while eating nothing but monosodium-glutamate-flavoured crisps. It's 968 pages of junk food for the mind, and it doesn't half give you indigestion.

It also gives you precognitive powers, in the form of an eerie ability to predict the plot far in advance. Gosh, the hero and heroine are going to meet after long separation—looks like their interim lovers will have to be killed off—yep, there they go, both of them. Gosh, two major villains are written off in book 4 after plummeting from great heights, yet *no one saw them land*.... Yep, here they are, luxuriating in new villainies for book 5.

Connoisseurs of fantasy hackwork will also enjoy the random variations in magic ability with the needs of the plot. One moment it's, "Alas, my powers are weak so far from my home city...." A few pages later, when said powers have got the authors out of a tight spot by doing something totally unprecedented, the explanation is, "My powers have grown with practice." As if this weren't enough, there's also an emergency plot-twiddling device called the Destiny Stone which—like red kryptonite in Superman comics—exists solely to account for ludicrous improbabilities.

Unfortunately there isn't a Destiny Stone in Frank and Brian Herbert's *Man of Two Worlds*, to account for the fact that the Dreen, omnipotent alien mind-masters, are helpless to withstand one mind-rotting earthly substance—basil.

Piers Anthony, who seems to be getting a lot of mentions today, introduced a cunning plot device in his novel *Refugee*: the airlock that doesn't lock. Because you can't lock the airlock, space-pirates have it easy: they just haul alongside and board the hero's refugee craft for several chapters of cruelly overwritten rape, loot and pillage. So popular a pastime is space-piracy, and so impossible is the invention of a lockable airlock, that our hero's ship is harrowingly raped, looted and pillaged no fewer than eight times in 333 pages. Crowded place, space.

Onward! Just as Heath Robinson's gadgets are held together with tatty lengths of knotted string, so a really unconvincing SF plot needs to be tied up with frayed threads of coincidence. I enjoyed watching a master plot-bodger at work in Anne McCaffrey's *Killashandra*, whose heroine arrives on a strange planet and promptly nips out in search of bootleg beer. As she takes her first swig there's a coincidental police raid, forcing her to take refuge in a randomly chosen house where, coincidentally, the chap is waiting who wants to kidnap her, whip her away and maroon her on an island lost in a vast archipelago. Undaunted she escapes to another island, which coincidentally is about to be visited by the erstwhile kidnapper, who coincidentally fails to recognize his victim and falls in love with her instead. And so on: it all has a certain lurching, ramshackle charm.

But it's hard to beat the ingenious plot device of Asimov's *Robots and Empire*, a diabolical gadget which for extremely complicated financial reasons must operate for fully 150 years to make the Earth's surface radioactive. But, enquires a particularly cunning henchman, *suppose somebody turns it off before then?* The moustachio-twirling arch-villain's answer, translated from the pseudoscience, is: "Har har, fear not, I'm putting a padlock on the controls."

I'm glad to report that there were a few fine works amongst all the grot. Indeed, a few of those mentioned above are pretty good despite odd lapses: *Heart of the Comet*, for example, which David Brin keeps telling me was squeezed off this year's Hugo ballot only by the overwhelming popularity of *Black Genesis*. Plenty of inoffensive books haven't been mentioned at all: unfortunately, as that man Amis once put it, long extracts demonstrating inoffensiveness can be wearisome. Or to phrase it another way, it's easy to spot a spider on the wall of a room but very hard to prove the room is spider-free. It's easy to point out evidence that an author has cocked it up—not so easy to convince you that a whole book is not only free of incidental cock-ups but also positively good. Let's just say that the two best books I've read this year are John Crowley's *Aegypt* and Jonathan Carroll's *Bones of the Moon*. Your mission, should you choose to accept it, is to decide whether you agree.

I don't unfortunately have time to say anything about the really *legendary* bad books which are so bad that they never even got published. American fans pass round a famous yarn called *The Eye of Argon*—the Eye in question being "the jewel protruding from the idol's eye socket, its masterfully cut faucets [*sic*] emitting blinding rays of hypnotizing beauty." Go to the bar, buy a drink for someone who's worked at reading old slushpiles, and they will tell you about the Piers Anthony manuscripts which even Grafton won't print. One of these fabled turkeys is reportedly called *Mercycle*. It is all about mermaids on bicycles. 'Nuff said.

When Conspiracy is over I'll be trudging back to the endless prairie of review copies, where all the plots start to look the same, where all the *titles* start to look the same ... one recent parcel contained three fantasies by two different authors sharing the same publisher, and they were called *The Wizards and the Warriors*, *The Wordsmiths and the Warguild* and *The Wizard and the Warlord*, and I moaned and hid them all under the desk. You're all probably feeling just this ghastly sameness after listening to an hour of me—so let's stop.

Thank you all.

1987

A major critical error appears near the end of this tirade: the supposition that there was a Piers Anthony book too awful to be published. To universal screams of disbelief, Mercycle *has since appeared.*

Follies of '88

THE CONVENTIONAL WISDOM

Very early in their productive lives, fans learn that convention reports can be infused with remarkable cool and street credibility by avoiding such mundane topics as the convention. Staying in the bar and overhearing gossip is merely the first twist of the focussing wheel which will eventually provide that totally original and unpredictable view of the proceedings. To dwell at length on petri-dish breakfast food and Krakatoa bowel movements is always innovative and worthwhile; but true masters of the form will be careful to fill most of their report with minute descriptions of How I Got There and, if appropriate, How I Got Back Home. This is the approved formula for witty and individual reportage, as used by all the best practitioners. Six million fanwriters can't be wrong.

It's thus embarrassing to realize that virtually the only memories I brought back from Follycon last Easter involved the journey home. (Pause for standard excuse about total euphoria during the con itself, meant not so much to be believed as to avert destroying lightning bolts from Follycon committee folk too numerous to mention but largely called Alison.)

Ah, it all comes back, that endless Monday-afternoon rail journey. Geoff Ryman had a reserved seat but was too nice to kick out the dear little white-haired lady pretending with great thespian ineptitude to be asleep therein.

"No," Mr Ryman said nobly, "I'll slum with you lot in steerage."

We found seats, and Geoff leaned back in languorous anticipation of a long snooze after staying up all Sunday night, and the padded back of the seat fell irrevocably off. Behind was a lethal-looking cluster of edged metal brackets and mediaeval pointy bits. It was a bad train for tall fans, Geoff sitting sternly bolt-upright for the whole trip while Dermot Dobson, unable to do likewise because of injuries on the spinal frontier, groaningly paced the aisle and at set intervals rolled up his shirt to show off the surgical corset. This was on the whole less revolting than Martin Hoare's very similar gesture, repeated through the weekend, which allowed you to relish the interesting stigmata of his chicken-pox. A sickly lot, fandom.

As Robert Holdstock likes to claim after recounting some particularly awful incident of youth, I was not as sensible then as I am now.

Much later in 1988 I laid the groundwork for a heavily travel-oriented con report by attending the World Fantasy Convention in short bursts via commuter train—a grave mistake, not least because it reminded me of the Follycon incident so embarrassing and repercussive that I didn't want to sign my name to any account of it....

THE BOTTOM LINE

It was a convention, Jim, but not as we know it. I was braced for the fact that World Fantasy Convention really means World Horror Convention, but not wholly for the further translation to World Horror Professionals' Trade Fair For People With Expense Accounts.

Penetrating this event was an act more frustrating than it might sound, since the West London Ramada Hotel's front wall had this long row of glass doors, all offering delusive glimpses of Ian Watson drinking beer and all, as it eventually turned out, locked.... In the bar I found Bob Shaw, who piteously cried "A fan!" and babbled awhile of eldritch hotel prices beyond the grasp of sanity. In the book room, Greg Pickersgill was brewing blasphemous, unspeakable theories, which he then spoke, of convention profitability at fifty quid a head and whose pockets he thought were being lined. (I cannot believe his horrid insinuation that this high-turnover professional event doesn't publish accounts.) Terry Pratchett related with glee how he, Bob and Harry Harrison had requested beer to fuel them for a panel, only for the Gopher In Charge to explain it was soft drinks only because, "We're trying to make a profit, you know." It must have been the huge influx of famous American authors and publishers which made everyone go on, and on, about money.

Soon I saw the bright side of this, when famous American publisher Dave Hartwell lured me off for lunch. At last the gravy train had stopped at my station. Yes, he and Kathryn Cramer wanted to commission a major piece for ... *The New York Review of SF*? Sure enough, Mr Hartwell was exercising his vestigial fan credentials, and even permitted me to pay for my own food.

Returning from this spree, I was nobbled by evil Harry Harrison, who lured me with beer from the straight and narrow path, sat me with spurious friendliness at his side, and conveyed via his usual genial mix of spittle and animal impressions the words, "I've always wanted to make this introduction, Dave!" From across the table came a slow voice saying, "I've read your reviews of me," and I gazed into the argute visage of Stephen R. Donaldson. It is merely to be recorded that my heart did before too long resume its beating.

Free wine kept appearing in an endless succession of sponsored parties, clearly a good thing were it not that I missed all the later and more debauched ones through having to run for my train exactly as London SF fandom moved in for large-scale gatecrashing. The first time I looked into the main programme, it was full of a mass autograph session hampered just slightly by the shortage of mere credulous fans to beg the autographs. (A scheduled reading by six *Interzone* stalwarts was later dropped at the discovery that the audience was outnumbered by, well, six to one.)

Next time I noticed the programme, an extraordinary mid-afternoon banquet plus awards ceremony was in progress—allegedly the highlight of the convention. Its actual £20-a-head food was reputedly invested with all the bowel-churning terrors perfected by the Union of Hotel Caterers; the cruellest rumour concerned a table mix-up which led to three mere fans, possibly the only persons present who'd actually paid for the meal themselves, being bumped from their places in mid-hors d'oeuvres. I believe the committee gave them some alcoholic compensation, but Charlie Brown and Andy Porter were later beset with suggestions for striking *Locus* and *SF Chronicle* headlines based on the fact that one of these unfortunates was called Stephen King. Lots of people won awards; the Ramsey Campbell Award (as the British Fantasy trophy is affectionately known) went to Ramsey Campbell, and Karl Edward Wagner walked out in strong hysterics because—if I interpreted him correctly— David Hartwell had given too many awards to David Hartwell.

In some ways it was probably a good trade fair, replete with luxury, freebies, influential business contacts and smoke-filled rooms. A mere change of name might eliminate the bewilderment and recriminations arising from the fact that many fans understand something slightly different by the word "convention". On my final, empty-pocketed journey home (note the traditional demands of this classic literary form) I was saved from rail-borne dehydration only by the solicitude of Diana Wynne Jones, who will be getting another rave review shortly.

The Plain People of Fandom: Is that all? What about the ever so embarrassing bit you mentioned?

Myself: Rats. I was hoping you'd forgotten that.

THE STATE OF THE ART

Despite my age and dignity I'm still not immune from totally cretinous actions, and Follycon saw one of my regular lapses. Given three tons of grubby papers to sign for contributors' and editors' copies of the Steve Jones/Kim Newman *100 Best Horror Novels* anthology of fave raves from the grave, I drunkenly allowed myself to be led astray by the wiles of Ramsey Campbell's daughter. The woman tempted me and I did sign, adding an extra L. Ron Hubbard on this sheet, a spurious H. P. Lovecraft on that.... Reader, be warned that such momentary follies can make life bad for a long, long time.

After a terrific wigging from S. Jones, I managed to blot my crime from memory. (OK, I'm not wholly bad, I did offer to locate sufficient contributors to the book who had sufficient compassion and/or sense of humour to accept copies with signed endpapers "defaced" by the abominable Langford.) Guilt surged up all over again at the rumour—gleefully passed on via the Malcolm Edwards transatlantic gossip line—that Harlan Ellison himself was going to kill me for this. Guilt geysered from my ears at the news that the surplus multi-signed copies were to be sold to idiot collectors at one hundred bloody pounds. "Suddenly," as Steve wrote to me in an otherwise almost forgiving letter, "it doesn't seem so funny any more, does it?" Er, no, squire.

The book was much in evidence at the Fantasycon, though with Grafton-like acumen the publishers had made actual copies hard to find—limited to specimens of the amazing super special expensive edition which turned up at a late-night launch party while I was on a train, and faded again at the light of day. This party saw the great alleged Pickersgill/Pringle Purloining Project, eagerly related by Steve and Kim to everyone who would listen: "They tried to nick books costing £100 each" is one story, and "You expect the books lying round at a launch party to be freebies" is the other.

Next day I had a glimpse of Neil Gaiman's copy, and was furtively relieved to find that late authors like M. R. James and Robert E. Howard had also signed—officially—via astral rubber stamp; while my own acts of folly were as nothing to the inadvertence of those who'd signed too near the edge and run into trimming trouble (half a Brian Aldiss here, two outlying loops of an otherwise missing signature there, like dismembered relics of who knows what foul crime). And what was this rumour that Ramsey Campbell Himself had succumbed once or twice to the same loathsome temptation as me? Or that ... but let's not be contentious, since the recriminations are now past.

Thus my embarrassing confession for this issue. I still cringe a little at the memory of those fraught months between Easter and Hallowe'en. Reader, know that promiscuous forgery leads to no good, and desist!

(Signed)

Claude Degler.

1989

Endless Loops

"Software," said Charles Platt in menacing tones, "is a *disease*. Never get into software, Dave."

I laughed. They laughed when I sat at the keyboard, but then I started to hack the operating system. There comes a turning point in life when with horror you find yourself thinking, If (DayOfWeek=Thursday) and (DayOfMonth in [15..21]) then DoBSFAmeeting; ... with a semicolon. It is a bad sign when you end sentences with semicolons.

The program counter clicked to the next instruction. If BSFAMeeting and (Month=January) and FoolishPromiseToPaulKincaid[November] then OhShit;

I was a featured speaker. I had been writing nothing but software for a solid month, and my brain was firmly embedded in one of those spaces that Bill Gibson writes about but never, never visits. I ported myself along a British Rail communications interface to the Paddington data terminal and ... stop that ... got to the celebrated BSFA pub. Buzzing fragments of indexing routines were milling behind my eyes before I'd so much as touched a drop, while before my eyes was Gamma, who had touched a drop.

"Accept data," this SF landmark seemed to say. "I am now Barrington J. Bayley's literary agent. Data entry terminates." He fell over.

Unreality error in central processor, I thought. Some ideas are too perfect and appropriate to be spoiled like this by coming true.

"What's happening tonight?" "I think it's a slide show." "What?" "The barman said." "No, Langford's talking." "Oh, *him*." "What about?"

"Himself. As usual," interposed Greg Pickersgill.

Thinks: If I open my mouth, all that will come out is 64 kilobytes of hex core dump and error messages.

"Slide show ...?" "Gosh, they've arranged the chairs in rows for us. They never did that for the BSFA before." "Langford's going to...."

"Who are you lot?" said the new arrival with the slide projector, before anyone could ask him to renew his membership.

"You didn't confirm your booking," added an implacable barman shortly afterwards, logic centres firmly locked against unauthorized tampering. Had he taken massive bribes from slide-show organizers? No, once again it seemed that a committee person had faithfully followed the traditional BSFA algorithm of If AllSeemsWell then Repeat DoNothing until CockUp;

61

Over the ensuing squabble came doomy Pickersgillian rumbles of "THIS IS SHABBY! THIS IS SUPPOSED TO BE A NATIONAL ORGANIZATION!"

I huddled in a corner, trying to scrape semicolons from the ends of my thoughts and wondering if I was going to be let off. But Gamma was slurring into a telephone with the resource and acumen which has made him what he is today (i.e., a man whose income is 10% of poverty-stricken Barry Bayley's). In mere minutes, powerful data compression routines had squeezed the entire meeting into the legendary Troy Club.

This, as will emerge, was all too appropriate. A venue resembling the Black Hole of Calcutta though less airy and wholesome, the Troy Club is best known as the site of innumerable launch parties for Brosnan/Kettle collaborations called things like *Spew* and *Secretions*. "You should join," secreted Gamma, fondling a representative of the management. "All sorts of SF people are members. Terry Pratchett, and, er, me ... and there's Terry Pratchett, and whatisname who writes those Discworld books, and, and...."

System in naked terror mode, I conveyed. Unable to accept input. Mr Kincaid had decided I was giving a talk after all. The eager BSFA crowd was pressed hard against my chest, making it something of a challenge to draw breath and hold them spellbound. I duly failed to hold them spellbound with the story of the unpublished *Guts!*—called by Ramsey Campbell "The first horror novel I don't even dare to read!"—which had become the first horror novel that even Grafton Books don't dare to publish.

(They accepted and paid for it in 1987; by the week of that BSFA meeting they'd just ticked their way into breach of contract for non-publication. Over the last year the authors have fielded upwards of eight hundred enquiries about publication date—six of them not from Neil Gaiman—by advising that seekers after truth write to Grafton editor Nick Austin and bother him. Nick himself dives under tables and out of windows when he sees me coming.)

Better to draw a veil over my reading from the *Guts!* chapters tastefully called "The Chyme of Midnight" and "The Lights Are Going Out", which probably went Repeat ReadWordNotLoudEnough; If EndOfSentence then PauseNotLongEnough; until EndOfMS; ... Like that but less terse and exciting. My audience seemed to be many echoing miles distant, a neat trick in a bar scarcely larger than a British Rail toilet.

Eventually firm hands were pressing beer on me, too late to lubricate thoughts still all tangled in algorithms and program loops. Abi Frost and Avedon Carol united to claim the existence of deep structural flaws in the programming of my outmoded hairstyle. I tried to explain to Owen Whiteoak that he'd taken and quoted with ghastly seriousness a remark ("Do we all have to gafiate now?") which I'd made with cheerful irony. He looked blank, as so frequently he does. I failed to convince Paul Kincaid that important parts of me seemed to have been left behind in random-access memory. Gamma gave an impressive demonstration of how much spittle he could balance in his beard before falling over again. Greg Pickersgill probably said something. I probably misheard it.

Next morning, eyes still not quite in focus (which had been routine for two weeks), I toyed with the idea, glimpsed dimly at the BSFA thrash, of writing some science fiction. But the programming work was calling and there was no time. Charles Platt was right, you know.

```
If (Software=Disease)....
If (Blood=PriceOfAdmiralty)....
Question:= (ToBe) or (Not ToBe)....
```

Is anyone out there well-informed on the cold turkey cure?

1989

I don't know why Kipling's line about blood and admiralty sneaked in here, but hope that this note will at least stop people asking. (Somewhere in the Amber series, a Zelazny hero enters severely wounded and remarks with Total Cool and Implausibility, "If blood be the price of admiralty, I've just bought me a naval commission.") The good news about Guts! *is that in 1993, now working for another publisher, Nick Austin clamoured to see it again. The bad news is that he rejected it. It was Nick who sent me the still-treasured letter usefully informing me that he'd been sitting on a (different) book submission for five years. I had, in fact, been aware of this.*

Some Informal Remarks Toward the Punctuational Calculus

I'm honoured to be so acknowledged by Orycon State University, for my research work in punctuation ... one of the few areas where Britain still leads the world. (The other one is books about the Queen.)

Of course it was an American research team which first managed to completely and utterly split the infinitive, and your big-budget facilities like the Del Rey laboratories have succeeded in producing and publishing the tiniest subliterary particles. How thrilled we all were when the *New York Review of Science Fiction* used critical path analysis to show that the structure of *Dhalgren* is a double helix—a breakthrough which promises that one day we'll crack the semiotic code and discover what it's about. American achievements all: but Britain still proudly maintains the largest breeding group of semicolons in captivity.

It's thanks to our punctuation research that the British Isles have produced fanzines with names like *Hyphen, Slant, Dot,* and *Llanfairpwllgwyngyllgogerychwyrndrobwllllantysiliogogogoch*—which is Welsh for "asterisk."

I must take this opportunity to dispel the ugly rumours about my own research work, in particular that brutal experiments have been conducted on live question marks and that unqualified staff are allowed to perform irrigation of colons. We carry out vivisection only on *volunteer* punctuation marks, all of which are first completely anaesthetized by immersing them in copies of *Analog*. This induces a profound stupor, or as we call it in the trade, a comma.

Our latest achievement is the world's first trans-punctuational surgery, carried out on a schizophrenic double-quote mark which turned out to be a pair of linked Siamese apostrophes—now living happy separate lives in different sentences.

Another exciting project is our attempt to synthesize a completely new symbol which will look blurred but vaguely convincing no matter where it appears, and can thus be inserted whenever you're not sure what the right punctuation is. We have an advance order for four billion of these, from Harry Harrison.

When Michael Bishop and I were guests at Orycon in 1989, the crazed committee thought it a jolly droll idea to make the opening ceremony a formal induction into their university faculty, and some appropriate remarks were requested. This is still not sufficient excuse.

To conclude my words of thanks, I'd like to give you a live demonstration of how Britons use what you call a period and we call a full stop.

1989

Fun With Senseless Violence

As it says—or ought to say—in the programme, my subject this evening is weaponry and senseless violence, which is why there are quite a lot of you listening in this big hall. If I'd made the mistake of giving a talk with a feeble title like "Peace in Science Fiction", we'd be much cosier in a much smaller room, all six of us. This is called knowing your market.

Yes, it's a truism that all too much of the science fiction scene is scarred by vast tracts of destruction left in the wake of colossal future armies and space-fleets, all bristling with ultimate doomsday weapons which seem to need as little reloading as those six-guns in the Western movies—you know, the ones that turn out to be at least 256-guns. For this one hour the committee has given us permission to revel in merry thoughts of global war and military supremacy, before getting back to sober realities of life like the Hugos and the Worldcon site selection.

To help you enrich your own lives with gratuitous science-fictional violence, I promise to give full instructions for building a lethal cold ray, to explain why all Isaac Asimov's robots are shamefully in violation of the First Law of Robotics, to reveal the logical power source behind the galaxy-busting artillery in your favourite space operas, and to mention L. Ron Hubbard.

Last year was a significant anniversary in my own career of senseless violence. It was just about 25 years before that I first strayed into a bookshop and was fascinated by the garish spaceships and death rays on the cover of Bertrand Russell's *History of Western Philosophy*. Fortunately I couldn't afford this, and bought a lot of cheap remaindered science fiction instead. My fate was sealed.

The first really bad results of SF obsession showed up in 1979, when, urged on by megalomania, flattery and electric cattle prods, I lost my convention-speech virginity, by giving a talk with the tasteful title "Genocide for Fun and Profit".

This was based on the first book I'd written all by myself, *War in 2080*, full of futuristic military hardware and destined to make an enormous splash in the international remainder market. Although it was supposed to be non-fiction, the book took its inspiration from SF ... which is the posh way of

---

Perhaps the original seed of this survey was a passage about sf side-arms in James Blish's classic More Issues at Hand: *"Harl Vincent invented one which covered you with hundreds of buzzing, spinning little black discs, which wore you rapidly down to nothing but a curl of greasy smoke; the wicked temptress in the story carried this in her index finger, a notion I am glad Freud died before encountering."*

saying I ripped off hordes of ideas from my favourite literature. Especially the sort of trigger-happy stuff where every minor skirmish sounds like this extract from my own very early story "Sex Pirates of the Blood Asteroid":

> A nearby galaxy exploded.
>
> And at that fateful signal, each of the arch-fiend Nivek's countless ships and planetary installations discharged the full, awesome power of its primary projectors, the blazing beams of destruction combining into a hellish flare of starkly incalculable incandescence against which no possible defence might prevail!
>
> Nivek snarled in rage. "Missed...."

You'll be glad to know that this villain is duly brought to book and made to face charges of "multiple genocide, ordinary genocide, genocide with mitigating circumstances, accidental genocide, genocide in self-defence" and many more.

One can't help noticing that fashions in genocide have changed over the years. Most writers are now a little bit more cautious than my mentor Doc Smith, who with schoolboyish enthusiasm used to let his clean-cut heroes wipe out every single member of every unfriendly race, thus ensuring that they wouldn't be tempted to do it again. Whatever it was. Afterwards, the victors could pronounce a simple but touching epitaph, such as "QX! Hot jets and clear ether! In sync to the skillionth of a whillionth of a nanosecond!"

With his very late book *Subspace Encounter*, there were signs that Doc Smith was developing posthumous qualms about all this. One of his characters actually remembers what it said in the Boy Scout Handbook and blurts out, "Genocide is supposed to be reprehensible." Unfortunately, his next word is: "But..."

Of course Britain's very own Robert Lionel Fanthorpe left out the But in his novel (if that's the word I'm groping for) *Power Sphere*. The verb in this book's very last speech has clearly influenced the jargon of the Pentagon: "'And that,' said Salford, with grim irony, 'is how Agent 1117 extincted a rather unpleasant race!'"

L. Ron Hubbard in *Battlefield Earth* rather felt that before wiping out a planetful of gooks and erasing their whole lousy biosphere, one should have some definite moral justification. He therefore made it clear that his fiendish "Psychlos" are aptly named, since they've allowed their brains to be adjusted by those hated cultists called psychiatrists—as opposed to the ideologically sound opposition, based in Los Angeles and East Grinstead.

The Orson Scott Card approach is substantially more humane. Here, after first slaughtering the tastefully named Buggers right down to the very last arthropod, his caring young hero consoles them by feeling, at great length, guilty about it. The resulting depth of emotion brought tears to my nostrils.

Both Joe Haldeman and James White, who are such notoriously nice guys, stop a long way short of this. Their favourite approach is to have it discovered—after only a fractional micro-genocide or so—that there has been a mistake. The original first contact message, saying something like "Greetings, Earthling scum! We come to annihilate you painfully and rape your planet," turns out to be a misprint. After shooting all their interpreters, both sides can live happily ever after.

Nobody could accuse Jack Chalker of being prejudiced—when he throws a genocide, *everyone's* invited. In the climactic Well World book, he shrewdly covers up his own spot of indiscriminate mass slaughter with a version of the traditional escape clause, "With one bound he was free!" Yes: having blasted the entire universe into a smoking heap of superstring fragments, he has it repaired again before anyone can notice. Well, replaced with a copy actually, but a really good one. Philosophers and TV scriptwriters love this kind of temporary total annihilation, since you can do it every week without spoiling series continuity.

Piers Anthony does something rather similar in *Being a Green Mother*, which admittedly is a fantasy but which deserves a mention here because of its contribution to the very scanty archives of Post-Genocide Dialogue. After the heroine has wiped all life from the Earth in a slightly overstated temper tantrum, we're faced with the burning question of what, precisely, should Mummy say to a daughter who's just obliterated the entire human race? The answer, from the Piers Anthony Book of Etiquette, is: "I think we should talk, dear."

For the sake of fairness I'd like to taunt more British authors, but unfortunately my compatriots rather tend to shirk the important issue of genocide, thanks to something which New York publishers call British gloom. Long before the cheerful interstellar slaughter can begin, your typical British future society has poetically gone down the tubes, owing to famine, plague, floods, triffids and reading too much J. G. Ballard.

I suppose the most worrying authors are those who, claiming to be inspired by the late great Robert Heinlein, explain that their alien heavies just have to be bombed into extinction because there is no choice—because they're the Universe's toughest, meanest, deadliest, most unrelenting critters, who in defence of their twisted, perverse views will fight on, tooth, nail and tentacle, asking no mercy and showing no quarter, so long as a single one survives.

This looks like quite a strong argument until you notice that the same authors tend to praise Man (rarely, for some strange reason, Woman) as the Universe's toughest, meanest, deadliest, most unrelenting critter, who in defence of his noble, idealistic views will fight on, tooth, nail and nuclear handgun, asking no mercy and showing no quarter, so long as a single Jerry Pournelle survives.

One can't help thinking that should a lot of suspicious and technologically superior aliens get their ideas about us from this kind of deeply philosophical science fiction, it could cause some problems in interstellar diplomacy. The message would appear to be: "Hi there, alien weirdos! We're rough, tough, mean, deadly, xenophobic, and will listen to no argument short of racial extinction, ha ha!" This might not be the best way to persuade the Galactic Federation to overlook our terrible social lapse of being (ugh) carbon-based. But, as usual, I digress.

In my rather short career as a weapons physicist in the 70s, I got interested in how all the hardware of interstellar annihilation actually worked ... not to mention its terrible side-effects. I have gathered statistical evidence that doomsday machinery capable of taking out more than three planets without reloading has an absolutely devastating and incurable effect on one's prose style.

Here for example is a modest little attack with energy beams, as described in one of the least brilliant SF novels ever published, *The Troglodytes* by "Nal Rafcam". These troglodytes, like the book's readers, are completely speechless ... so we don't know the motive behind "their master plan to reduce the world to utter disaster", but this is how they begin:

> The speechless ones moved into the camp. Their lethal machines were triggered and like a flash of lightning the whole camp was ablaze from the huts on the rim of the camp right through the camp. Everything was cinerated. Every living person was killed the moment the deadly emissions from the tribe's machinery pierced through the camp's superficial structure. So instantaneous and final were these lethal rays that the destructive act was over in but a few minutes.

Larry Niven has philosophized somewhere about how space drives can make ever such good weapons and vice-versa. This was actually anticipated by our troglodytes, whose spacecraft zooms through the atmosphere driven by two enormous lasers. One is at the back and heats up the air in order to drive the ship forward "much in the fashion of a jet". The other laser points forward and clears the atmosphere away from in front of the craft. To engage full reverse thrust, you need only leave one of these lasers fully on while simultaneously not turning off the other.

For some reason this cunningly designed ship fails to work for more than a few pages; it then turns into a badly written fireball and takes all the flying troglodytes with it. As the author mournfully remarks, "No human could have endured the immense heat, let alone superhumans."

I will tactfully not mention the mighty battle lasers described in Fritz Leiber's otherwise jolly good book *The Wanderer*. In particular I am not going to mention the way the beams are luridly visible in space, and even less am I going to mention how they continue to be visible, speeding away to infinity, for several seconds after the firing stops. This is obviously where George Lucas did his research.

I'm not quite certain where Frank Herbert did his, but in *Dune* you can get even more spectacular results with one puny little laser. Here every important person and building is protected by a total defensive shield which repels bullets, missiles and so on. Its one tiny flaw is that if a single unsporting terrorist should fire a single laser bolt at one of these invincible shields, there's a terrific fusion explosion which utterly destroys the laser, the shield, everything inside the shield, and about forty square miles of real estate. With defences like this, who needs enemies? I don't know about you, but I'd be inclined to leave my shield turned off and just risk the odd bullet or missile.

So much for laser shields. That reminds me that for particle beams in real life, the Earth's own magnetic field is a big problem, since it makes them bend in a rather limp and Freudian way. In the 70s some weapons physicists hit on the idea of firing *uncharged* particles which wouldn't swerve in Earth's field. Since neutral particles are bloody hard to accelerate, the cunning plan was to use protons and hire someone to attach electrons to them as they left the accelerator's muzzle at close to the speed of light. The only other thing I remember about this wondrous scheme is its nickname, "Sipapu"—supposedly an old American Indian word meaning neutral hydrogen beam weapon.

I think the most *economical* particle gun of all time must be the one Charles Harness invented for his story "The New Reality". This gadget fires exactly one photon. A carefully angled prism then places this single photon in a dreadful quantum dilemma, where it has to make an awkward decision with no chance of hiding in the statistics.

According to the author, the poor thing's only choice is to vanish in a fit of embarrassment. Since this naturally wrecks the law of conservation of energy, the side-effect of Harness's single-shot photon gun is to destroy the universe. Luckily his hero falls through the hole into a nice new creation and can start saying the usual things like, "And I shall call you ... *Eve!*"

As a change from all those coruscating beams of hot stuff, SF writers have always had a sneaking fondness for cold rays too. I never understood how these worked until I found the scientific explanation in a 1930 story by Bob Shaw's favourite author, Captain S. P. Meek. Since you can focus a beam of light or heat through a lens, the obvious trick is to put a big thick piece of cardboard in front of your heat source and let the lens focus the resulting *absence* of heat into a searing pinpoint of spine-chilling cold.

"Even at two miles," says the Captain's wicked scientist, "I could produce a local temperature of three hundred degrees below zero." (Fahrenheit. I hope.)

The marvellous thing about this cold projector is that, just as with John W. Campbell's Hieronymous Machine, you can cut production costs by leaving out most of the parts ... such as the heat source we started with. The pocket version is merely a powerful lens with insulation sprayed on one side. No batteries needed, and never again will you run out of ice at parties.

My own variant of this astounding piece of super-science involves a multi-kilowatt audio amplifier which takes its input from a very high quality earplug. (Two earplugs for the stereo version.) The hugely amplified lack of sound produces a deafening blare of silence which could really mess up enemy communications for miles around, and would enormously improve the Worldcon business meeting. Which reminds me that it was the famous 18th-century wit Sydney Smith who said, of Ian Watson, "He has occasional flashes of silence that make his conversation perfectly delightful."

Just because I'm a physics chauvinist, I shouldn't overlook exciting biological handguns like the Delling in *Whirlpool of Stars* by "Tully Zetford" (who we are not supposed to know is really Britain's very own Ken Bulmer). A Delling appears to be a precision-engineered water pistol filled with some horrid goo distilled from the remnants of convention room parties. In a half-hearted attempt at the Lionel Fanthorpe thesaurus record, Zetford tells us with subtle understatement what happens when this is fired at you.

> Giffler melted.
>   His body deliquesced. It oozed. His head flowed and collapsed and sloughed. Still upright, he melted and shrank and collapsed, his body shimmered like a blood-drenched jelly. He shrank and oozed and formed a contracting pool of scum on the yard stones.
>   The man in black, Goton Telander, walked out of the Custom House door, He still held the Delling. With a finicky motion he flicked his fingers and the electronic and neural circuits whipped the gun back up his sleeve. It had all been so very slow and yet so very quick.
>   Giffler had been destroyed....
>   A robot vacuum cleaner and scrubber darted out on rubber wheels and began to suck and clean the spot where Giffler had died.

Good old hotel room service; they never give up.

The oldest form of biological warfare consists of poisoning wells, or forcing visitors to drink British hotel coffee. An exciting new slant on this technique comes from the fantasy novel I've already mentioned, by an author who had better remain nameless but lives in Florida. The book's very wonderful and enlightened heroine exerts her special powers and detects that there is indeed something objectively wrong with a village water supply. I quote: "Anyone who drank in it would be sickened, and clothes washed in it would remain unclean. The soul of the water reeked of its special pollution." In a powerful and moving feminist statement, we then learn why. The buried water-main had been walked over by ... a woman. No comment. Absolutely no comment.

Appalling biological weaponry usually works a bit less quickly than that: you know, the alien enemy infiltrates us and arranges over a long, long period to addict hordes of people to sinister pleasures which are so hard to give up that [*cough*] the addicts won't [*cough cough*] stop even when told it's [*cough cough hack spit cough*] killing them. Addictive pleasures like, for example, science fiction conventions.

The idea of slowly-acting weapons brings me at once to Isaac Asimov, who in his later years became unable to write a sentence like "He was instantaneously disintegrated in a puff of smoke" without expanding the action into several long chapters, full of explanatory dialogue, visits to the toilet, and new additions to the Laws of Robotics.

What Asimov has failed to reveal in all his books is that positronic robots themselves are a long-term weapon against humanity. His feeble excuses for the lack of robots by the time of the Foundation series merely show that he's part of the cover-up, and evidently in the pay of that malevolent alien consortium known to Earthlings as the editorial board of Doubleday. The truth is that robots were banned by the Galactic Empire because they were too dangerous.

Asimov gives the game away in his first few robot stories. The positronic robot brain operates, we are told, by the internal creation and annihilation of—surprise!—positrons. When positron meets electron, the annihilation energy is in fact over a million electron volts, producing a burst of hard gamma radiation. Inside one of these positronic supercomputers, this must be happening billions and billions of times per second, with gammas and X rays spraying out like nuclear halitosis. Obviously it's extremely hazardous to stand anywhere near a robot ... especially when it's thinking.

This is confirmed by Asimov's own novels and their descriptions of his most robot-infested planet of all, a place called Solaria, where (a) there are hardly any flesh-and-blood people left, while (b) the few survivors eventually become genetically weird and grow funny lumps on their heads. It all hangs together, you see.

But, you are asking yourselves—those of you who aren't snoring or wondering who this Isaac Asimov is—but surely my analysis is totally demolished by the other well-known fact that hard radiation causes Asimovian robot brains to seize up so fast as to leave no time even for a traditional chorus of "Daisy, Daisy ...."? If robots already spew out gamma rays, how can this be? I will tell you. Control yourselves.

High-energy gammas from an external source will produce random electron-positron pairs as they pass through matter. These will appear in the robot mind as wrong and illogical thoughts from outside, such as an irrational desire to write a trilogy containing more than three volumes. Of course the robot itself can detect this malfunction and intelligently deduces the whole scenario I've just explained, intelligently realizes it's been leaking harmful rays in defiance of the First Law all its life, and as a result, intelligently suffers immediate brain death. Which, just like the best-seller lists, demonstrates again that intelligence *doesn't* have much survival value.

Now of course a *real* SF hero or heroine would never stoop to pointing gamma sources at defenceless robots. This is no way to deal with a villainous artificial intelligence which has just gone insane and announced, "Yes, *now* there is an L. Ron Hubbard!" Instead, traditionalists have a choice of three ecologically sound disposal methods which do not consume fossil fuels, or lead to hazardous waste. The only objection is that outside the glorious pages of science fiction, they may not always work.

Method one involves logical subtlety. The mighty-thewed, pin-headed SF hero cries, "Accept input: everything I say is false!" The world-dominating electronic brain can only reply *Fzzzt crackle crackle*, and seizes up with its display showing the final, defiant message, "Please contact your hardware dealer." Other good questions to blow the minds of computers are, "Why is a raven like a writing desk?", "What is the sound of one waldo clapping?" and "Do you realize I haven't backed up my data this week?"

Method two is not easy to distinguish from method one, and consists of the Very Dumb Question. Thus Patrick McGoohan in *The Prisoner* painfully typed in the word "Why?" and totally destroyed a hyperintelligent computer complex which might reasonably have come right back with "Why not?" Or even, "Because."

Method three is sensitive and emotional, with the heroine placing one defiant hand on her brass bra to declaim, "There are limits to your power, Machine! You cannot love ... or weep." Whereupon the mad computer's only remaining option is to die of embarrassment.

Of course, in science fiction, these low-budget weapons consisting of pure information are also popular for use against people. I suspect that writers— pallid, flabby and inept creatures that they are—like them because they're easy to lift and require little skill to aim. The idea is that this deadly data, once it gets into your mind, will cause you to fall over twitching, bleeding from the eyeballs and frothing at every orifice, like a very young fan who's just read his first William Gibson story.

These infant fans all seem to think that the notion of brain-bursting information—"concepts that the mind cannot stomach"—was invented by Gibson in the 1980s. Just to show off my superior erudition, I can't resist pointing out the weird coincidence that it cropped up twice in October 1969, with the appearance of two similar works, Piers Anthony's *Macroscope* and the first episode of *Monty Python's Flying Circus*. Remember the sketch about the funniest joke in the world, which no one can hear and live? The German version supposedly goes: *Wenn is das Nunstück git und Slotermeyer? Ja! ... Beiherhund das Oder die Flipperwalt gersput.* Not many people know this is a quotation from Wittgenstein and translates as, "Whereof we cannot speak, thereon we must remain *aaaaaaaaaaargh.*"

Anyway, British SF pundits go on about how Fred Hoyle used the idea of unthinkable information years before, in *The Black Cloud*, 1957, and really offensive nitpickers like myself remind them that the world's funniest and deadliest joke features in a poem by that famous American, Oliver Wendell Holmes, who in 1894 died laughing.

Which is what I nearly did when I read about the methods of the arch-villain in Charles Sheffield's recent "hard science fiction" novel *Proteus Unbound*. This fiend has the unsocial habit of driving his potential enemies insane, by mercilessly beaming them animated pictures of himself dancing backwards in red tights. Talk about psychological warfare.

All these non-macho software weapons sound too much like magic spells to the true fan of hard science fiction, who insists that stories be based on rigorous extrapolation from known scientific facts about antigravity, faster-than-light craft, instantaneous communication, infinity generators and time travel....

For example, people were quite cruel to Bob Shaw for his astrophysical cover-up in *The Ragged Astronauts.* Just as you're fretting that the twin planets sharing a common atmosphere can't possibly work, Bob cunningly inserts a mention that this is, er, another universe, where *pi* happens to be exactly three. In other words, anyone wanting to prove the set-up is impossible must first ask Bob for the value of the gravitational constant in these foreign parts. The reply is always: "It's defined as whatever makes my solar system work."

I pointed out if you decide like this to make your own rules, it seems entirely reasonable that this different universe will also have its own special grammar, syntax and spelling, so that the publishers could save a fortune in proofreading. Mr Shaw's reply was not printable, but by the end of the third book (*The Fugitive Worlds*) the use of an intergalactic mega-weapon has changed the value of *pi* to ... about three and one-seventh. You can imagine people stalking around scratching their heads and muttering, "That circle looks a *different shape* somehow."

Funnily enough, no one seems to protest half as much when writers dream up space drives that change another important constant by furtively pushing our universe's maximum speed limit up towards infinity. And not many authors have picked up on the very useful implication that if c approaches infinity and Einstein's dear old $E=mc^2$ still works, you get an awful lot more output from a nuclear reaction. I mean, the fusion of one hydrogen atom could provide all the energy you need to zoom right round the universe detonating suns and wrecking galaxies, and there'd still be an infinite surplus which would have to be either stored in infinitely many batteries or converted back to a single subatomic particle.

I assume that this kind of rigidly scientific power source is what makes AKKA work. AKKA, you might possibly remember, is the plot-saving gadget from Jack Williamson's *The Legion of Space*, which when all else fails can be hauled out of your sleeve to destroy entire invading spacefleets, plus any odd moons and planets that stray into the line of fire. It's conveniently portable, it needs no batteries, all the parts can be bought from Radio Shack except for the bits of wood, and I've always been impressed by the luck of the inventor who first stumbled on this world-wrecking principle and just happened not to be pointing it at anyone, or at the earth, or the moon, or the stars....

Similarly, the eponymous plot device of Barrington J. Bayley's *The Zen Gun* (1983) is carved from rough wood and does not require ammunition, but on one of its more interesting settings will detonate suns at three light years' range by projecting a murderous blast of pseudoscience (based on the sometimes disputed theory that gravity is not a pull but a push). By way of safety catch, this apocalyptic facility can be used only by a trained Zen master who is too enlightened actually to use it.

My favourite device with no visible power supply appears in David Duncan's *Occam's Razor*, where an eccentric mathematician scores high marks for style by announcing, "Gentlemen, we are about to short-circuit the Universe!" It's a slight anticlimax when the fabric of space/time is rent asunder, and the world's nuclear arsenals disabled, by a collection of wire frames supporting films of aqueous solution—or in lay language, soap bubbles.

This is all because of topology, which was just making its first shy appearance as an explanation for everything in SF. Previous explanations for everything included atoms, rays, radium, magnetism, mesmerism, and General Semantics: invoking one of these magic names automatically meant that you didn't have to explain any more. Of course new catch-phrases still arrive every year or so. 1950s futures were full of people taking cooling drinks of heavy water. Later on they did their hair in gravity waves, and today's SF characters can't so much as tie up a parcel without resorting to superstrings. Not to mention burying their dead in a supersymmetry.

(I once planned a trend-setting story to be called "Cyberfractal Wetware Meets Gödel's Infinite Black Hole Designer Psychosis in the Quantum Gutter"; but I found it had already been written ... by almost everybody.)

One of these current hot subjects is chaos theory, which was particularly brilliantly not predicted in the SF novels of Colin Kapp. These are fabled for grandiose weaponry and conspicuous consumption. *The Patterns of Chaos*, for example, has a plot device which will make your forebrain bulge with galactic concepts until the sense of wonder comes spurting from your ears. See, there are all these planet-wrecking hellburner bombs which have been travelling between galaxies for an awesome seven hundred million years, and they're aimed at the hero. In a subtle refinement of suspense which would have brought tears to the eyes of Henry James, they keep just missing ... but going off closer and closer. One of them in fact misses the hero by less than one metre. Well, as the author somewhat reluctantly explains, one metre and 16.1 hours.

All this is as nothing to the super-artillery of Kapp's follow-up *The Chaos Weapon*. This massive device projects devastating bolts of pure entropy, so vicious and irresistible that they could ... they could turn Hal Clement and Arthur C. Clarke into 1960s New Wave writers, or even cyberpunks. With power like that, it will come as no surprise that the Chaos Weapon has to be fed with an ammunition belt of suns, while its hellish beam is focused by a ring of ten black holes. Things certainly look bad for the hero when he gets hit by its full output.

Fortunately it's only a glancing blow ... which merely bounces his space-ship (I quote) "against the elastic walls of the continuum itself". I love this traditional SF picture of the fabric of space as a kind of rubberized canvas which an enterprising art thief could cut right out of its metrical frame.

Bouncing off it does lead to some sticky problems: to quote Kapp again, "the ship was not circumventing the light barrier but had become enmeshed in it." But our hero soon makes a comeback and proves the worth of the indomitable human spirit by diving out of the airlock with another planet-wrecking hellburner bomb "clasped under one arm"—and the Chaos Weapon is put out of commission faster than you could say "contracted wordlength".

It was that book that made me realize again why it can be almost soothing to read violent space operas full of megaweaponry and exploding planets. In more than 92% of cases, by careful use of outrageously lousy physics and a level of literary craftsmanship which makes the physics look quite good, the authors manage to convince us that these universe-busting arsenals could never conceivably work.

This thought comforted me in my years of working for the British Ministry of Defence under the terrible shadow of fear that nuclear weapons would be dropped. Our lab technicians were so clumsy that the most likely place for one to be dropped was on my foot.

I think that's about enough senseless violence for one programme item, but I'd like to leave you with a cheering thought about science fiction and its uplifting moral effects. Although pundits keep claiming that porno potboilers and splatter movies excite their fans into real-life acts of imitation, I'm glad to report that despite a lifetime of violent SF I have never once disintegrated a hostile galaxy, or used a huge gamma laser to blow up the sun, or even wiped out a single measly planet in a multi-gigaton antimatter blast. Not once.

And I hope that everyone in today's SF community, with the possible exception of Greg Bear, can say the same.

Thank you.

1989

Best Foot Forward

One neglected literary form, as *Interzone* knows, is the covering letter you send with your deathless manuscript. Thanks to industrial spies, I've secured several examples familiar to editors all over the world, and especially in Brighton. The challenge is to detect the subtle reason why in each case the recipient reached for his or her trusty rejection slip without finishing the covering note, let alone starting the manuscript. Match your wits against the professionals!

Dear Editor,

What you're waiting for is a new idea to shake up the fuddy-duddy world of science fiction. Well here it is! Based on the mindbogglingly innovative concept of Earth being struck by a giant alien meteor with startling results, my novel *Lucifer's Footfall: The Forge of Shiva* is...

Dear Sir,

I see you publish science articles, so you'll love my enclosed poem *The Joy of Superstring Theory*, a true epic in nineteen thousand heroic couplets. Also, it is allegorical too. Mrs Gilbey of our village Literary Circle thought it was VERY INTERESTING and I know you will not need no more recommendation....

Sir,

I cannot reveal my blockbuster plot to you as yet, since you would steal it and have it published under some house name by one of your tame hacks, thereby defrauding me of millions. I am on to the little games of you so-called "publishers". Before submitting the outline I want a firm contract guaranteeing a seven-figure advance and 110% of gross film rights. For the present I am not revealing my address—attempts to trace me and steal my notes will be useless. Kindly reply via the classified advertisement columns of...

Attention: Editor,

Revelations chap. xiii clearly shows us the clue. We know it takes Halley's Comet 76 years to complete one orbit but are you aware that if you add 2000

David Pringle of Interzone *magazine insists that he has received variants of all these letters. Almost.*

AD to Archbishop Ussher's 4004 BC and divide the total by 76 it goes exactly 79 times? Since 1990 is actually the year 2000 this shows that the Second Coming will occur on 12 July. My manuscript conclusively proves...

Dear Mega-Ed,

I was having this totally ace game of *Bludgeons and Blackguards* with my friend Irving when we realized the excitement of our role-playing campaign would make an incredibly triff novel! So here, based on that month of fun, is *Lepermage of Elfspasm*, a brill fantasy dekalogy in which a lovable crew of Elves, Dwarves, Cats, Boggits, Men and a token Voluptuous Nymph go up against the Cold Dark Dread Force of Chaos Blood Death Evil, which...

Darling Editor,

I saw your picture in *The Bookseller* and at once knew we would become *very* close friends! I am 19 and *very* experienced. Perhaps we could have lunch together. Or breakfast. Of course I will be quite delighted to buy the meal! (Don't you love champagne?) Here is my photograph for you to keep. To fall in love sight unseen—it's like something from a mediaeval romance, isn't it? Speaking of which, I know you'd like a peep at the enclosed MS of my richly romantic historical novel, *I Was Edward II's Teenage Groupie*...

Hi, Editorperson,

There's never been a novel like this! Imagine the excitement of a plotline in which all the past Dr Who's meet up with Darth Vader, Superman, Gandalf, Marvin the Paranoid Android, Indiana Jones, Crocodile Dundee, Captain Kirk and Spock, Snoopy, Judge Dredd, Roger Rabbit, James Bond, E. T., Mickey Mouse, Rambo and Jimmy Swaggart! I am sure a big outfit like yours will have no trouble sorting out copyright problems, and then...

Deer Idiotr,

Plees find encloased my novvle, it is handwrote Im afraid but you will not Mind this becuase GENIEUS cant be mistakken can it? No retern post encloased sinse this will nott be nessary as you will See...

Dear Sir or Madam,

The MS herewith is a *very first draft*. I could change almost anything on request. For example, in the slave bondage orgy scenes I am open to suggestions (your knowledge must be so much greater than mine). Just say the word and I'll alter the lard to cod liver oil, or the protagonist's name to—well, it's a teensy bit obvious, should we tone it down to Steelram or Goatfetish? Also there are details about bestial fellation which need checking in the light of your mature experience. I'm willing to take advice on any point. Just send a fully detailed letter of instruction and comment, and...

Editor, dear Editor,

Ever heard how George Orwell's best novels were bounced by several major publishers before they got to be international best-sellers? Well, history repeats itself, and my enclosed *Big Brother Farm* has actually been rejected by *exactly the same* wilfully blind publishing outfits as Orwell's. To add to the astonishing coincidence, I have chest trouble just like him. Knowing all this, can you afford to take the chance of not...

Dear Skiffy Editor,

This is a guaranteed SF best-seller—you don't even need to read it! My change of name will assure its success. I have the legal documents all ready to fill in: the final decision is yours. Do you prefer Isaac Amizov, Alfred C. Clarke or Roberta Heinlein? I had also thought of H. G. Whelks, but do not think this would be such a good seller...

To Whom It May Concern:

Not merely a work of high entertainment—my novel is *more*. Here in fictional guise are the truly shocking *facts* about the *conspiracy* of scientists, theologians and armed librarians who *control* us. Intentionally I have given over six chapters to *exposing* the jealously guarded truth about *gravity* alone— not a pull as *Communism* would have you believe, but a *push*! Unless you too are blind to reason or controlled by *laser signals* broadcast from *Chinese UFOs*, you cannot fail to....

Dear Gagged Lackey of the Thatcherite Junta,

Your lickspittle rag won't dare publish this, but...

You see, of course, the common fault in all these? Not one of them addresses the editor correctly, as "O Mighty Being From Whose Fundament The Illumination Of The World Proceeds".

1989

Ansible Review of the Year

A *live fanzine* is what I'm expected to give you now (at least, according to L. Ron Hubbard's Pocket Programme of the Future). I am not too good at this subtle impersonation stuff; at the Masquerade I was denied a spot prize because they said I'd totally failed to look like a human being, and pretending to be a fanzine is harder still. [Waves copy of *Ansible*.] Try to think of me as being printed in two columns of invisibly tiny type. I want to see you squinting. I want to see bloodshot eyes throughout the room ... yes, most of you are ahead of me there.

Well, the historical background of my little SF newsletter *Ansible* doesn't really bear examination: but this is the Fan Programme, where the lid gets ripped off, and if it isn't Greg Pickersgill will rip it for you. So first, a bit of clarification. Some new fans may have the horrifying idea that *Ansible* is named after the faster-than-light communications gadget found in the works of Orson Scott Card. I wish to deny this terrible charge and point out that it's named after the faster-than-light communications gadget found in the works of Ursula Le Guin. Mr Card pinched it, in shameful imitation of me.

I've always wanted to ask Ursula Le Guin whether there was meant to be a hidden significance in the word. After I'd published my first few issues, Chris Priest wrote in gleefully to tell me I was the proud editor of a newsletter whose title was an anagram of Lesbian.

That first issue appeared at Seacon '79 in this very hotel. By the time I reached double figures I'd actually achieved the breakthrough of publishing a few bits of news, in between the vulgar remarks about people like Chris Priest. But *Ansible* was always keen to print up-to-the-minute items like extracts from such famous novels as *Neuron World*:

> This was the Stygian darkness of which poets wrote. This was the pit of Acheron of which the creators of classic prose made mention. This was the kind of darkness which made thick, black velvet seem like chiffon by contrast. This was

---

A performance which probably makes no sense at all, much of it having actually been written during Conspiracy (the 1987 Worldcon held in Brighton, England, and elusively chaired by Malcolm Edwards). One would-be-controversial panel title, "Why Have the Americans Hijacked the Worldcon?", caused more of a stir than its planners had intended. The MCFLF flyer appears by the vigorously withheld permission of Chris Priest.

the kind of darkness that turned pitch into translucent polythene, when the two were placed side by side....

This was the back page of ... *Ansible 9*!

Thank you, Lionel Fanthorpe. The same issue carried an anonymous flyer inviting people to join a dynamic new fannish political movement:

M.C.F.L.F.

Are you a *Middle Class Fan*? If so, you are a member of a nice but persecuted minority, and you are invited to close ranks with those of your own kind. The MIDDLE CLASS FANNISH LIBERATION FRONT will protect *your* interests.

You are a *Middle Class Fan* if:

1. You live in the HOME COUNTIES, the THAMES VALLEY or a SMART SUBURB.
2. You possess a DEGREE, a PROFESSIONAL QUALIFICATION or a WORD PROCESSOR.
3. You buy at least ONE HARDCOVER SF NOVEL a year.
4. You prefer J. G. BALLARD and URSULA LE GUIN to LARRY NIVEN or ANNE McCAFFREY.
5. You SECRETLY COLLECT SF as a HEDGE AGAINST INFLATION.
6. You have PUBLISHED SF PROFESSIONALLY.
7. You have had a REJECTION from *Asimov's Sci-Fi Magazine* (same as 6).
8. You have a TRENDY DISABILITY, such as deafness, literacy or wit.
9. You are ABLE TO READ WITHOUT MOVING YOUR LIPS.
10. You DONATE BLOOD or support the EQUAL RIGHTS AMENDMENT.
11. You read THE SUNDAY TIMES, FOUNDATION or ANSIBLE.
12. You think WORKING CLASS FANS do actually smell a bit.

Are you a MIDDLE CLASS FAN? Now is the time to sit down with a nice cup of tea and be counted. Just fill in the form below....

TO: D. WEST, 17 Carlisle St, Keighley, West Yorks, BD21 4PX.

Yes! I am a *Middle Class Fan* and proud of it, and wish to join THE MIDDLE CLASS FANNISH LIBERATION FRONT. Please send me full details of how to look down on people, type out my own litho plates, make macramé pot-holders, cook vegetarian dishes and produce my own Christmas cards. I enclose £20.00 (American Express and Diners Club accepted)....

Who actually wrote this flyer remains a closely guarded secret, but computerized textual analysis hints that the style seems strangely influenced by that of *Inverted World, The Space Machine, The Affirmation* and *The Glamour.*

Other popular *Ansible* features included Hazel's Language Lessons, which reached their high point with the vital information that the word *komaria* in Kikuyu means "to touch somebody reprovingly or threateningly with a stick and say 'wee!'". David Garnett's serialized Dictionary of Science Fiction Terms only lasted long enough to cover the letter A, thank God, though some fans out there are still waiting hopefully for the promised Part Two: From "Bastard" to "Buttock".

The actual news items were sometimes a tiny bit less reliable. For example, in issue 44 I put in a rude bit about how Colin Wilson had been interviewed by Lisa Tuttle and spent all too much of the session going on about how he liked young lady interviewers in tight jeans. This was a deplorable misprint and I have to apologize: sources close to Lisa later corrected me and pointed out that Mr Wilson had been far more interested in asking the colour of her knickers.

Before I go on, I'll just read some selected critical responses quoted in back issues of *Ansible*:

"It's a riot!" said *Foundation* (well, Colin Greenland anyway).

"As a newszine, it is the Emperor's New Clothes," enthused Mike Glyer in *File 770.*

"The cosmic adventure of the ultimate soldier on a desperate mission beyond death!" observed Timescape Books.

The *British Fantasy Newsletter* complained that *Ansible* is: "Not nearly as controversial as its reputation belies."

"We demand an immediate public apology," wrote Andre Norton's attorneys.

"Fandom," declared Greg Pickersgill as early as the second issue, "is a damn sight better life than pushing peanuts up the Pennines with your penis."

US fan Roy Tackett remarked, with characteristic tact: "There is, somehow, something attractive about the thought of sitting back and watching the English get nuked."

Robert Heinlein wrote, enthusiastically, "Our teeth grated, and my nipples went *spung!*"

"We thought of suing you," added Fred Harris, "but you haven't any money."

And William McGonagall had the last, deeply moving word: "And when Life's prospects may at times appear dreary to ye, / Remember Aloys Senefelder, the discoverer of lithography."

I think this establishes *Ansible*'s credentials for sober, hard-hitting, no-nonsense, factual journalism. The following review of the last twelve months consists, I must warn you, of items even *Ansible* couldn't bring itself to print. Switch off your tape recorders and put your short-term memory in neutral, please—and remember the definition of fanzines I once found in that famous SF novel *Come, Hunt an Earthman* by Philip E. High:

"A *Zine* is a terror weapon. It rends and distorts, twisting the structure of the target completely out of shape."

AUGUST 1986

An exciting new science fiction magazine was launched, called *Amazing Stories* and edited by Hugo Gernsback ... no, sorry, that must have been in 1985. I forgot to say that *Ansible* is sometimes a tiny bit late with your actual news.

In Sweden, twenty-six fans were injured in a zap-gun battle fought over the hot issue of whether "bheer" should be spelt with an "H", or with two.

Thanks to a leak in the Cabinet it was revealed that the British government had successfully issued court injunctions in Australia, America and the United Kingdom which for sixteen shameful years have prevented an allegedly "subversive" and "politically embarrassing" book from being published. Its title is, of course, *The Last Dangerous Visions*.

In a very loud public statement, Harlan Ellison commented: "That's not fucking funny! The book is finished, complete, and the manuscript is all ready to be delivered. I'm just waiting for the final rewrite job on one last story, by L. Ron Hubbard."

SEPTEMBER 1986

John Brunner wrote to *New Scientist* magazine complaining that his expensive word processor wouldn't print out the Sanskrit and Middle English characters which he constantly needed for his daily correspondence. The next issue featured Harry Harrison's strongly worded reply, saying that there was no problem at all if one simply translated it all into Esperanto. The week after that, Sam J. Lundwall sent in a trenchant letter from Sweden, complaining about the way insular Englishmen like Harry Harrison talked about Esperanto and science fiction as though they owned it, when in fact both had been invented in Continental Europe in 1887.

SF fandom was plunged as usual into controversy when the Pope published a science fiction novel called *Immaculate Genesis*: there were worries about massive Hugo bloc-voting by members of the little-known "Catholic" cult which has been openly condemned by several British governments since the reign of Henry VIII....

"Gosh wow, fans, this is all a bit of an embarrassment for us," said the chairman of the Vatican City Worldcon bid.

OCTOBER 1986

A dynamic new writers' organization, the SFWGB—Science Fiction Writers of Great Britain—was founded, to grant to British authors their inalienable rights of fame, royalties and the pursuit of free booze in a private room well away from the fans. Any writer would be qualified to join if he or she had published three stories in SF magazines anywhere in the world, except America.

Joanna Russ wrote an angry public letter to complain that the announced Conspiracy '87 programme is sexist, since it features masked balls.

NOVEMBER 1986

The Moral Majority developed a simple new scientific test to determine whether SF and fantasy books are Godless, immoral, and deserving of being burnt. Books which are suspect—i.e., which have been published—have their entire print runs stacked in Death Valley and napalmed. If God doesn't miraculously save them (explained the Reverend Jerry Falwell), this will be a direct condemnation from on high. Most fundamentalists condemned this approach as "half-hearted" and "wishy-washy", suggesting that we should get straight to the root of the evil by extending the same technique to authors.

Arthur C. Clarke and Isaac Asimov received an advance of six hundred billion dollars for a proposed novel to be written by both their word processors in collaboration. (This was originally going to be done via a specially set-up geosynchronous satellite linkage, but it turned out that Asimov's word processor was afraid of heights.)

The working title is *2000 and Foundation*: this will reconcile the Clarke and Asimov future histories by revealing that all along, the secret directing intelligence behind the mysterious monolith and the Second Foundation has been John W. Campbell.

DECEMBER 1986

London's post office workers held their traditional, seasonal celebrations of Saturnalia in Trafalgar Square, with wild orgiastic dancing around a huge blazing bonfire of undelivered Conspiracy hotel booking forms.

Geoff Ryman abandoned his plans for a twenty-five-minute play adaptation—for performance at Conspiracy—of Samuel R. Delany's *Dhalgren*. "It wasn't challenging enough for me," he said. "Instead, I'm now planning to do a fifteen-minute monologue version of *Stand on Zanzibar*."

JANUARY 1987

The Society for the Promulgation of More and More Science Fiction Awards announced an exciting new trophy, the Volsted Gridban Memorial Award For Consistent Integrity. This would be presented as a consolation prize to authors who after ten years of publishing SF still haven't received any other sort of award. Unfortunately, the judging committee couldn't find any writers who qualified.

The British SF Association finally paid heed to the critics who complained that its magazines didn't have the popular appeal which would attract a wide audience. Membership increased tenfold on the appearance of the new tabloid version of *Vector*, retitled *The Daily Sci Fi*. Highlights of the first issue were the nude picture of Anne McCaffrey on page 3, an Agony Aunt column run by John Norman, and the feature article *10 Tell-Tale Signs That Show Your Neighbour Is A Trekkie*.

Swedish fandom was once again plunged into all-out war, as usual. An agonized press release reports: "This is the most appalling and shameful scandal to have rocked world fandom since science fiction was invented by Sam J. Lundwall in 1887." The issues involved are a bit unclear, but the central dispute seems to be about whether or not Otis Adelbert Kline was or wasn't a better writer than Captain S. P. Meek.

FEBRUARY 1987

Convention fans were horrified by the recent discovery—unearthed in an old copy of *Fahrenheit 451*—that books are inflammable and could be used as weapons to set fire to convention hotels, or even more probably, convention hotel managers. A hastily proposed amendment to the Worldcon constitution requires that these dangerous items be peace-bonded—sealed shut with wheelclamps borrowed from local police—before they can be allowed at conventions. "Even that may not be enough," said a spokesfan. "We dropped a copy of *Battlefield Earth* from a height of 100 feet on to a volunteer gopher, and it seems that even with peace-bonding, these books can be pretty dangerous...."

Meanwhile, Ian Watson joined the Freemasons.

MARCH 1987

A new science fiction magazine was announced from Davis Publications Inc: *Vincent Omniaveritas's Magazine of Cyberpunk*, full of hard-hitting, action-packed, information-dense essays demonstrating conclusively that "cyberpunk" SF is infinitely more wonderful than any other form of literature since Gutenberg. It is hoped that after the first year, the magazine size can be expanded to allow the inclusion of some fiction.

Later that month, riots erupted in the streets of Stockholm as Swedish fandom debated the issue of whether professional magazines should be bound up with staples. (One bloodily divisive side issue concerns the rival merits of the two spellings "sthaples" and "staphles".)

APRIL 1987

At the Easter convention, old-time fans complained again that the traditional feel of fanzines had been destroyed by all these computers and laser printers. They called for a return to the golden years when fanzines were created on old-fashioned IBM Selectric typewriters and reproduced by traditional handcrafted offset lithography.

In Britain, H.M. Government denied scurrilous rumours that they planned to introduce a tax on books. "We've worked out a much fairer approach," the Chancellor of the Exchequer announced. "We're bringing reading into line with television—with a simple, no-nonsense tax on the receiving apparatus. The annual tax will be levied on all users of *eyes*. As a special bonus, a single licence will allow each individual to operate as many eyes as he or she wants, provided they're all kept in the same house."

In line with Government educational policy, there will be large discounts for illiterates.

MAY 1987

D. West published his longest fanzine article yet: "Repeat Performance", a dazzling 144-page analysis of something or other, which explores transsexuality, baked beans, investment strategy for unit trusts, how to make your own toilet paper, the reasons why the rest of British and American fandom are a load of wankers, and the morality of mud-wrestling. All these strands are brilliantly drawn together into D.'s final conclusion, which is that writing fanzine articles is a waste of time and only an idiot would do it.

The 1986 Heineken Lager advertising campaign received vast numbers of nominations for the Hugo Award, in the categories Best Novel, Best Non-Fiction and Best Dramatic Presentation. After long debate the Worldcon committee brilliantly compromised by shortlisting it under Best Fan Artist.

JUNE 1987

Greg Pickersgill had a nifty new idea for a team event which could fill a twelve-hour stretch of fan room programming at Conspiracy ... synchronized ceiling watching. Competitors would lie back and stare in unblinking silence at the ceiling, excluding all thoughts from their minds and thus demonstrating that they had enough grim mental self-sufficiency to read even Piers Anthony novels. Unfortunately this suggestion never made it to the Conspiracy programme-planning meeting, since Greg accidentally spent that day practising the advanced techniques of his new sport.

Brian Aldiss announced his new literary project. Thanks to massive popular demand from his bank manager, he's working on an immense sequel with one of the following tentative titles: *Helliconia's Edge*, *The Helliconia of the New Sun*, *Chapter House Helliconia* or *Helliconia August Bank Holiday Weekend*.

At the same time, Bob Shaw came to an important realization about his *Ragged Astronauts* series. In the first book he established that he could bend the laws of physics as much as he liked, since this is a different universe with different physical constants. His new brainwave is that this different universe will also have different rules of grammar, syntax and spelling! As he told *Ansible*, "This could save a fortune in proofreading!"

JULY 1987

The London "Forbidden Planet" bookshop attracted attention with its 100-foot-tall papier-mache display model of J. G. Ballard, made entirely from recycled copies of the fourth Conspiracy progress report.

In America, a Senate investigatory committee received anonymous letters from Puerto Rico and Cincinnati, accusing the last six TransAtlantic Fan Fund administrators of being heavily involved in shipping arms to Iran ... as well as legs to Iraq and fishnet tights to West Yorkshire.

Swedish fandom achieved another historic first! "This is the proudest and most exciting development ever," says Ahrvid Engholm's enthusiastic press release about the first use of tactical nuclear weapons in a fan feud.

AUGUST 1987: CONSPIRACY

In a savage confrontation on Friday night at the Worldcon, hotel liaison person Katie Hoare was confronted by six psychopathic hotel managers wielding flick knives and bicycle chains. Later, a spokesman for the RSPCA complained that this sort of graphic violence was totally unfair to hotel managers.

The fan programme item "Why Are Americans? How Dare They Continue To Exist?" was expected to be controversial. Happily, after mere hours of discussion and only a few minor flesh wounds, fannish common sense prevailed—Mike Glyer and the entire Los Angeles SF Society agreed to having been totally in the wrong, and promised to correct their errors by applying at once for Welsh citizenship.

This dramatic conversion was brought about by the diplomacy of Greg Pickersgill, who smoothed over all the weekend's international frictions by clearly explaining the proper definitions of important fannish terms. For example, "intolerably imperialist cultural chauvinism" translates as "being American", and "understandable patriotic spirit" merely means "insulting Americans".

After nasty experiences with slimming drugs earlier this year, Bob Shaw was happy to announce from under a Fan Room table that he'd switched to an exclusive diet of the new and organically produced appetite-suppressant called "gin and tonic".

Fans were delighted to hear that Britain's most famous unreadable author, Robert Lionel Fanthorpe, has turned his black belt to good use and made three million pounds from evangelistic mugging. In a staggering act of generosity he has used the money to set up an independent foundation for the promotion of fine SF ... Fanthorpe Services Inc. The first major classic unearthed for publication by the associated imprint, Thousand Year Rule Press, is "Leo Brett's" famous *March of the Robots*.

> ("Strange metallic things; things that were alien to the soft
> green grass of earth. Terrifying things, steel things; metal

things; things with cylindrical bodies and multitudinous jointed limbs. Things without flesh and blood. Things that were made of metal and plastic and transistors and valves and relays, and wires. Metal things. Metal things that could think. *Thinking metal things....*")

Several major pundits have already praised this to the skies as the work of a true master—world-renowned critics and authors like Algis Budrys, Orson Scott Card, Anne McCaffrey, Gene Wolfe and Fred Harris.

Despite initial worries about Scandinavian feuds being carried on at Conspiracy, Swedish fandom won everyone's heart by simply sharing a bottle of whisky and passing into a mass coma. The only sour note was struck when a hotel barman tried to charge them corkage on the miniature. (Oh dear, these old gags will creep in.)

Mike Glyer protested hugely at the insensitivity of the Committee in allowing a Fan Programme item with an offensive title. *The Ansible Review of the Year* is a clearly chauvinist name in that it fails to grant equal time to the vast majority of SF newsletters called *File 770*. In a controversial reply published by the convention newsletter, Martin Tudor offensively and publicly stated, "Er, sorry." Mike was so affronted by this that he unilaterally boycotted the hotel swimming pool.

The Ministry of Defence refused to comment on persistent but elusive reports that an unidentified floating Malcolm Edwards had been sighted hovering 200 feet over Brighton beach. Sceptical observers pointed out that although the Committee has been investigating these rumoured brief sightings for five whole days, there was still no hard evidence that con chairman Malcolm Edwards exists.

At this point I'd better stop, for the usual reason that I stop doing an issue of *Ansible*. It's not so much the constraints of time and space; it's just that I can face only so many lawsuits and death threats per issue. Even now I have a terrible feeling that at tonight's SFWA party, Fred Harris and I may be booked for a mutually enrichening exchange of hurled drinks.[1] If I get out of this hotel alive, I'll promise to think about beginning to consider starting work on *Ansible 51* ... real soon now.

Meanwhile, thanks for listening.

1987

---

[1] This feeble attempt to establish precognitive powers is transparently a later afterthought. [Ed.]

Somewhere Near Penrhyndeudraeth

The good thing about this freelancing is that you can declare a holiday whenever you like. The bad thing is that you don't. I dimly remember a time when my Civil Service employers allowed me to take evenings and weekends off.... After calculating that we hadn't had a proper holiday for 00000110 years, I realized the computers were eating too deeply into my once sensitive and fannish soul. Hazel packed the car with luxuries (clothes, food); I added the essentials (books, booze); and we rattled off into the sunset, which is also the direction of Wales.

Toiling up through the Marches and the torrid zones of bilingual road-signs, into a landscape of mountains intermittently visible between the sheep, I took notes for a long-planned but never written article on Welsh as she is wrote. The Welsh are eager to confuse the vile *Saeson* or English, but unlike the similarly disposed Irish are hampered by having a relatively straightforward language. Translating the town of Wrexham into *Wrecsam* seems mere perversity, and few *Saeson* are likely to be confused by a *tacsi* rank, a double-decker *bws*, a walk on the seaside *promenad*, an eighteen-hole *cwrs golff*, or a drink at the *clwb* (necessitating a visit to the *toiledau*). In Caernarfon (trans: Carnarvon) Castle, the historical bits include such conundrums as *William I (Y "Concwerwr") o Dapestri Bayeux*. Spoken Welsh is something else, and every evening a hotel TV would gush incomprehensibly: well, almost. "*Llanfairpwyllgwyngyll telefision gogerychwyrndrobwll social security llantysiliogogogoch....*"

This was Gwynedd, the sheep-infested northwest corner of Wales which contains most of the surviving Welsh speakers, notable mountains and tourist traps. (Statistic: Wales houses 1% of the population of the EC and 15% of its sheep.) Here the planned essay and our fannish street credibility ended with a loud simultaneous bang, at Portmeirion.

To fandom, Portmeirion means Patrick McGoohan's resoundingly triffic 1966 series *The Prisoner*, and by extension its fan club's Portmeirion festivals, and the mild tedium associated with any media group which focuses all its energies on a single cult object. Under that burning-glass of fanatic devotion the object seems to wither, like *Star Trek* actors dwindling from sequel to sequel. Yawn, snooze, and where's the Jacqueline Lichtenberg Appreciation Society when we need it? This is known as prejudice.

But: "We're coming back here," said Hazel before we'd so much as un-packed, and in defiance of all intricate forward planning we spent the rest of our week at Portmeirion. There has probably got to be a reason for this.

Firstly, despite the urgings of common sense, the place wasn't specially tricked out for the "Prisoner" series. Barring a few obvious items (to the best of my belief there are no sliding doors, craggy subterranean corridors lined with juke-boxes, or rocket launch silos) and some mild surprises (the reality is smaller, and cunning camerawork made it seem to front on open sea rather than a mere estuary), the late Sir Clough Williams-Ellis's village really is like that. It's a colossal folly, a Gothic-Italian dream, a Disneyland of real architecture put together as the ... as the fanac of a real architect.

All is crammed into a tiny fold in the coastline, a combe which funnels down to the estuary while the dottier buildings cling to its sides and the clifftops. Near-garish colours predominate; I can think of no other context in which my aesthetic adviser Hazel would reckon an arched belvedere painted pale mauve looked somehow right. Personally I loved the jackdaw resourcefulness. That sinister Green Dome of the TV series has an impressively intricate façade which turns out to have been half of a giant manorial fireplace. The staggeringly ornate plaster ceiling which posed over us at dinner-time had been transported wholesale from some condemned country house and reassembled from a stack of truck-sized fragments. Seven vast Ionic columns acquired on one of Sir Clough's whims (and then stored for 30 years before use) have been incorporated into the landscape, and we spent a fruitless afternoon hunting for the alleged eighth. Odd salvaged gargoyles, cornices, balustrades, statues, urns, crenellations, arches and colonnades are scattered everywhere ... not to mention a brace of cannon and an errant Buddha. Even the part where we stayed (some buildings are "hotel rooms", some are shops, most are self-catering cottages) sported weird bas-reliefs and statue-niches from goodness knows where. The designer modestly called it his Home for Fallen Buildings.

I have a nervous feeling of evoking a mere architectural junk-heap. Actually the overall effect is weirdly integrated and witty. As you wander around, there comes a realization there there are *no* accidental perspectives: viewed from any angle, the place has its own daft perfection. By cunning use of the sloping combe, a three-storey cottage called Telford's Tower dominates its corner of the skyline. A wholly non-functional "Campanile" stands even taller, and the Dome looms like that of St Paul's. None of these is actually anything like as big as our own perfectly ordinary Victorian house, but dizzy height is forced on you as an optical illusion. Speaking of suggestion, I kept wondering whether the innumerable and inexplicable old paintings of erupting volcanoes which line the walls of the "Town Hall" breakfast- and dining-rooms weren't intended as a cruel allusion to the dreaded holiday tummy....

Around the village are woods big enough to get lost in, which we promptly did, straying among forgotten exotica (bamboo, in North Wales?) and remnants of nineteenth-century gardens—fortunately I was sufficiently out of breath not to recite the whole of Swinburne's "A Forsaken Garden" into the teeth of the salt wind. A lost beach was heaped with the endless white skeletons of sea urchins; a grim little glade offered forlorn headstones and graves which proved to belong to a bygone someone's dogs. The Gilbert-and-Sullivan spirit of the village didn't penetrate this far, but there was the same sense of infinite remoteness from word processors and bank managers.

The funny thing about Sir Clough's fantasy world is that it's as durable as his favourite Ionic columns—robust enough to absorb and ignore tourists, cars, all the tentacles of a mundane Outside. Portmeirion's façade is curiously solid, with no peeling plastic or fairground impermanence. The spell extends even to the one place which does sort of drop to a different level of unreality: the "Prisoner" souvenir shop, lying behind the very door which in the series opened on Number 6's palatial lodgings. Again all was illusion: there's only one tiny room in there, containing Max Hora.

Max used to live near us in exotic Reading, Berkshire. A leading light of the "Prisoner" society, he's genuinely achieved his own fantasies. Imagine a high-tech fan offered the SF bookshop concession in the Houston control centre, or a John Norman devotee given his own bondage parlour. Max *lives* in Portmeirion, drives a remaindered Mini-Moke from the series, spends his winters writing booklets of "Prisoner" memorabilia, and in the summer flogs them to visitors. This is the place to buy your Patrick McGoohan photos, videos, badges, ballpens, notepaper, postcards and bumper-stickers (advt.). Max will also sell you a "Rover" weather-balloon: mere seconds after our arrival we found him coaxing one to sail across the central piazza's ornamental water, for the nostalgic benefit of yet another visiting TV crew.

I sipped much beer with this entrepreneur (fandom will always find a way), and heard the inner secrets of the tiny community of Portmeirion residents, living in odd corners of Sir Clough's follies like rats in the walls ... but the demented magic of the place still didn't fade. Outside in the warm evening, the village was empty and judiciously floodlit. Mere lack of population failed to lessen it or to evoke that grey abandoned-stage-set hollowness: Hazel and I would wander happily around flower-scented paths, past many a Palladian pediment or rococo grotto, until too tired for more. Damned if I try to analyse it further. You had to be there.

As indeed we decided to be, only a few months later, for a full week. Two Welsh holidays in a single year! I still don't know how I managed to justify it to that harsh taskmaster Langford who makes me work such long hours at the keyboard: but a way had to be found, since by the time we got home Hazel had already made a chart and was ticking off the days.

One thing led to another. On and off we've spent several weeks in the place since that great discovery in 1986, and learned that the uncrowded evenings are by far the best times; that it is unwise to rent the cottage outside whose bedroom window the local peacocks like to emit unbelievably hideous cries; and that falling in love with that whole corner of Wales can lead to the financial madness of buying a holiday flat just down the road in the shadow of

Harlech Castle. You don't need to visit so often when, every time you set off from Harlech on a shopping expedition, you can just see Portmeirion across the wide estuary, gleaming like some coveted toy from the pre-plastic era.

Time to hire another car and plan another Harlech trip...

1986

The Village is pretty much the same today, and the Prisoner shop still operates. Unfortunately 5,271,009 people crowd in there every day of the high season: if you want to feel a little of the magic, try to book a room overnight.

Hugos and Critical Mass

The first time I ever received an award from the wonderful world of SF was an occasion of slight embarrassment for me.

There had been a now mercifully forgotten fuss about the secret machinations behind the Nova Award, traditionally presented to the wrong British fanzine at the Birmingham (England) SF Group's annual Novacon. Plied with beer, I had volunteered to reform the selection procedure, and after earth-shattering consultations published the three-volume set of revised Nova voting rules (with the seven appendices) which was supposed to end controversy forever. What was a little embarrassing was the fact that in 1977, the first year of my new, enlightened voting system, I won the bloody award....

It took mere seconds to come to terms with glory and brace myself to receive a tasteful certificate, suitable for framing. Little had I realized the infinite artistic resource and sagacity of fandom. The architect of the 1977 trophy was Birmingham's—as opposed to America's—Ray Bradbury, and he really went to town. What still stands seventeen inches tall on my library mantelpiece has to be seen to be disbelieved.

First comes a marble base, and then a squat gilt cylinder, and on top of that a second marble slab, from which rises a proud column of purple and gold anodized aluminium with holes in it through which golden starbursts may be seen, and this is topped with a sort of platform chequered in glittery orange and turquoise plastic, supporting a chess-knight crafted from the same turquoise glitter, having in the side of its head an ingenious trapdoor which discloses strange cogwheels and watchsprings within, this whole crowning section of the artifact being enclosed in gilded wire loops carrying little balls to represent the planets in their orbits or (possibly) electrons caught in the act of defying the uncertainty principle. It is difficult to dust.

Some say that all this was intended to symbolize the works of the 1977 Novacon guest of honour, John Brunner, who nevertheless did not sue. Certainly the guest in the following year was Anne McCaffrey, and I distinctly remember the Nova winner leaving a thick trail of plastic wings and claws as he proudly carried off the 1978 award, modelled on the sort of dissolute dragon one imagines being favoured by Thomas Covenant the Unbeliever.

How I came to write this one is a mystery. Usually, discussions of Hugo awards bring me out in a red-hot bubbly blush. But this was ConFiction (the Dutch Worldcon) ... men in clogs, carrying tulips and wearing windmill beanies, must have twisted my arm.

These wondrous trophies of a bygone age (before the Novas settled down to being tasteful glass paperweights on midget plinths) came rather forcibly to mind when I read some bitchings by a British visitor to a recent US Worldcon. There had been a display of Hugos from times past, and the writer waxed rude about how shabby and unimaginative the Conspiracy '87 Hugo bases had been. They were, in other words, small and wooden, and you could get one into a suitcase. In fact—I will remark, preening smugly—you could get two into a suitcase.

Compare the glory of the 1988 Nolacon base, rising in a transplendent epoxy cone resembling giant inverted broccoli, towering above smaller recipients and generally looking not so much like an award as something which, if God noticed, would provoke a repetition of that distressing and undemocratic police action at Babel. My own representatives at Nolacon wept tears of relief and opened champagne with a liberal hand when I failed to win one of the things. "It would have given us," they said, "the freight of our lives."

Came Noreascon 3 in 1989, and my luck was in. Since for closely guarded financial reasons I wasn't there, my old pal Martin Hoare picked up the Hugo for me and subsequently forwarded the bill for his medical expenses. His slow progress back to Britain was charted by postcards of skyscrapers with captions like "Hugo Award, south elevation", and involved numerous sceptical Customs searches. While awaiting his arrival I asked a returned British editor, John Jarrold, what the 1989 Hugo actually looked like. He thought for a bit. "A green toilet seat, covered with a load of balls."

In due course I found that this was a shade unfair and that the Noreascon trophy possessed an artistry somewhat beyond the level of the 1977 Nova Award. It also possessed a high-pressure grease nipple and no instructions on its use, but that's another story. What had reduced Martin to a shattered wreck was that it was exceedingly heavy (ten pounds or so; a hefty marble dais was involved in the construction), exceedingly if not Nolaconnishly large (about sixteen inches high and ten across the base), and exceedingly fragile (one was documented as disintegrating in a crash of lost marbles within minutes of its presentation).

"I had to take it completely apart, and glue and screw it together again in England," apologized my faithful courier. "And even then, Customs gave me a hell of a time. All those suspicious ball bearings and metal parts...." I didn't question him too closely about whether the high-pressure grease nipple was original or a later interpolation from his workshop. He had suffered enough.

But his tales of hissed warnings at the 1989 Hugo ceremony ("*Careful*, it's a heavy bastard!") inevitably suggest the bad-taste scenario in which some frail and elderly author, beloved by us all, accepts the Hugo and is at once felled to the ground by the weight of our adulation...

Let's point no querulous fingers at past award designers, but make a note for the future. Most Hugos are likely to travel by air immediately after the convention, and what looks great at the presentation (not to mention terrific on the mantelpiece at home) can still be a nightmare to transport. Perhaps coming Worldcons should either refrain from trying to go beyond recent years' physical pinnacles of award grandeur, or should budget for the crating and shipping of things like the gigantic black monolith planned as the Hugo base for 2001.

Having now ruined my chances of any future awards, I'll close by reporting a conversation with an imaginary member of the ConFiction committee.

I asked: "About your own Hugos ... have I provided you with a base for discussion?"

"We have been thinking," he said, "of an enormous, traditional clog."

"But," I protested, "would not the Hugo itself, being a chrome-plated rocket thirteen and a half inches (or 35 of your Terran centimetres) high, seem incongruous in the context of a clog?"

"Aha! You have never seen our high-fashion, stiletto-heeled clogs? Our winners—not one of them from Holland—shall wear their Hugos home, and hop in stately procession from the ceremony."

He smiled, and vanished as mysteriously as he had come.

1990

The Moving Accident

Hazel and I have *actually moved*. We have *changed our address*. (Silence.) An *epic transition*, that's what we've achieved. (More silence.) Come on, surely such a unique and earth-shattering event deserves a round of applause, a shower of sympathy and wreaths, a rushing of International Red Cross parcels to the afflicted zone? ... Oh. Oh, I see. Other people do it too, you say, just as other people get married and spawn and die and (except conceivably in the last case) also regard the whole thing as a pretty cosmic event. You may have a point there, yes, but mere logical argument isn't going to stop me droning on as though I'd just fought World War III over the last couple of weeks, or personally witnessed the coming of the Antichrist, or received an impeccably produced fanzine from Keith Walker.

Long ago and far away—well, a few years ago in our old house a mile away—Hazel and I developed grandiose plans to avoid having to move. Shifting all those books, those typewriters, those filing cabinets, those fanzines, would be a fearful nightmare, we told one another wisely, and how right we were. Our scheme for universal domination and perpetual immobility involved an intricate land-swapping deal which I dreamt up one night after six or seven pints of inspiration. The old house at 22 Northumberland Avenue had a ridiculously long garden (the shed at the far end was only dimly visible through a blue haze of distance, and it was wisest to take a few days' provisions when setting out to trace the lawnmower), while along the side of said garden ran a disused pathway giving access to a local school which actively didn't want access from that side, as evidenced by the thickly rusted lock and chains which gave the iron street-gate a cheery prison aspect.

Phase I of the Master Plan went rumbling into motion as I sent successive letters to the school headmaster, the local education authority, the council planning office, and the Royal County of Berkshire Property Department, plus solicitors, building societies and suchlike riffraff, and (for reasons never too clearly explained) the Superintendent of Parks and Woodland. In phrases too fulsome, verbose and polysyllabic to be set down here—I have *some* pride—these letters contained a thickly camouflaged version of Langford's Plan. Stripped to its simplest terms by ruthless use of Occam's Razor, symbolic logic, and imperfectly recollected episodes of *Foundation*, it went: "I've thought of this way to hugely enhance the value of our property by a land swap which will do no one else any good at all...."

After a pause sufficient for the traditional monkeys to have polished off Shakespeare, submitted all the tragedies to *Asimov's* and collected a "futility" rejection slip for each, the forces of Berkshire began to move. "Yes," they replied. A year and a half after my letter, our garden became fifty feet shorter

101

and several feet wider, and next to the house there was now room for a glorious extension to accommodate wild orgies and the ever-increasing book collection, preferably in different rooms. A year after this golden moment, the council even got round to fencing the new bottom of the garden, cutting us off forever from the distant horizon where the shed would have been if it hadn't come to pieces in my rough hands as I struggled to lug it closer to the house. You can imagine what I'm like with fine wine-glasses of cut crystal, when I have this effect on garden sheds.

When it came to removing the six-foot wooden side-fence separating us from our new strip of asphalt garden, Langford the Engine of Destruction was in his element. (*The Plain People of Fandom*: Bet you broke a lot of hammers and tyre-irons doing that. *Me* [startled]: How did you know that?) The rotted wood became a daily bonfire, much admired by the school's warped pupils, who climbed up a still needed section of fence to gape, merrily hurling each other's clothing and exercise books on to the pyre. When they started doing the same with fragments of fence and Hazel's favourite elder-tree, it was time for the fannish intellect to take action. Early one morning I stole down the garden and thickly anointed the top of that fence with gooey black duplicator ink. The sounds which ensued ... but I digress.

Manifestly we'd never need to move house now. Illimitable space was ours for the taking, requiring only that we build a few brick walls around it. Starry-eyed, Hazel and I sketched out an extension barely smaller than the original house; only with difficulty did I prevent her from adding minarets and pinnacles, and only with even greater difficulty did she block my plans for a vast cellar from which real beer could be hand-pumped to the office, the library, the dining room, the bedroom....

"Ha," said the architect whom we summoned from the vasty deep. "Wouldn't be surprised if they've got an easement here." With sudden violence he flung back this iron lid set in the newly-acquired land, something we'd hitherto failed to notice, and vanished down a brick shaft into the bowels of the earth. Strange cries echoed from the depths, as though he'd met an alligator or a Harlan Ellison story. He returned slightly flushed, which prefigured his next words: "Main sewer," he carolled happily. "Can't build anything big on that," he continued in a paean of joy. "That plan of yours is right out," he concluded, barely able to contain his ecstasy.

"So?" we asked suspiciously.

"So we'll just have to stick to one storey, that's all, and that means I can find you some standard designs which will be much easier to draw up—"

"It'll be a box!" Hazel shrieked. "I've seen these standard extensions, and always it's a horrible little rectangular box just stuck down there by the side of the house looking like nothing on earth and completely out of keeping with the Edwardian brickwork! A *box*!"

The architect paled slightly, then rallied and drew himself up to his full height of not very much at all. "Naturally anything which I design will be a symphony of brickwork which at once blends imperceptibly into the original scheme and highlights its inner beauties in an, as it were, contrapuntal mode," he did not say, but it was along those lines. Haughtily he flounced away, while Hazel and I looked at one another with a wild surmise.

And sure enough, with the speed of a striking sex-crazed strooka (my favourite SF simile, culled from Ken Bulmer's remainders), there came a fantastically detailed set of plans, even covering the brand of tea the builders were to drink while not engaged in their traditional 15-minute work break. Hazel looked at the plans. I looked at Hazel, and cowered slightly.

"IT'S A BOX!!!"

"What it is," I said unconvincingly, "is that the flat roof highlights the beauty of our sloping one, as it were contrapuntally, while the robust dissonance of the picture window at the front provides a striking yet satisfying contrast with the totally different design of the existing sash windows. Apart from that, it's a rotten little box."

"Send it back and make him change it," said Hazel with finality.

The small but perfectly formed architect was all too ready to change it, asking only for a few more days of Creative Thought and a corresponding number of noughts added to his fee. "The way you want it, it's more *expensive*," he said plaintively. "I was trying to save you *money*."

"A tent would have been even cheaper, but we didn't order a tent either," I distantly observed, and realized my mistake as a red gleam came into the tiny architectural eyes and somewhere an invisible cash register went *ting* to indicate the swelling of our bill by several pounds' pique money.

More time passed, months creeping by with the glacial inexorability of some vast, ponderous force of nature or even the post office itself. Three years from the formulation of the Master Scheme, we were finally ready with plans, detailed planning permission (without which you are not allowed the smallest erection in this crowded country) and even the all-dreaded building regulations permission (which ensures not only the continued employment of building regulations inspectors but also that whatever you finally construct will be safe, sturdy, enduring and too expensive). It was February, 1982. The glorious transformation of 22 Northumberland Avenue, Reading, into a fannish paradise seemed assured.

Then we called in the builder.

I still have nightmares about the builder.

Ming the Merciless would have gaped in sick envy. The galaxy-smashing supervillains of our favourite literature were relegated to mere delinquents by comparison with the bale-fires of destruction which coruscated in our builder's eyes. Not that he was unsympathetic: he couldn't wait to start. First he would bore innumerable large holes through the wall of the upstairs front room, headily disregarding obstacles like plaster and wallpaper.

"But that's my office!" I wailed. "The whole point of building this extension rather than moving is so I can keep working in my office."

After the holes had been gouged out and jacks inserted to stop everything collapsing, the demon builder then proposed to demolish the wall of the room underneath and, with all phasers blasting on maximum intensity, to ravage unchecked through the remaining habitable enclaves downstairs, finally overrunning every other room with fire and the sword on the flimsy pretext of rewiring and laying new gas pipes.

Then, it seemed, he would consider building the new bits.

"But," I said, and babbled incoherent things like "7000 books ... desks ... typewriters ... filing cabinets ... duplicator ... copier ... computer..."

"Furniture," Hazel suggested.

"That too."

"All that'll have to go into storage," said Genghis Khan cheerily, unwilling to let mere chattels obstruct his merry path of devastation.

"No," said Hazel, 0.3 nanoseconds after the builder's departure.

"Tomorrow to fresh woods and pastures new," I agreed.

Like lapsed believers or lapsed atheists who rush at once to the opposite extreme, the failure of our five-year master plan sent us straight out to the forbidden temples of Reading's estate agents.

There was the pushy agent who loudly insisted that we had to sell our house through him as a first priority before even considering beginning to think of looking at any others: he would have done well with the Feckle Freezer Co., but we never dared go back in case he started flogging us insurance, double glazing and encyclopaedias. There were all the dim agents who listened carefully to our demand for a large old house in the university area with at least four bedrooms, and months later were still posting an unending succession of brochures for small modern three-bedroomed shoeboxes in scrofulous new estates several miles outside Reading. There were the reclusive or hermetic agents who wrote down our requirements in tedious detail but for some reason never came up with anything at all—doubtless not real businessfolk but front organizations for the CIA. And there were the friendly agents who'd sold us 22 Northumberland Avenue and even remembered us: can it be that sensitive fannish faces do indeed stick in the mind? Or had I merely been wearing my propeller beanie on both occasions?

We staggered home with a small pantechnicon load of papers which (after elimination of anything small, new, misplaced, or liable to make certain critics cry "It's a box!") reduced themselves to three possibles.

Only three? That evening we stalked through fog all round the university area of Reading, which bristled with *FOR SALE* signs bearing the names of already-visited agents who were obviously in a conspiracy to conceal these homes from such unworthy buyers as us. Whenever we enquired about one of these palaces, there'd be a sudden look of consternation from the relevant agent; a panic-stricken search through the records; an emergence with smiles of vast relief: "Ah, we've *just* sold that one..."

As it happened, we only went over three houses and came to a final decision mere days after the quest began. One contained more rooms than we'd ever dreamed of, straggling in a narrow way over four or five storeys with little rooms everywhere: trouble was, there weren't any big rooms, as so necessary for drunken fannish riots and the not all that different meetings of the almost famous "Pieria" writers' mob (wherein non-sober folk like Rob Holdstock, Mike Scott Rohan, Andrew Stephenson, Garry Kilworth *et al.* gather together to piss on the newest Langford story. This is all quite democratic since I have the reciprocal right to praise their latest efforts). The second house stank of death, not merely because the owner had died there mere weeks before, but also owing to the jolly decor of brown from top to bottom, the murderously jagged-edged gas mantles (yes, gas mantles) which jutted everywhere and did me an injury not convenient to describe, the vast garden which resembled the Amazon rain forest in everything including size and wrapped the whole gloomy house in a hideous dank embrace....

We bought the third house, 94 London Road, a Victorian semi dating from 1878. It's rambling and peculiar, from the weevil-infested cellar to the upper reaches where thin air makes it difficult to breathe. There are inexplicable oddities like the narrow room twenty-four feet long up on the second-and-a-half story; the mysterious wires and pipes which erupt from walls or ceilings, run a little way and disappear into holes like startled mice; the nodes on various walls where gas-mantle outlets were sealed off, not always successfully, as the Southern Gas emergency service can testify; the apparent cupboards on upper floors which give access to long grimy crawlspaces in the angles of the roof and offer an endless bounty of small birds' skeletons; the skylight which looks not at the sky but into a hidden roofspace lit by two more skylights, one of which is not ours; the owls which hoot and moan high up in the sinister Tower of Flints.... Perhaps I exaggerate.

The proprietor of all this was a Mrs Vieri, widow of a button importer, which did at least explain the five million buttons packed in neat boxes up in the attic room. (Not to mention the constant trickle of further buttons which are still emerging from cracks in every floor and skirting-board.) "Actually she's *Lady* Vieri," dribbled the friendly agent, "and I think she's Einstein's granddaughter or something as well." Every estate agent loves a lord, and Hazel too was much taken by this close encounter of the noble kind—even if she should have learned better after meeting that self-confessedly famous skiffy author Lord St Davids, who in tones of paralysing tedium told her all the things he had done in various wars, several times.

Luckily Mrs Vieri's title proved to be an off-the-peg Italian one picked up via her late hubby, which doesn't really count, so Hazel stopped grovelling and started making friends—to such good effect that we were shifting books into the long-neglected upper rooms of 94 London Road long before actually owning the place. I will only add that Mrs V. was then officially 65, the actual figure of 72 not being admitted except to people she'd known more than say

45 seconds, and was at once extremely small and hideously dynamic: I pale at the thought of her 30-mile walks every Wednesday, not to mention little hobbies like caring for about a dozen "old ladies" of 80-odd, supporting all local hospitals single-handed, and running every charity within ten miles. Sometimes I feel even more useless than I look. However...

However, we had the problem of selling our house. It was easy, as it turned out. Someone walked in, peered around, announced his intention of converting the place to flats (*flats*! It was Ballard's "Billennium" all over again), and airily made a cash offer. "Selling your house is easy," we bragged for three months while the slow process of buying 94 London Road creaked on: surveys, oaths signed in blood that we would destroy much lovable wildlife (wet rot, weevils, *Anobium punctatum* alias common furniture beetle alias—all right —wood-worm ... everything but death-watch) to pacify cruel Sir Jasper at the building society and have him give us a mortgage, lengthy waiting while the people who were selling Mrs V. a house tried to finalize their divorce and decide which half of the house which of them would be selling....

Proposition: No house deal is ever completed. Proof: The people who are moving in have to sell their former house while those moving out have to buy a new one. Extend by induction to infinity. For financial reasons all purchases/ sales in this infinite chain need to be completed on the same day. Now, by Murphy's Corollary, at least one transaction in the chain will fall through.... The world is only saved by the existence of *first-time* buyers, naive and dewy-eyed creatures who don't have houses to sell and who wonder why estate agents fall upon them with flattery and blandishments. Additionally there are those who leave their homes for the hereafter or (the same as far as disappointed estate agents are concerned) rented flats. This glum aside leads us to:

The disaster came, of course, mere seconds before contracts could be irrevocably exchanged for the Northumberland Avenue sale and the London Road purchase. Our friendly converter of formerly nice houses to flats had had time, after all the delay, to discover that on the whole Reading Council was inclined to piss from a great height on such perpetrators of vileness. "Quite right too," said Hazel, "except just this once." No chance of planning permission. No chance of our other old friend building regulations permission. Suddenly, after three months during which it hadn't been on the market, we found ourselves the proud owners of an unsold house. The transition was so swift that I'd turned away three prospective buyers with the words "It's sold," before the lethargic estate agents mentioned to me that it wasn't. Everything would have collapsed utterly had I not persuaded another rapacious Sir Jasper at my bank to hand over a vast temporary loan, allowing us to buy the new place with nothing to worry about bar interest rates not as generous as Shylock's.

In mere days we'd sold the house again, this time to a repellent chap from British Rail who came round with his tame builder in tow. Said builder kept going "tut" at things like our wiring, windows, walls, floor, ceiling, roof, doors and other really quite minor points, and at the end of the tour explained that it would cost nearly £3000 to make this rotten little slum inhabitable. Having inhabited it for six years without social obloquy, I felt peeved: but the thought of that bank loan interest made us gulp and accept a slightly insulting offer. As with pimping or writing for Robert Hale & Co., there is no way to deal in property and keep one's pride.

Then it was time to move, a really cheapo economy-style move since we couldn't afford real removal men nor trust them to know which boxes of books were too flimsy to be stacked (the ones labelled *Priceless Masterpieces* contained irreplaceable treasure in the shape of books by or featuring me). "Fear not," said mighty Martin Hoare, "I'll repair my lovable old London taxi and we can shift most of the stuff in that." Five years later he still means to repair that taxi, the wheel-rims of which have now sunk interestingly through the tyres.

The alternative low-cost removal van proved to be owned and driven by a vibrant entrepreneur whom Mrs V. continually addressed as "young woman" since Mrs Removals was a mere debutante of 65. From time to time I still have to wander up to that long room three flights of stairs from the front door, and assure myself that these two ladies, plus a Hazel suffering from general prostration, plus ineffectual me, did somehow get our 7000 volumes up there during a heatwave. It's the sort of achievement which makes Erich von Däniken write books explaining how the primitive, cave-dwelling Reading tribes could never have coped without the aid of flying saucers armed with antigravity winches, teleportation units and gigantic, pyramidal removal men. He would have added a second fleet on discovering our further feat of stuffing all the heavy furniture upstairs as well—as required by the satanic Mortgage Pact, which demanded that the ground floor be wood-wormed and damp-proofed real soon now, meaning that every floorboard was at the worm-hunters' mercy....

Shortly afterwards there was a distressing little scene with the man from British Rail, who rang and at great length enumerated all the remedial things which he now realized had to be done to our appalling heap of wattle-and-daub in Northumberland Avenue, things which he claimed to have realized *since* the traumatic verdict of his builder, and anyway, um, er, as it were, he was withdrawing his offer, so there. I suppressed the urge to shout something ideologically unsound like "I suppose you can't afford even a bleeding hut on your pitiful strike pay!" (BR having roused great wrath in me lately by standing between me and many a merry event in London, thanks to being on strike). Subsequently I rang our estate agents to say, "That bugger's cocked the whole thing up, soddit!" ["Mr Batten has chosen to reconsider his purchase offer in the light of what he claims to be unacceptable renovation costs."] I'm ashamed to admit being hugely cheered by the response: "Ah, we know about him—don't you listen to what he tells you—he can't afford to buy any house at all now, on account of he's lost his job for being such a militant union agitator that even the union didn't want him around any more...."

Almost instantly we resold the place, to a chap who went to Cambridge: "So he must be all right, mustn't he?" said Hazel. "Not as all right as if he'd been to Oxford," I allowed, "but he'll do."

But this tiny saga of horror beyond one fan's comprehension does not come to any tidy end. We had a quick fannish housewarming, largely distinguished by (a) Grand Tours of the house inflicted by Hazel on anyone who dared to scale the heights or plumb the depths; (b) famous Abigail Frost, who took note of Hazel's "no smoking" rule and left for a quick fag—via the front window, offering all of London Road (otherwise known as the A4) a long glimpse of turquoise-stockinged legs, and puffing her way about the front garden in her exotic party ensemble until everyone inside had had the chance to say, "With Abi there you don't need to hang out a red light."

Then Armageddon came. The gasmen found *another* leak (emergency team summoned, huge holes in front garden, Langford returns swayingly from One Tun meeting to find a Hazel-lettered sign on the front gate saying BE-WARE OF THE PIT). The dreaded wormfolk ripped out and replaced (in fetchingly different colours) the various squashy spots of downstairs flooring which proved to be supported by mighty joists whose texture now resembled a loofah. The formerly musty and disgusting cellar sprouted a smart new ceiling, a series of air-vents, a new fuse box (all my own work) and strip lighting, making it inappropriate to install the planned cask of Amontillado. A pervading pong of embalming fluid indicated the chemical damp-proofing injected into all ground-floor walls, the injection holes being filled with the little plastic bungs we still can't help calling tappens. A further pervading pong of vermicide had something to do with the hideous deaths of innumerable woodworm, at a price suggesting they were individually tracked down by private detective agencies and hit with small gold hammers.

Let's pass over the roof repairs (involving scaffolding which as it was dismantled burst intriguingly through the front window to where a visiting Mary and Bill Burns were, briefly, asleep), the endemic woodlice, the Great Slug which ravaged at will over the breakfast-room carpet, the leaky window-frames, the drunken fireplace (quite rectilinear before it was "repaired"), the pigeon-hole (a rotted gap in what builders call the undereave soffit, enabling pigeons to mate noisily in the ceiling over Hazel's sleeping head, not to mention playing Rollerball with bits of loose slate when other amusements palled).... You will get the idea. A 109-year-old house is full-time work for the rest of one's life; but we do rather like it.

"Never again," said Hazel. "We're never going to move again."

"That's what we said in 1976," I dreamily recalled.

"Aaaaargh!" concluded Hazel; and, on the whole, I agree.

1982

Hazel and I have still not moved again. Nowadays there are lots more than 25,000 books to worry about ... but I've grown rather subdued about the size of my collection since touring John Clute's.

The Leaky Establishment: The Final Drips

I feel a little bit guilty about the subject of this talk. It wasn't entirely my fault; I woke up after convention chairman Steve Green had *persuaded* me, and found the words "You are giving a Novacon 14 talk on your book *The Leaky Establishment*" tattooed on my typing finger. Dimly I remembered the terrible hours of coercion in the bar, and how Steve finally clinched it by offering me a two-week all-expenses-paid holiday in lovely Ireland at the home of Anne McCaffrey. It was either that or give this talk.

The guilt is because I reckon I'm here on false pretences: I ought to be talking about science fiction, or at any rate fiction, and most of *The Leaky Establishment* is in fact autobiography. It does actually contain an SF idea, and an exceedingly daft one too, but... Once or twice I've read a few chapters to people (this was before all my friends bought earplugs), and was boggled to find that they fell about laughing not at the jokes but at what I thought were ordinary, unfunny details of Civil Service life. Like the routine way in which, in my part of the Civil Service, large randy security men were forever groping your thighs on the pretext of searching for suspicious lumps of plutonium hidden in your jockstrap.

Perhaps I should start by explaining how I ended up chasing neutrons for five years at the Atomic Weapons Research Establishment—a job which has failed to impress anybody in the whole world except Greg Benford. "Why did you quit Big Science Biz?" he asked me in tones of concern. I told him how much a grateful British government pays its weapons physicists, and he fainted.

So it is time to tell the true story at last. A story of shame and degradation, of pitiful struggling against implacable necessity, and, above all, of hangovers. Long ago in the mists of 1974 I woke up with a hangover—some things never change—and discovered that all my mates at Oxford had been applying for jobs. I personally had been too busy celebrating my physics finals, such a major event in the Langford career that I celebrated more or less continuously for six months before it happened.

Since I was more sensible then than I am now, I decided not to become a freelance writer. The lure of a free pint of fizzy beer at Novacon 14 was balanced by the fact that in '74 I'd only sold one short story, to Ken Bulmer, for £13.30 payable in several instalments; while my masterpiece "Sex Pirates of the Blood Asteroid" had merely collected rejection slips, from both the *Christian Science Monitor* and the *Times Literary Supplement*. Accordingly I nipped

---

More autobiography. See also the short story "Leaks" in this very volume.

round to the Oxford careers office and enquired about vacancies for top-salaried executives with a Jag provided by the company. What I cunningly kept up my sleeve for the time being was that at a pinch I was prepared to settle for an Aston Martin.

Of course it turned out that all the really cushy jobs had been snapped up, right down the line from Chairman of ICI to saggar maker's bottom knocker. Sneering at my pitiful grovellings, they explained that there were only five things for late, hungover physicists to apply for, and one of them was a UB40.[1] I went away with the other four application forms and started inventing lies about my star-studded career to date.

Oh dear, it all comes back, like the curry I had at Mancon. I applied to IBM and they lost my application in the infallible data-processing system. I applied to the Post Office, and I needn't tell you how that application got lost. I applied to ICL, famous lame-duck computer company, with the promise that my as yet untapped talents could make them even lamer. They actually invited me to spend a luxurious weekend at one of their places, and it was there that I made a huge tactical error—one which I am not repeating at this convention. I tried to demonstrate what a reliable, responsible programmer I'd make, by not drinking much. I should have known this was a mistake when I reflected that ICL had already taken on Martin Hoare.

What was left was the Ministry of Defence. I approached their interview room with an ominous sense of doom and foreboding—which was in fact another hangover—convinced they were going to expose my pitiful ignorance with sudden trick questions like "Newton's laws of motion: how many are there?" or "E equals mc *what*?" Inside, this evil-looking fellow stared at me with the sort of expression seen on Joseph Nicholas's face as he weighs the literary merits of the latest Perry Rhodan novel. He said: "Mr Langford, just one simple question. Can you explain to me the nature and significance of the Mössbauer effect?"

Thus it was that I became a scientific officer at Aldermaston; and only years after, when I'd shaken the radioactive dust of the place from off my shoes forever, did I tell anyone that the day before that interview, I'd been doing an Oxford physics practical on the Mössbauer effect.

There were a few other formalities, such as being Positively Vetted—which only *sounds* like Civil Service jargon for a vasectomy. Large thugs covered in hideous scars kept breaking down doors to interrogate people about my sexual preferences—I got the impression that they received some slightly inventive answers. At least I've never worked out why at one interview I was shown pictures of melons and asked about my reactions.

Around then came the first of the amazing incidents which I couldn't resist putting into the novel but which nobody can believe really happened. It

---

[1] Note for foreigners: in Britain a UB40 is a document identifying you as someone receiving unemployment benefit. Don't ask about the preceding UB1 to UB39.... .

was my last week in Oxford, the morning after the college ball, and I was rudely awakened at an unnatural hour—about 12 noon, as I remember. I staggered out in my dressing-gown to find another security investigator in the hallway, who explained that while interrogating me for three hours on the previous day while shining lights in my eyes, he'd forgotten the most important question of all. "Mr Langford," he said, "are you ... a homosexual?" Suddenly I had the feeling that my perfectly ordinary dressing-gown was all covered with exotic brocade in the Oscar Wilde fashion. Summoning up all my courage, I said "No." He went away.

Meanwhile, inside my room, a certain lady whose name I will not drag through the mire, but whom I later married, was giggling uncontrollably into the pillow.

My dressing-gown may have caused the Ministry of Defence to doubt, but the balance was tipped in my favour when a month or so later I and several others got arrested for detonating parts of Oxford with fireworks. This apparently showed the right spirit. The Crown Court judge actually said more or less this, and I felt a slight twinge of unease when (after slamming one of my mates with a two-year prison sentence) he expressed pious hopes that Mr Langford's little prank would have no effect on his chosen career in the business of destroying human civilization as we know it.

So I started five surreal years at AWRE Aldermaston, and after the first six months I knew that no matter what it said in the Official Secrets Act, I could get away with putting almost every detail into a novel. Not only would everyone think it sheer fantasy, the MoD itself surely wouldn't dare admit some things were true.... One example that didn't get into *Leaky* was the time when as I was sitting casually in the reactor control room drinking tea, a reputable nuclear scientist came sprinting through, clutching an object of classified size [gestures with hands a classified distance apart] wrapped in a lab coat. This was in fact the core of Britain's Independent Nuclear Deterrent, which my superior officer wished to put away so he could get to the bank before it closed. It occurred to me that had I so much as moved my foot two inches and tripped him, there could have been a lot of interesting bits of plutonium on the floor, and later on some exciting newspaper publicity about the funerals.

As a matter of fact, the way they flung the radioactives around I'm surprised there wasn't a cardboard box by the main exit with a sign saying KEEP BERKSHIRE TIDY—PLEASE PLACE PLUTONIUM HERE. One of my colleagues managed to lose an uranium sample in the 50 yards between his office and the reactor: the area was mostly grass and we waited for ages in hope of seeing the results predicted by the best SF, such as a mutant clump of purple carnivorous grass entangling stray technicians in its deadly tendrils. All that happened was that one patch went a bit brownish, and the scientists stopped picking the mushrooms which every autumn grew round the reactor building in fairy rings. I thought it very sporting of them to let the security police have first pick just for once.

Some extremely nasty radioactive material was also involved in an experiment I designed, an experiment so classified that I can tell you nothing about it except that it happened in Nevada.... By the way, if any of you have actually managed to outwit my publishers and buy a copy of *Leaky*, I have a small correction for the text. Thinking that Nevada was classified, I wrote Arizona instead, and only when the book was published did I find that everyone knew which state the Americans use for their underground tests. (Speaking of which, I came across the interesting fact that in one such test, a beam of radiation was supposed to go through a little hole to do things to a poor defenceless bit of test material—and the beam missed the hole by a quarter of an inch. You may have had misgivings about the American strike capability, but I bet you hadn't realized they could fail to hit something at two hundred yards' range with an atomic bomb.)

Where was I? There was this experimental capsule, whose destination I cannot reveal to you, incredibly fragile yet containing extraordinarily dangerous substances. It stood on a laboratory bench, and all that remained was to put the lid on. A trained British craftsman set to work; the lid stuck and wouldn't go on straight; and he started hitting it with a big hammer. I don't quite remember how I and five other scientists managed to teleport outside the suddenly closed door.

After all this it was no surprise when Aldermaston had its big flap about plutonium contamination. Some people contained so much of the stuff that their doctors were starting to notice it as a weight problem. The famous unofficial signs appeared in the AWRE library, saying "To avoid assembling a critical mass, staff are requested not to gather in groups of more than 5 and to remain at least 0.6 metres apart (1.2 metres if wet)." Everybody who'd so much as looked at the plutonium entry in the periodic table was ordered to report for checking under the Whole Body Monitor, an elaborate device using sophisticated electronics to tell whether or not you still had a whole body. Aldermaston's enthusiasm for investing in this essential safety equipment was so great that the nearest monitor was twenty miles away at Harwell.

I duly went there and had my inmost secrets probed: they warned me that there could be a certain amount of experimental error in the reading, and those of you with an intensive scientific training may judge that this was correct. Here's the letter I eventually received from the Superintendent of Personnel Safety:

> Dear Mr Langford,
>   The estimate of plutonium in the lungs resulting from the whole body monitor tests at AWRE Harwell on 19 October 1978 is minus thirty-nine nanocuries. This result has been passed to the Dose Evaluation panel for consideration ...

You may mock, but I found it strangely reassuring to know I could playfully nibble a full 39 nanocuries of Pu before reaching the zero level of contamination. (By the way, those on the inside never refer to it as plutonium or Pu: you show you're on friendly first-name terms with the stuff by calling it "plute".) One good reason for my state of extreme purity and cleanliness—at least back in 1978—was that I spent most of my time playing with computers instead of entering the regular Independent Deterrent Egg'n'Spoon Races. With the Aldermaston computer system, what got contaminated was my brain.

The set-up at AWRE bore about the same relation to real computers as (in the organizational field) the British SF Association Ltd does to IBM. The advanced programming facilities available to Britain's crack nuclear scientists consisted of a wide choice of FORTRAN. The computer itself lived in a sort of blockhouse guarded by swarms of security men almost as merciless and brutal as those at Seacon '84. Nothing could penetrate the system's impregnable defences! Nothing, that is, except the coded information flowing along handy, tappable cables to terminals around and even off the site. By terminals I mean, of course, teletypes. The whole thing must have been under a preservation order as a magnificent example of 1950s industrial archaeology.

Again, I hit the problem of things which people refuse to believe. I had a bit in *Leaky* about an exciting arcade-action Space Invaders game which ran on a teletype. I've given up trying to persuade anyone that this was mere cold historical fact. You had to be there. There was real sense-of-wonder in reading the official manual which went on about the elaborate defences of the AWRE computer operating system, and then finding you could crash the whole network by compiling a perfectly legal program in FORTRAN.

My favourite memory is of a useful little feature which the computer staff themselves proudly offered to users: it was supposed to make it easy to scan through the information you had stored in the machine. It did. It also made it easy to scan through all the secret password files. They took the feature away again quite quickly when I pointed this out; I suggested an OBE for contributions to national security would be in order, but the mean buggers wouldn't give me one.

Computers are boring and I can hear the crash of catatonic bodies in the aisles, but I can't resist telling about the amazing Aldermaston micro. One day somebody had the bright idea of filling a van with radiation detectors so they could cruise the streets just like the TV-licence people, spotting illegal nuclear stockpiles. Like the one accidentally acquired by the hero of my book. (All the van ever did detect, I gather, was a radioactive patch on the road near Mortimer in Berkshire. Fell off the back of a lorry, I suppose.) I drew the short straw and had to suss out a microcomputer to analyse all the rubbish picked up by the detectors—I suppose it would have been embarrassing if hordes of security guards had burst from the van and riddled someone with bullets, only to discover he was merely carrying an outsize luminous watch.

The trouble was, this was the MoD and there were budget problems. I could sign for as many things as I liked which cost £50 or less, but the full weight of bureaucracy would land on the back of my neck if I dared write out a single chitty for a forbidden amount like £50.10. We ended up buying some cheap chips, and persuading a technician to build a micro from scratch, while I spent eight weeks of my life writing machine code for the wretched thing. At last the great unveiling came, and to my ill-concealed surprise the whole shambles worked, and the AWRE bigwigs looked on it and saw that it was good. So of course it was junked. After all, the project could now be given a big budget, and with a big budget there was no point or prestige value in Langford's nasty little shoestring computer. They spent a few thousand on a pretty minicomputer instead, and I was secretly pleased when it failed to work as well.

This was of course quite logical in bureaucratic terms, in the same way that it was logical for the scientists who actually did AWRE's work to inhabit horrible disintegrating wooden huts on the far side of the marshy bit of the site, while mere parasites like typists and security men got luxury purpose-built offices near the main gate. Again, the logic of seniority meant that I had to be secretary of two nuclear policy committees and take all the minutes, my chief qualification being that I was the only person on either committee who was deaf. The solution was to sit next to the committee chairman in an attitude of sycophancy and ignore all distractions, such as other people's voices. Those minutes were Impressionist works of art, whole vistas of unspoken meaning conveyed in a few deft words like "The chairman agreed. The chairman disagreed. The chairman could not endorse the first proposal but was in sympathy with the second ..." Scarred by my appalling experiences on such committees, I find I'm now wickedly prejudiced against exciting events like BSFA meetings, even when the speaker is someone charismatic like Alan Dorey. In fact, especially when ... no, I mustn't be cruel.

I'm also prejudiced against engineers. My main contact with engineers at Aldermaston was when one rang up, explained that his section had spent two years working on some new and ever so classified substance, and could I now do all the theoretical background work for them in, say, one week? Ever willing to oblige (which means, ever willing to find an excuse for putting off my own urgent work), I asked for some vital information like the density of the stuff. "Density?" he said, as though I'd made a suggestion so obscene he didn't want to admit he understood it. "I'll ring you back," he said. After a week of what I suppose must have been massed research efforts by his entire engineering team, he rang me back. This time he sounded actively hostile: "I've got the information you asked for. We've measured a piece of the material. It's 5mm by 10mm by 25mm, and it weighs umptitum grams. Can you work out the density from that?" Faintly I assured him that with the aid of mainframe computers I probably could.

Speaking of engineers leads naturally to engines and, specifically, cranks. Every so often I'd get appalling wads of badly duplicated bumf in my IN tray:

as well as security regulations, there would be new theories of physics submitted to AWRE's front office and passed to the nearest convenient sucker (me), just in case they contained the ultimate secret of life, the Universe and everything. One chap had a brilliant, self-consistent theory of atomic and nuclear structure: I particularly liked the way in which every single element as yet discovered by science was a special case, an exception which proved the fellow's general rule. One of the predictions of this revolutionary theory was that nuclear weapons couldn't possibly work, and I thought it kind of the author to let us know. However, I was prejudiced against him because he didn't even believe in the Mössbauer effect....

The best bit of alternative science to land on my desk was Robert Kingsley Morison's *An Experiment with Space*, which I have here—

> Strenuous but pathetic attempts have been made by terrestrial air forces to obtain possession of extraterrestrial knowledge by capturing an alien space vehicle.... This book suggests a more sensible approach. *An Experiment with Space* not only lessens the chance of a national monopoly on levitation but also takes us beyond the stage of idolizing the Space Brothers. Robert Morison conceived a simple idea for generating levitational forces in 1969; but not until August 1979 could he assemble enough scientific and philosophical thoughts for a book. Anyone who succeeds in mastering gravity will make possible a vast expansion of humanity's horizons—thus enabling men to change.

He doesn't say what it'll enable women to do. Anyway, the front cover blurb spills the Secret: "Internal vortex lifts 9-metre disc by space dynamics: angular velocities of 20000 to 40000 revs/min mean molecules moving at 11 km/s. YOUR PLANET NEEDS YOU to consider and investigate possibilities that may radically transform civilization. Like neutralizing gravity and debunking materialism." The general idea is that molecules at the edge of this spinning disc are moving at orbital velocity and therefore the whole disc will naturally drift off into orbit. One of us dropped the author a note asking why CERN at Geneva, with particles circling its storage rings at nearly the speed of light, hadn't passed the orbit of Pluto long ago. I understand the reply was that that was part of the worldwide cover-up, and that to fool the public CERN had been secretly bolted down.

My collection of anecdotes about the horrible grottiness of Aldermaston used to be endless. Those MoD policemen fondling helpless young scientific officers' thighs. The amazing gate security system whereby all attempts to smuggle out plutonium were presumed to happen in the evening so there was no need to spot-check people or cars at lunchtime (this, no doubt, based on close study of office hours at the Kremlin). The 5-megawatt reactor from the days before the energy crisis was invented, which blithely threw away its entire heat output into the surrounding air (yes, it was a swimming-pool reactor; yes, somebody did fall in). The even more conservation-conscious site heating, with live steam being carried round a five-mile perimeter fence by aboveground pipes which not only leaked at the joints but to boost heat-loss by radiation were painted black. The Royal Visit, with the Queen being treated to a display of amazingly incontinent MoD guard-dogs. The local newspaper which really believed and printed the story that AWRE scientists had to drink twelve pints of beer each day to flush neutron contamination from their bodies...

Well, I could go on forever, and by the time I'd finished writing the bloody book—including all this and more—I felt I had gone on forever. (The same drained feeling is experienced by many people who've read it.) So for further sordid details I refer you to the novel itself: just go to any major bookshop and they will explain they've never heard of it. Except for Rog Peyton, who with a huge and enthusiastic smile will say, "Sold out." That's the hardback: I'm glad to say Sphere Books decided to publish a paperback conveniently in time for Novacon, but unfortunately they picked Novacon 15.

I got out of Aldermaston in 1980 for half a dozen reasons. One was that, as I've said until even I am bored with hearing me say it, I found I was earning less than civil servants who were of technically lower rank but worked in boom areas like the Department of Unemployment: this was galling to my elitist soul. Again, Joseph Nicholas used to spit on me in the streets, and big Rob Holdstock would accost me saying, "I want to know what you do vivisecting those poor neutrons at Aldermaston: I won't understand a word of it but I have a right to know!" Again, the MoD mandarins wouldn't even let me take unpaid leave to extend my coming TAFF trip to America. Again, I had contracts to write some books and wanted to do them in peace, without security men poking their soiled fingers into my nice clean prose as they did with *War in 2080*: "We don't like the implication here that neutron bombs are harmful," they would complain. I had actually written that neutron bombs would kill more people for a given size of explosion: the preferred way of putting it was that "enhanced-radiation devices require a lower energy yield for the same military effectiveness" and are thus jolly good for the environment. Other reasons for disaffection included conscience, an ever-growing dislike of having my thighs groped, and the thought that one day I could write rude things about the whole place....

You may wonder whether any of these rude things got me into trouble. I did have one alarming phonecall: "This is Aldermaston Security. We're somewhat upset by this book of yours, *The Leaky Establishment*, and we'd advise that all copies be immediately withdrawn from sale pending a possible court action." While I was still saying fluent things like "But" and having heart attacks, the voice burst into coarse laughter and revealed itself to be my former friend Paul Barnett, alias John Grant. By way of apology he dedicated the next

John Grant book to Hazel and me, but Hazel in particular is not wholly certain that this is a high honour. The book is called *The Truth About the Flaming Ghoulies*.

I wrote my first rude things about AWRE in *New Scientist*, under a pseudonym of course—"Roy Tappen", who later became the hero of the book. Following this ... well, here are the inner secrets of how books get commissioned. Maxim Jakubowski had told me it was worth going round to Frederick Muller Ltd with a few book proposals, because they were owned by Harlech TV, had pots of money and gave you super expense-account lunches. So I made an appointment to drop in and discuss a heap of brilliant book ideas which I then quickly wrote. "What time?" they asked. "Oh," I said casually, "how about an hour before lunch?"

Katie Cohen, the Muller editor, smiled sweetly as she tore each of my ideas to tiny little shreds until there was a hollow reverberating emptiness in both my briefcase and my brain. "You haven't any more ideas?" she said. In panic I searched my pockets and found a crumpled xerox of the New Scientist article, and said "Maybe I could base something on this, sort of semi-autobiographical...." For the next half-hour Katie did the most brilliant selling job I've seen, convincing herself what a wonderful novel this could be, while I sat there, silent except for strange inner rumbles and hoping for lunch. At last she looked at her watch.... "Send us a synopsis and we'll send you a contract," she said. "And now I'll have to say goodbye because I'm lunching with someone."

After that, there seemed nothing to do but write the book—otherwise the day would have been wasted altogether. The trouble is that, having disposed of that particular section of my autobiography, the next novel should logically be about the joys of freelance writing and how proud one feels to create the vital raw materials of the remainder trade. This, alas, is the sort of thing that's so depressing, it's fit for nothing but the Booker Prize shortlist. Maybe I'll write a relatively cheerful SF novel about nuclear holocaust instead.

If so, I must try to pick a better title than *The Leaky Establishment*—the problem with which is that if you mention it often enough to an audience, the word "leaky" has a subliminal effect and people keep leaving for the toilet. In fact it's beginning to work on me as well, and if you don't mind, I'd like to be excused...

1985

Fizz! Buzz!

Chatting recently about timeless values of human culture such as the price of booze, I had a moment of feeling desperately old. In a relative sense: Chuch Harris remembers with a gloat how he achieved beer bloat for only half a groat or a quarter of a goat, and doubtless Harry Warner's early memoirs record the first hairy eofan rubbing two yeasts together and crying "Eureka! I've invented hangovers!" My own sense of crabbed antiquity comes when young fans hear with open disbelief my senile reminiscence of, "When I started drinking beer, this stuff was one and fourpence a pint...."

It wasn't "this stuff", of course, but some foul fizz served in the pothouses of South Wales to schoolboys who didn't know any better. Knowing better and making my lemon-sucking face at the mere memory of the bouquet, I mused that even at 7p a pint I wouldn't fancy the muck now ... though one does pay thirteen or fourteen times as much for something very similar in the average con hotel. Then memories started trickling back: Proust sailed into the wastes of lost time at the remembered nibble of a biscuit, but Langford is made of sterner stuff. The remembered taste of iron filings... *In beer veritas.*

There would be half a dozen of us in those smoky pub sessions, all from the now vanished Newport High School, thrown together by vague friendship, throbbing absence of girlfriends, and the natural human urge not to be at home with one's parents. Long evenings of this noble if negative pursuit had to be got through; it was my ever-evil pal Dai Price who introduced the familiar and direly hazardous game Fizz-Buzz.

If you are very lucky, you won't have met it. Semi-drunken cretins sit in a circle, counting in turn, clockwise round the ring: "One." "Two." "Three." At five, and every subsequent multiple of five, the current sucker must instead give a stentorian cry of "Fizz!" At seven, and its multiples, the word is "Buzz!" and the order of play reverses direction. Anyone failing to make the right noise at the right time must take a huge swig from his beer (amateur rules), drain the glass and buy another (tournament rules), or knock back any drinks in front of him and buy a round for the entire party (insane idiot rules).

Well, it beat South Wales's two permissible conversational topics: women (deeply frustrating since none of us knew any) and rugby (even more frustrating since, precociously beer-raddled, we couldn't play the national game without wheezing and falling over).

There was actually a weird satisfaction in doing this daft business right, "the solemn intoxication which comes of intricate ritual faultlessly performed" (thus Dorothy Sayers on bell-ringing)—except that the ritual wasn't *that* intricate, and even the double thrill of "Fizz Buzz!" at multiples of 35 failed somehow to reach orgasm level.

Thus Dai and I concluded that the "game" lacked intellectual challenge, at least until so late in the evening that remembering one's name also began to present difficulties on the order of Fermat's Last Theorem. Tentatively we started attaching electrodes to the hitherto sluggish rules. One early experiment, which even the thickest of the gathering could handle, was to assign "Oink!" as the, er, buzzword for all multiples of 3. Dai soon developed a particularly obscene "Oink!" whose mere enunciation came under the heading of gamesmanship. The corpse of the rotten game began to twitch slightly.

"Burp!" for multiples of 11 was the next remorselessly logical addition. By now, some us were sweating, concentrating intently, and falling over a good deal sooner than of yore (see above, under *Tournament Rules*). Then came a quantum leap into genuine mathematical abstraction: "Clang!" was what you had to say each time the count reached a prime number. (After savage debate, the dogma of pure mathematics was cast aside and 1 was ruled to be a prime.) It was around this stage that I stopped remembering petty things like closing times or how I'd got home afterwards. Sanity was finally eroded by the two-pronged introduction of "Pow!" for perfect squares and "Zap!" for powers of two. Was 1 a perfect square? (Yes.) Was it a power of two? (We decided that $1 = 2^0$ was a special case and didn't count.)

By now, the alert and intelligent reader will have gathered, there were no bloody landmarks. Pale, strained faces ringed the table, soddenly trying to follow a count which began not 1 2 3 4 but "Clang Pow!" "Clang Zap!" "Oink Clang!" "Pow Zap!" (There was some arcane rule about the order in which you had to pronounce the shibboleths, but this luckily escapes me.) And it was a supreme moment of triumph if, swaying and incapable, we successfully galloped into the straight with "Oink Buzz!" "Burp!" "Clang!" "Oink!" "Fizz Pow!" ... and, at last, the first number in our counting system which came through in clear. "Twenty-six!"

I have never quite worked out what the other pub regulars thought of us, but they used to look worried.

The suggestion of "Ping!" to mark cubes was perhaps unnecessary. Perfect numbers also received short shrift. The whole thing broke up with a serious Dai Price plan to insert a special term for members of the Fibonacci series. ("As you well know, Professor, this runs 1, 1, 2, 3, 5, 8, 13, 21, 34 ... not that *you* need to be told, but we must assume there are some ignorant readers out there." "Quite, Carruthers. Shut up.") An appropriate word in this context might have been, "Argh!" Rather than debate whether 1 should now be intricately coded as "Argh Argh Clang Pow!" owing to its double appearance in the series, we all went to university instead.

I arrived in Oxford, and many splendours and miseries duly followed, but the demented game wasn't so easily escaped—not merely because I inflicted it on university SF group fanatics who madly programmed the Nuclear Physics

Dept computers to generate all the correct responses, up to ten thousand. (When I write *Advanced Fizz-Buzz—the Dungeon Master's Guide*, I'll know where to do the research.) Though in a weird way I owe a lot to Fizz-Buzz, such as a lifelong interest in maths, those nonsense sequences were bloody hard to shake off. *Tenser, said the Tensor ... Tenser, said the Tensor....* People claim to have been driven half round the twist by obsession with Charles Hinton's coloured cubes for visualizing the fourth dimension (*circa* 1904). Not being quite intellectually up to that, I still suffered years of fizzes and oinks and clangs running round in my head like mathematically-minded squirrels. It didn't even have the vague aesthetic respectability of something like Mark Twain's supposedly unforgettable jingle *Punch, brothers, punch with care! Punch in the presence of the passenjare!*

(En route I also invented numerous variants like Cantorian Fizz-Buzz, played with all the real numbers between 0 and 1 with special grunts for transcendentals—*you* go first, thanks; Big Fizz-Buzz, in which anyone reaching the first transfinite ordinal during the course of a normal pub session must pronounce the rune "Someone's Been Cheating!"; and, after a crippling attack of Douglas Hofstadter, Self-Referential Fizz-Buzz incorporating Strange Loops....)

The funny noises within my skull did eventually fade away, but as a possible side-effect I seem to have spent most of my working life doing vaguely mathematical things, from doomsday-weapon simulations to back-of-an-envelope futurology. This abysmal nostalgic wallow has therefore given me the final answer to those who mumble about wasting time in pubs. Placing a hand on my chest and speaking in manly resonant tones, I can say: "I owe my whole career to lousy bitter and Fizz-Buzz." (Death comes on swift wings to anyone who responds, "What career?") Of course it's kept me from certain pinnacles: my failure to write *The Hitch-Hiker's Guide to the Galaxy* can be blamed entirely on my schoolday conditioning to think that, for the reasons above, 26 is an infinitely funnier punchline than "Oink Buzz!". I mean, damn it, funnier than 42....

1986

If the pub game described here seems bad enough, beware of its distant cousin Sprodzoom—where ritual exchanges (of gestures rather than sounds) have been elaborated by insane Cambridge mathematicians and computer scientists into an intricate system of protocols for sign-language "conversations" where form is everything and there is no content; where the gesture code itself can and must be continually redefined and expanded during a game; where, in advanced versions, inanimate objects become players.... Preliminary symptom: circles of sf fans on the floor waving their arms and legs at each other. Leave the room immediately.

Slightly Foxed: The *Million* Columns

1: THUD & BLUNDER

The essence of "Golden Age" detective fiction was that the author should outsmart the reader. However, after smiting your forehead once too often in admiration of all that ingenuity, you could begin to develop a slight headache and hope that sooner or later the wretched authors would outsmart themselves.

It happened fairly often, of course. Dorothy Sayers's fictional mouthpiece Harriet Vane confessed quite cheerfully that she never wrote a whodunnit without six major howlers. Some authors would chart their corpse's steady drift down the Thames to sea, forgetting the complications produced by the fact that (as A. P. Herbert testily told them in the 1930s) the river below Teddington is tidal. Others planned murder with electrified doorknobs, chessmen, teapots—with never a thought for a decent earth or return circuit, without which the victim is apt to say, "I felt a funny tingle," and stroll on.

Mistakes big enough to ruin the story are rare. Here, though, are four examples from famous authors....

In its early days, the Ellery Queen writing team made a great point of using remorseless, watertight logic and playing utterly fair with the reader. It would thus be fun to catch the Queens in a massive error of pure logic.

Sure enough, this happened in *The Greek Coffin Mystery* (1932), one of those confections of elaborate false clues and solutions. An important red herring depends on the colour of a red or possibly green silk tie. The confusion arises because ... wait for it ... a minor character is colour-blind and therefore (the Queens insist) consistently and unambiguously sees red ties as green ones *and vice-versa*.

This is reminiscent of that theory that abnormally tall, thin figures in El Greco's paintings show that the artist suffered from an eye defect, presumably astigmatism, which caused him to see people as oddly tall and thin. Obviously the questions to ask are: (a) Assuming the eye trouble, how did El Greco see his own canvas? (b) If someone can always tell red from green, how could he

---

For its brief life (1991-3) Million *was the sister magazine to* Interzone, *complementing it by covering all the popular fictional genres except sf and fantasy. Its subtitle was "The Magazine about Popular Fiction"....* "As opposed to Interzone, the magazine of unpopular fiction," I said incautiously within editor David Pringle's hearing.

ever get their names mixed up? Having thus reasoned that the "colour-blind" chap must be a liar and villain, I was disappointed when the inexorable logical analysis never again mentioned him.

It was equally dismaying to fall through the flaw in a book by the late great John Dickson Carr, whose macabre working-up of suspense might sometimes have become clichéd, but who outstripped everyone else in the ingenuity of his eighty-odd variants on the Impossible Crime in the Locked Room.

In *The Case of the Constant Suicides*, alas, Carr's research slipped. "Carbonic acid gas ... one of the deadliest and quickest-acting gases there is" is cunningly administered in a chamber with no gas fittings, no gas cylinders, no chemicals or apparatus which could have produced gas. The idea looked promising and, in 1941, novel. The snag was that Carr got carbon monoxide and carbon dioxide mixed up, and the evil mastermind was supposed to have done his deed by placing, under the bed, a deadly block of quick-acting dry ice.

(In fact, since CO_2 will eventually suffocate you quite as handily as any other sort-of-inert gas, the book could easily have been patched up by dropping the rubbish about "deadly" and "quick-acting", and the scene where someone nearly faints at one whiff of the fatal vapour.)

Sometimes, as above, the author's gimmick is so neat that to invoke the real world seems cruel and unfair. "The great tragedy of science—the slaying of a beautiful hypothesis by an ugly fact." The same tragedy afflicts the book which I suspect is Dorothy Sayers's best, *The Documents in the Case* (1930).

The gimmick of *Documents* appeals hugely to my personal technophilia. Its plot turns on the proving of the "unprovable"—whether the organic poison in the fatal fungi was natural (making the death a mere misadventure) or a deliberately added, chemically identical synthetic. Enter that little-used forensic gadget, the polariscope....

The technical points are that asymmetric organic molecules will twist the polarization of transmitted light according to their "handedness"; that only one of the two mirror-image forms of such a molecule is produced in living tissue; that a synthetic will be an equal mixture of both forms with the left-hand and right-hand "twists" cancelling out; and that, viewed in the polariscope, the natural poison is thus optically active while the synthetic is inert. No wonder the book's last page has the Director of Public Prosecutions gloomily imagining "expert witnesses displaying an asymmetric molecule to a jury of honest tradesmen ...".

Poor Dorothy Sayers. "There was nothing wrong with the plot," she said bitterly in 1932, "except those infernal toadstools." The selected poison was muscarine, being the reason why the Fly Agaric fungus is not a reliable health food. And muscarine *isn't* optically active: no version of it, natural or synthetic, would do anything exciting in a polariscope at all.

Sherlock Holmes seemed to have a far more, dare we say it, elementary lapse in "The Priory School", where he deduces the direction of travel of a long-gone bicycle from its tracks on open ground: "The more deeply sunk impression is, of course, the hind wheel, upon which the weight rests. You perceive several places where it has passed across and obliterated the more shallow mark of the front one. It was undoubtedly heading away from the school."

Presumably, had the front-wheel track overlaid the back one, that would have indicated the opposite direction. But few criminals are so fiendishly cunning as to ride their bicycles backwards.

This time, there's an extra twist. After years of being taunted about these tracks, Sir Arthur Conan Doyle finally went out and experimented with his own bicycle. While admitting that the original deduction was flawed, he defiantly pointed out that "on an undulating moor the wheels make a deeper impression uphill and a more shallow one downhill, so Holmes was justified of his wisdom after all."

You know my methods, Watson....

1991

2: BANNED IN NEW YORK

There's no more painful route to popularity than having your book clash with real-world prejudice. The *Satanic Verses* case is too uncomfortably familiar; the *Lady Chatterley's Lover* trial is still talked about after three decades. But does anyone remember the 1920s prosecution of James Branch Cabell's *Jurgen: a Comedy of Justice*?

This is one of the finest fantasy novels ever written, though now somewhat lost in the modern genre's turbid flood of trilogies. Its tone is polished and ironic, its erudition wonderfully silly (Evelyn Waugh called the book "that preposterously spurious artefact"), and its message severely moral.

In brief: Jurgen, a failed poet turned pawnbroker, regains his youth and spends it as unwisely as he did the first time round, in a series of regrettable affairs beginning with a Guenevere not yet married to King Arthur. He shamelessly promotes himself from chapter to chapter: "Preliminary Tactics of Duke Jurgen", "Shortcomings of Prince Jurgen", "Economics of King Jurgen", "How Emperor Jurgen Fared Infernally", "The Ascension of Pope Jurgen".... Despite having his pick of beauties, he finally chooses to return to the familiar scolding of his wife Dame Lisa, an undoubted ratbag.

How could any moralist object? Enter John S. Sumner of the New York Society for the Suppression of Vice, who in January 1920 persuaded a grand jury to indict Cabell's publishers for selling "a lewd, lascivious, indecent, obscene and disgusting book entitled *Jurgen*, a more particular description of which said book would be offensive to this Court and improper to be spread upon the records thereof...." From that point Cabell's fame rose, and his royalties ceased, until the trial in October 1922.

Although *Jurgen* contains not one unequivocally naughty passage, there is a vein of amusing double-entendre when Jurgen is (in his favourite phrase) dealing justly with some woman. As Cabell put it in a private letter of 1919, "Much can be done by starting off the reader with the honest belief that a sword or a staff is actually being discussed, and then permitting the evil-minded, such as you, to become suspicious."

A casual reader might think it prophetic that in Chapter XXXII the hero is condemned by invaders from "Philistia" led by a huge, prurient dung-beetle with a retinue of black-and-white-clad pages carrying weapons: "You are offensive because this page has a sword which I choose to say is not a sword. You are lewd because that page has a lance which I prefer to think is not a lance...." This bit was actually published later as *The Judging of Jurgen*, a joke on Sumner, and incorporated into subsequent editions of *Jurgen* itself.

The publishers, McBride & Co., had already had misgivings, and before publication the author offered a cunning plan: "I am making six expurgations, with modest asterisks to mark them, in six of the immaculately proper chapters, and am calling attention thereto in the preface as all that was necessary to conform the book to the standards of the most squeamish. Result, the reader will imagine something very horrible indeed to fill in these lacunae, and will take the really ticklish portions for granted as having passed the censor...."

It didn't work. Sumner himself might never have noticed a book which for three editions had been appreciated and reviewed as mere literature. Unfortunately, a troublemaker got into the New York *Tribune* with a gleeful piece about how *Jurgen* "gets away with murder", and the hunt was on.

The taint of lawsuits like this is that they force defendants into a false position. In 1920 one simply couldn't say, "Yes, there are some harmlessly rude double meanings, and so what?" The defence brief had to insist otherwise, with endless evasions like: "There is no reason for taking in a wrong sense the reference to the sceptre."

(Context: "Emperor" Jurgen is cohabiting with a lovely vampire in Hell. It is pitch dark. "I was in the beginning suspicious of your majesty," she says, "because I had always heard that every emperor carried a magnificent sceptre, and you then displayed nothing of the sort. But now, somehow, I do not doubt you any longer.")

So the defence was a tissue of fibs. Had the case gone to the jury, there was a plan to put dodgy passages in context by reading out the entire book. "The recitation would have taken six and one-half hours," explained Cabell's friend Louis Untermeyer. "At the very conclusion, just as [the reader] was tottering from the stand and the jury was being waked by the clerk of the court, I was to tower to my five feet seven and cry *Encore! Encore!*"

But, to balance the bad luck of *Jurgen*'s spicy press coverage, the case was concluded by unexpected good fortune when the judge accepted the plea for a directed acquittal. Yes, he allowed, certain passages were suggestive in a veiled way of immorality, but "it is doubtful if the book could be read or understood at all by more than a very limited number of readers." Ah, that's all right then.

Best of all ... *Jurgen* pretends to be a translation of mediaeval tales from "Poictesme" recorded by the nonexistent scholar Gottfried Johannes Bülg. Earlier, Cabell and a pal had in all innocence published a spoof controversy about Bülg. Clearly the judge had read this, and his summing-up was influenced by the book's being "based on the mediaeval legends of Jurgen." Might he have taken a different line had he known that Cabell made it all up himself, naughty parts included?

Prosecuted by a ridiculous prude, defended by untruths and quite possibly acquitted by mistake, *Jurgen* went on through countless editions. Cabell's next book was respectfully dedicated to his benefactor, John S. Sumner.

A final dig appears in his *Figures of Earth* (1921), whose hero obtains children by a magical ceremony to which not even Sumner could object. He draws three asterisks on the floor and, with his wife, steps decorously over them. Both then await the coming of the stork.

1991

3: Bound & Gagged

Once upon a time, being regularly tied up with stout ropes was not so much a luxury offered by strict disciplinarians in Soho ... more a regular occupational hazard of thriller heroes. And, of course, their girlfriends.

As a plot mechanism, having our hero tied up serves several useful purposes. The writer gets a rest from the exhausting work of writing action-packed adventure. The villain can gloat sinisterly about how this locked cellar will shortly fill with water, gas or rabid hamsters, while the Iron Maiden swings inexorably closed, the concealed time-bomb ticks towards detonation, etc. And our hero will presently display his ingenuity by freeing himself with one mighty bound.

But how many ways are there to escape a scientifically knotted cocoon of stout manila rope? For my instant survey I passed over James Bond (who despite his name is not trussed up often enough to be statistically significant) in favour of Leslie Charteris's hero Simon Templar—the Saint. Anticipating postmodernism, the tied-up Saint likes to harangue gloating villains: "I've got such a lot more to do before the end of the volume, and it'd wreck the whole show if I went and got bumped off in the first story...." (*The Saint vs Scotland Yard*, 1932.)

Let us be statistical.

Excluding omnibus volumes, ghastly TV-series and comic-strip fictionalizations, and one disappointing novel ghosted by Harry Harrison of SF fame (*Vendetta for the Saint*, 1965), there are thirty-six "canonical" Saint books stretching from 1928 to 1964. Over such a period anyone might change, and the Saint certainly does. Progressing from beer-drinking dealer of rough justice to suave jet-setter and wine connoisseur, he put away childish things, among them the simple pleasure of being roped and tied.

World War II marks the division. Up to 1945 there are twenty-five books in which the Saint is tied up (by my count) no fewer than seventeen times, averaging a 68% bondage factor per volume. If you add notable occasions on which he's locked away (in jails, cellars, one ship's cabin and one ordinary room), the figure rises to 92%. After the war Templar doesn't seem to get tied up at all.

Did Charteris tire of the good old routine? Perhaps, but my suspicion that these episodes exist mainly as narrative padding is supported by the fact that the Saint is never tied up in short stories. Ritual trussing and escape use too many of a mere few thousand words, and after 1948 all the canonical Saint stories are shorts. (Before, many were novellas—much roomier, at two or three per volume.)

Any Charteris villain would have been glad of the following data, showing precisely what tactics to avoid:

Before you tie up Simon Templar, it's most advisable to search him. Fifty-nine percent of his amazing escapes involve simply cutting the ropes, since in a rather un-English way he keeps a knife up his sleeve. Arch-criminals neglect the importance of confiscating this implement, perhaps because the ploy was tried in the Saint's first book (*The Saint Meets the Tiger*, 1928), and the impudent fellow proved to have a razor-edged cigarette case in reserve.

Admittedly, the Saint is versatile with his knife. On two occasions, even while the arch-fiend is gloating at him, he keeps up a stream of repartee while imperceptibly slicing away behind his back. When dropped into the Thames, securely attached to fifty pounds of scrap iron, he holds his breath and patiently works the knife free (*The Saint Goes On*, 1934). Suspended by trussed wrists from an iron ring with a hundredweight block of stone roped to his feet, he goads the villain into using his knife to cut the rope which supports Templar—whereupon, rather than plummet to death, he grabs the ring one-handed, pulls his other hand loose and, while supporting his own weight *and* the stone's with his right hand, puts a firm half-nelson on the Napoleon of Crime with his left. Blimey. (*The Ace of Knaves*, 1937.) Dangling by his hands from another iron ring in traditional dungeon style, he abandons shoes and socks to wield the inevitable knife with his toes (*The Saint On Guard*, 1945).

Other errors for the Ungodly to avoid are:

> Being bluffed into releasing your victims and hauling them out of range of the bomb you have placed under the floor (*Enter the Saint*, 1930).
>
> Accidentally dropping your key to the mantrap in which you have caught the Saint, within his reach (*The Saint Meets His Match*, 1931).
>
> Allowing your attention to stray as you mix tons of cement to entomb him, thus permitting him to char his bonds with a girlfriend's cigarette lighter and escape without your

knowledge from the deep pit you are in process of filling up
(*The Saint vs Scotland Yard*).

Having him whipped by a gigantic black torturer; the
first lash will so enrage him that he bursts thick leather straps
with insane strength (*ibid*).

Elsewhere, Templar relies on confederates to free him, abrades his bonds by
conventional use of rough brickwork, or—mystifyingly—distracts his captors
with a trick exploding cigarette, invokes the spirit of Houdini, and slips free of
formerly quite secure knots.

Those who merely lock him up do no better, since they madly allow him
to retain a palmed lockpick (*Saint Overboard*, 1936), a complete set of burglar's
tools (*The Saint in London*, 1934), or two beer bottles which he can fill with
earth as a makeshift respirator to survive the poison gas while digging his way
out of the cellar (*Alias the Saint*, 1931).

One hardly likes to complain about these plot devices being incredibly
crude, when the tales themselves are usually great fun. Far more soothing to
call it sportsmanship; any villain with a sense of style leaves some loophole in
his trap.

Indeed, this also applies to heroes. Simon Templar himself is not terribly
good at holding on to prisoners. After one ruffian in *The Saint vs Scotland Yard*
has spent all night hacking a huge hole through our hero's own massive cellar
door, we are told: "Simon realized that he had been incredibly careless." You
bet. What totally unexpected means of escape had he overlooked? He'd left his
captive with a knife....

1991

4: The Worst Crime in the World

There's an eerie, phosphorescent glamour in dire writing. The legendary *The
Stuffed Owl: An Anthology of Bad Verse* has been endlessly reprinted and imi-
tated since 1930. Bad movies and bad SF (especially bad SF movies) have had
similar loving attention in recent years. What about rotten crime fiction?

S. J. Perelman pioneered its study with his 1930s squib "Somewhere a
Roscoe", extolling Robert Leslie Bellem's work for pulp magazines like *Spicy
Detective*. This private-eye genre was highly formalized. A gun was always a
roscoe, and never went Bang but said—or sneezed, belched, stuttered or
barked—"Kachow!", "Chow-chow!", "Chow!", "Ka-chowp!", "Whr-r-rang!"
or in extreme cases "Blooey—Blooey—Blooey!"

Similarly, the corpses (mostly voluptuous; "the warmth of her slim young
form set fire to my arterial system", etc) all got variants of the same stylized
epitaph. "She was dead as": a pork chop, a stuffed mongoose, an iced catfish,
a fried oyster, six buckets of fish bait, vaudeville, George Washington's cherry
tree....

A later scholar, Bill Pronzini, has widened the investigation in *Gun in Cheek* (Mysterious Press, 1982) and *Son of Gun in Cheek* (ditto, 1987). Sometimes he struggles to extract humour from material which is merely God-awful, but many unspeakable gems are unearthed and Pronzini has the affection for his victims without which no celebration of appallingness can succeed.

Here's a tiny selection, illustrating the special qualities needed by what Pronzini calls "alternate crime classics":

EMOTIONAL EXCESS. "He rushed to the canal, sobbing, and, with a prayer ... threw himself into the water. Happily, in his despair, the poor child had forgotten that he knew how to swim." (Gaston Leroux, *The Perfume of the Lady in Black*) "The fire from my ears, my eyes and my throat congregated into a lump and shoved off the top of my head." (Michael Morgan, *Decoy*)

GENRE INCESTUOUSNESS. "Zarzour *looked* like a murderer—he *acted* like one—and he kept talking about committing the perfect crime. Now according to every precept of mystery fiction, he definitely should *not* have been the actual killer!" (Eric Heath, *Murder of a Mystery Writer*)

STRIKING WOMEN. "She was as lovely as a girl could be without bludgeoning your endocrines." (Stephen Marlowe, *Killers Are My Meat*) "She ... unearthed one of her fantastic breasts from the folds of her sheath skirt." (Michael Avallone, *The Horrible Man*) "I looked at her breasts jutting against the soft fabric of her dress, nipples like split infinitives." (Max Byrd, *Fly Away Jill*)

PROFOUND DEDUCTIONS. "It was evident by the look of fear in his eyes that he was frightened." (Thomas K. Makagon, *All Killers Aren't Ugly*) "He had been shot, poisoned, stabbed and strangled. Either someone had really had it in for him or four people had killed him. Or else it was the cleverest suicide I'd ever heard of." (Richard S. Prather, *Take a Murder, Darling*) "Let's not forget, in the midst of all this fun, that whoever killed this guy is a killer." (Shelley Singer, *Free Draw*)

SINISTERLY MALFORMED VILLAINS. "I feel it in my hump that something is going to happen!" (Edward Woodward, *The House of Terror*) "Freddie's tongue shot out from between his lips like the fangs of a poisonous snake." (J. C. Lenehan, *The Tunnel Mystery*)

THE INVESTIGATOR GETTING KNOCKED OUT. "Somebody stuck a red-hot poker in my ear and all my brains ran out of the hole. My bones turned into macaroni and I sank down into a gooey mass of tomato sauce that looked like blood. Then somebody began rubbing the end of my nose with sandpaper and there was a big balloon of pain tied to my ear." (Carl D. Hodges, *Naked Villainy*)

ATMOSPHERE. "The air was surcharged with an invisible something which seemed to surround the house. Even that phlegmatic, nerve-proof group were not immune to the tuning in of the premonitory cross-currents." (Florence M. Pettee, *The Palgrave Mummy*) "That was my first look at Merriwether

Manor, where Murder had rented a room ahead of me." (Jeremy Lane, *Death to Drumbeat*) "The anticlimax was terrific, it was catastrophic." (Arthur M. Chase, *Peril at the Spy Nest*)

HANDGUN EXPERTISE. "Lieutenant Freevich had fired almost a complete round of ammunition." (Hugh Pentecost, *The Steel Palace*)

DETECTIVE INTROSPECTION. "Inspiration splattered me in the face like a custard pie." (Michael Morgan, *Nine More Lives*)

DRAMATIC TAUTOLOGY. "'What?' I monosyllabled." (Florence M. Pettee, "The Clue from the Tempest") "Simeon Taylor was killed—beheaded and left to die...." (Hugh Pentecost, *Sow Death, Reap Death*)

CUNNING MURDER METHODS. By fire extinguisher: "They ... stuck a nozzle in each ear while they held her down and turned the extinguishers on." (Ennis Willie, *The Case of the Loaded Garter Holster*) By vacuum cleaner: "He held it there until he had drawn every drop of air from her body." (Sidney A. Porcelain, *The Crimson Cat Murders*)

STIFF UPPER LIP (BRITS ONLY). "'I say, Fitzhugh, why not go to the club? Nobody could touch you at the club!' Fitzhugh's lips twitched queerly. 'I—er—I imagine I'd be asked to resign if a gang of Chinese murderers came into the club after me.'" (Murray Leinster, *Murder Will Out*)

Enough. Pronzini offers several hundred pages of similar treats, recommended to all crime fans and/or masochists. People who like books like these will like these books.

Some masters of awful detection do emerge, so outrageous they're arguably good: McGonagalls of crime. Perelman's favourite, Bellem, is just one. The hideously productive Michael Avallone pushes the wise-guy school of cliché to fresh depths ("My bewilderment took on a couple of new glands."). My own soft spot is for the stupefying plots of Harry Stephen Keeler, driven by creaky engines of implausibility and coincidence ... like the one where the Hidden Last Will and Testament (I think it was) is splashed across the country on garish advertising posters which reveal their message only through *The Blue Spectacles* of the title. Another typical Keeler plot turn, which thrilled me when I was about fifteen, features a night train hurtling to destruction—*unless* the fugitive hero can contrive a warning light, his entire worldly goods consisting of a match and a thousand-dollar bill....

And speaking of diabolical plots, a future column will discuss the most unbelievable solutions ever offered for the traditional Impossible Crime in the Locked Room. The reader is warned.

1991

5: ANCIENT IMAGES

Years ago at a UK Milford SF writers' conference, a visiting American (George R. R. Martin) invited the massed authors to embarrass themselves. "I want you to cast your minds back," he said hypnotically, "to the very first image from literature that you can remember." This would apparently be Significant, though where the Significance lay was—and remained—unclear.

Around the circle, people started nervously responding with lofty scenes from noted works. It was like a job interview conducted by some company that had fallen for graphology, with candidates struggling to produce handwriting which clearly indicated uprightness, perseverance, loyalty, discreet ambition and absolutely no tendency to fall about in hysterical laughter at the idea of taking this test seriously. When it came to me, I felt it practically my duty to lower the tone with coarse honesty. Unfortunately I couldn't remember a decent flagellation scene from Billy Bunter, or anything beyond the title of the controversial (in my family, anyway) comic book *Goom: The Thing from Planet X*. Instead it would have to be....

No, not *that*!

In the event I did a brief rhapsody about *Biggles Hits the Trail* by Captain W. E. Johns, one of the ace pilot's rare excursions in the direction of SF. The plot was centred on a lost Tibetan mountain made mostly of radium. Inevitably this feature of the landscape was honeycombed with the dwellings of countless mad monks, who had harnessed the awesome force of radioactivity to their sinister ends.

For example, they used it to generate an innovative sort of static electricity that glued unwanted visitors' feet to the ground (much later I realized this was a pinch from Kipling's 1912 SF story "As Easy as A.B.C."). Some of my best schoolday nightmares involved the scene where Biggles and intrepid companions are pinned, just barely able to drag their feet in a crackle of sparks, while the monks' favourite pets advance fluidly on them—an inexhaustible stream of albino electric centipedes with enormous fangs.

But the image that remained was simply that of the brooding "Mountain of Light" itself, glowing fitfully amid the Himalayas. Good picture. Lousy physics, but a good picture.

The keen-eyed reader may have noticed a slight hesitation above. What, when Billy Bunter and even *Goom: The Thing from Planet X* were toyed with, was too embarrassing to relate? Confessional time: the answer is Enid Blyton, and the remembered scene was simply a loft full of apples, some of them rotten. Later I confided this to other writers, and one or two did say, shiftily, "Oh yes, I remember *that*."

This column's usual bibliographical rigour is being abandoned, as I can no longer place the short story involved. (A largish Blyton omnibus, illustrated? Please don't anyone sully the delicate bloom of my ignorance.)

Blyton was a highly visual writer, and that piece sticks in the mind as a thoroughly and even maddeningly memorable use of an image for didactic purposes. The context: some kids are helping an older female relative, no doubt an aunt, to store apples in the loft for winter. Only perfect, unbruised apples need apply. Of course one of the children bungles and admits one apple with the tiniest possible bruise.

The curtain is lowered to indicate some lapse of time, and rises on a scene of moral horror. Sadly the aunt shows the kids what has come to pass, with the flawed apple now a seething mound of corruption, spreading rot to dozens of others around it. The tableau had a suppurating intensity that H. P. Lovecraft would have been hard put to match. Unforgettable.

But perhaps I'd have forgotten Biggles's Mountain of Light without the underpinning horror of that slow-motion, dream-clogged flight from multi-legged peril, and perhaps the apple scene would slide quite easily from memory without its dreadful ensuing moral.

The point of Blyton's story was that between the two visits to the loft, the kids have been wanting a school friend to come and stay. A *naughty* one with a *bad reputation*, it's admitted, but they promise to set him a good example and reform him out of recognition. Sadly but kindly the aunt discloses the scene of fruity necrosis and pronounces her awful judgement. The bad always corrupts the good. That acquaintance might have only a tiny bruise of naughtiness on his soul now; but if you good kids associate with him, *this* will be the grim result. Shades of the prison-house...

One doesn't want to make too much of one brief story in Enid Blyton's colossal output. Elsewhere she has plenty of effective if not particularly memorable imagery: a quarter-century since I last looked at them, the Famous Five books conjure up a jolly montage of mildly exciting things like caves, darkness, lonely houses, secret passages, midnight feasts and conclaves....

But those blasted apples refuse to be forgotten because, I rather believe, that was the first time I'd ever resented a piece of writing as being both effective and unfair. Come to think of it, there were plenty of little bruises on my youthful soul, and Blyton was evidently condemning me to total running-sore status by about the age of fifteen. No appeal allowed. You can't argue when someone else has craftily picked the analogy beforehand, especially when it might contain a smidgeon of truth. (I've never investigated whether this particular sentence of damnation was one reason why librarians later took against Blyton.)

Inoculation confers immunity, at least a bit and at least sometimes. My own favourite great-aunt, who never stored apples and who did me a huge favour at age twelve by giving me the old Methuen *G. K. Chesterton Omnibus*, later took an interest in my mildly rotted soul and tried me on some pop-theology by C. S. Lewis. It was all there: deviously chosen analogies, plausible wheedling, yawning logical gaps. The Blyton blight once again. If that was what Christianity was all about, I wanted no part of it.

Although I've never encountered the awesome sight of a radium mountain burningly gently in the twilight, any old rotten apple can still make me wince.

1991

6: The Reader Is Warned

Elsewhere in *Million*, people keep doing nostalgia pieces on "Classic Books About Popular Fiction". How undemocratic. Hunting through my endless, tottering piles of non-fiction, I find an overwhelming preponderance of *non-classics*. Isn't it our duty to acknowledge these works too? Perhaps not...

For example, who now remembers my simultaneous nomination for Most Boring Book About Crime Fiction and Flimsiest Effort To Capitalize On A Popular Success—*The Wimsey Family* by C. W. Scott-Giles, Fitzalan Pursuivant of Arms Extraordinary (1977)? Its slender 95 pages of cod history and genealogy shed a truly astonishing lack of light on the Lord Peter Wimsey stories. Perhaps it appeals more to heraldry buffs than to lowbrows like myself who thought the Arms of Harriet Vane (pictured here) were features attached to her shoulders.

Ellery Queen is bigger game, being much respected as a crime author, or authors. Thanks to this and other factors, including a highly visible platform in *Ellery Queen's Mystery Magazine* editorials, the Queen opinions once carried great critical weight.

But look at the "classic" *Queen's Quorum* (1951, revised 1969), "A History of the Detective-Crime Short Story as Revealed by the 125 Most Important Books Published in This Field, 1845-1967". Anyone can argue with a Best Of list, but what makes this one so frequently embarrassing is the way its enthusiasm spills over into gush:

> Melville Davisson Post's *Uncle Abner* is second only to Poe's *Tales* among all the books of detective short stories written by American authors. This statement is made dogmatically and without reservation: a cold-blooded and calculated critical opinion which we believe will be as true in the year 2000 as we wholeheartedly believe it to be true today. These four books [the other three are by Doyle, Chesterton and Poe] are the finest in their field—the *crème du crime*. They are an out-of-this world target for future detective-story writers to take shots at—but it will be like throwing pebbles at the Pyramids.

You glean the impression that the Queens liked the Post book. If you were waiting for some actual justification of so much windy hyperbole, tough luck: this level of critical analysis is quite literally all you get.

Third time lucky, though: the next book to hand is so fascinatingly eccentric and useless as to deserve "classic" status in a category all its own. *Locked Room Murders* by Robert Adey (1979) consists of a long, numbered list of 1,280 stories about impossible crimes, with an appendix giving all the solutions. Some of these terse plot giveaways make boggling reading, and often induce a powerful urge never, ever to read the book. Here's a selection of personal favourites.

64. Victim, while in bath, was tricked into handling a copper spider through which an electric current was passed.

(One of Colin Watson's novels had an even nastier trick with an electrified beetle attached to a wall. The wall was made of porcelain and formed the back of a gents' public lavatory. According to Watson, there's an irresistible psychological urge to *aim* for any foreign body such as a beetle ... whereupon, *fzzzzzzt*.)

68. After killing, the murderer stepped into an incinerator and incinerated himself.

75. The killer, a midget, was still in the room hidden in a leather hatbox when the door was broken down. (See 366.)

91. The deaths were engineered by a person dressed as a werewolf....

100. The killer bought and left a block of frozen nitro-glycerin which exploded as the fishmonger attempted to break it with his hammer.

131. The killer entered the house disguised as an elephant, and escaped down a secret tunnel which he later nailed shut....

132. Victim accidentally threw a live cartridge into a live electric light socket. The metal base of the cartridge melted and it was fired as though from a revolver.

139. The mask had been smuggled out in the pouch of a stuffed kangaroo....

146. A ventilator above the corpse was removed leaving a small hole through which an armadillo, rolled into a ball, was lowered. It proceeded to deface the dead man. (Literally, I understand.)

147. Murderers got past guard to victim by impersonating a horse.

366. The killer, an African pygmy, was hidden in a coal basket when the entrance was forced. (See 75.)

369. The victims were strangled by a hybrid creeper.

519. The victim was killed by the lid of the old Victorian bath in which he was sitting, which fell on him when he picked up a rigged loofah.

534. The jewels had been stolen by a trained white rat whose hideaway was a footstool with a false compartment.

540. Webs spun across the magnifying lens of a telescope by a pet Venusian spider caused brain damage to the victim when he looked through it....

542. The bus was hidden under a stairway with a secret opening.

574. The house was built around the corpse.

634. Dagger was made from a plastic ashtray which after it had been used reverted on application of hot water (in a teapot) to its original shape.

706. The victim was being poisoned by a faulty central heating system and, in rising with desperate suddenness to escape it, struck his head on the painted base of a chandelier.

787. The murderer wore a tartan kilt and blended in with the scenery.

855. A line was looped under the victim's armpits and was attached at the other end to a captive shark. When the shark was released it raced off and dragged the victim overboard.

861. Victim is dehydrated, stuffed through the cell bars and then, once back inside, rehydrated.

890. The murderer drank the water in which he drowned his victim.

954. The victim, who had the peculiar habit of eating grapes from the wallpaper design, was poisoned by someone who knew of the habit and put cyanide on [them].

972. The stabbing was done by an already present diabolical floating machine which afterwards burnt itself out.

977. The poison had been administered by a red ant enticed by a scent on an envelope delivered to the victim.

1,281. After reading 1,280 mindboggling puzzle solutions, the reader's brain dissolved and oozed in twin streams from his ears.

One of the above is not authentic. I'm delighted to report that a new, expanded edition of this seminally dotty work is expected from an American publisher in 1991. Stay tuned.

1991

7: On the Twilight Edge

In classical detective stories, according to conventional wisdom, the supernatural may be introduced only to be explained away in the harsh light of rationalism. Stands to reason, doesn't it?

Thus Father Brown, whom unwary readers might suspect of mystical credulity, is always firmly reasonable about impossibilities: "I believe in miracles. I believe in man-eating tigers, but I don't see them running around everywhere. If I want any miracles, I know where to get them." ("The Miracle of Moon Crescent") Conan Doyle, to his everlasting credit, never infected super-rational Holmes with his own spiritualist beliefs. The Great Detective's closest approach to mysticism is a vaguely Kantian observation in the late story "The Veiled Lodger": "If there is not some compensation hereafter, then the world is a cruel jest."

All fictional rules are breakable, and if a supernatural build-up was good enough, then explaining it away can be irritating. Thus Greg Cox's recent *The Transylvanian Library: A Consumer's Guide to Vampire Fiction* includes *He Who Whispers* by John Dickson Carr on grounds of atmosphere, but petulantly deplores the way its vampire menace dissolves at Dr Fell's rational touch.

Interestingly enough, the fabled Detection Club of the golden years was less dogmatic about fantastic elements. According to Chesterton, after solemnly swearing never to conceal a vital clue from the reader, the new Club initiate was asked: "Do you promise to observe a *seemly moderation* in the use of Gangs, Conspiracies, Death-Rays, Ghosts, Hypnotism, Trap-Doors, China-men, Super-Criminals and Lunatics; and utterly and for ever to forswear Mysterious Poisons unknown to Science?" My italics.

True to this promise, many authors did indeed indulge with moderation in ghostly plot elements. For example, Ernest Bramah's blind detective Max Carrados would sometimes meet a bit of the dark world, such as electrically transmitted emanations from a plague pit....

In the same way, H. C. Bailey's undeservedly forgotten Mr Fortune has a couple of cases in the twilight zone. "The Profiteers" (*Mr Fortune's Trials*) features unpleasant heavies who die inexplicably at locations where their ancestors flogged and burnt women to death ... whereupon forensic expert Fortune notes that the bodies carry marks closely resembling the flogging and the burning, and the story ends uneasily. Another twilit tale, "The Rock Garden" (*Mr Fortune Explains*) has a "maybe it was, maybe it wasn't" apparition which sabotages a nasty and thoroughly modern scheme.

It's less surprising that the verbena-squirting Moris Klaw (of Sax Rohmer's *The Dream Detective*), with all his immoderate apparatus of psychic dreams and aetheric photography to solve mundane puzzles in a welter of italics and exclamation marks, should just once come up against the real thing in "The Veil of Isis". So, one is inclined to remark, what?

Such stories gain from their shock value when you meet them unexpectedly amid other, classically correct tales of detection. Anthologists who like the supernatural are often tempted to gather these pieces together. Sometimes it works; sometimes the collection falls prey to what I once christened the Vampire Effect. This happens when an editor is delighted by the impact of a normally staid "mainstream" author's one story which unexpectedly introduces a real supernatural horror. When the anthology is published, the editor reads lovingly through it and wonders why that piece seems somehow to lack punch as part of *Fifty Great Tales In Which The Heroine Turns Out To Be A Vampire....*

The Vampire Effect exerts its baleful spell in several existing anthologies. *The Fantastic Saint*, for example, gathers the Leslie Charteris shorts in which Simon Templar meets something extraordinary. Too often, the mere context is deflating: when Simon encounters another apparent con-man with a marvellous gadget, you know that this time the gadget will work, and when he investigates the Loch Ness Monster.... At least it's always fun.

A similar collection, *The Fantastic Stories of Cornell Woolrich*, does the late author a real disservice. Woolrich's best thrillers conjure alarm and dread from real-world shadows: he didn't need occult props and did not himself choose to reprint potboilers about slinky snake-priestesses (not even supernatural: she did her dirty work with envenomed cigarettes), accursed dresses commissioned by Satan (I kid you not) and rotting revenants. The better stories in the collection try to be ambiguous about their supernatural elements, but the dead weight of the book's title prevents this. Nudge nudge, *fantastic* stories, geddit?

One way of keeping the reader agreeably confused is to mix "real" and spooky detection in the same volume ... running the risk of irritating genre fans who prefer to read only one or the other. Dorothy Sayers's famous *Detection, Mystery and Horror* collections kept their genres segregated. A notable book that doesn't is *Carnacki the Ghost-Finder* by William Hope Hodgson, where on first reading you don't know which four cases will be solved "rationally" if rather clumsily. Since my old Panther edition promises "nine chilling supernatural hunts into the icy realms of other-worldly terror", anyone buying it on the strength of the blurb would presumably have been disappointed by nearly half the contents.

There are plenty more examples of detective authors dipping a cautious toe into unknown deeps—like "Word in Season", Margery Allingham's whimsical Campion story about a talking dog; or John Dickson Carr's celebrated *The Burning Court*, where the rational solution is meticulously explained only to be overturned in a vertiginous final chapter; or that nicely creepy children's disease with telepathic side-effects in Peter Dickinson's *Sleep and His Brother*. Let's end with a particularly neat example of "seemly moderation".

This is Dorothy Sayers's short "The Bone of Contention" in *Lord Peter Views the Body*, where Wimsey shows himself versatile enough to base rational deductions on spectral premises. The reasoning goes: (a) his horse shied violently at the supposedly haunted "Dead Man's Post" on the common; (b) when he earlier encountered the apparition of a death-coach drawn by headless horses (and remained open-minded about the supernatural possibilities), this sensitive horse was unaffected; (c) therefore the phantom coach was a tangible hoax. There's something satisfying about the quiet assimilation of a "real" haunt as touchstone for the fake one, even if many of us might have suspected (c) without any need for steps (a) and (b)....

But then, his insufferable lordship *was* full of whisky at the time.

1992

8: GOREY STORIES

Archipelago, cardamon, obloquy, tacks,
Ignavia, samisen, bandages, wax....

A welcome recent event in [British] publishing was the long-delayed appearance of Edward Gorey's collection of fifteen picture stories, or storied pictures, *Amphigorey* (Penguin £9.99). Since this column has never soiled its hands by being immediate or topical, we move in haste to the collections as yet unpublished in Britain—twenty further little books in *Amphigorey Too* (1975) and seventeen more in *Amphigorey Also* (1983).

For many years Edward Gorey has saturated himself in popular fiction, from Victorian melodrama and moral instruction through Edwardian splendours to golden-age detective stories. His laborious ink drawings and captions (the latter usually hand-drawn to look like print) tend to be both sinister and highly subversive of their fictional sources.

Children's stories, for example. *The Beastly Baby* echoes the secret if momentary thoughts of every long-suffering parent, with deadpan captions like "When it was taken bathing, it always floated back to shore, festooned with slimy green weed." Or, as the parents attempt in vain to slip away: "In public places, some officious person was certain to point out that it was in danger of being left behind." The hero of *The Pious Infant*, doomed from the outset to an edifying but fatal illness, is barely more appalling than Victorian moral exemplars: "He used to go through books and carefully blot out any places where there was a frivolous mention of the Deity."

[The Untitled Book] offers a surreal reworking of the one about glimpsing fairies at the bottom of the garden. To an accompaniment of nonsense captions ("Hippity wippity, Oxiborick; Flappity flippity, Saragashum...."), the impassive infant watches a succession of not altogether cuddly creatures emerging to dance. These include a large bat, a giant ant and what appears to be a kind of featureless fetish-doll. Suddenly the sky darkens as something indistinct but clearly very horrid passes overhead, and one by one the dancers disperse in panic while the unconcerned captions continue their cheery gibberish. Guaranteed to give alarming dreams to sensitive children, I'm sure, and a good thing too.

> *Opopanax, thunder, dismemberment, baize,*
> *Hellebore, obelus, cartilage, maize....*

Gorey's special interests of opera, ballet and crime—not to mention fur coats and white tennis shoes—colour many of the books. The most appalling of the lot must be *The Loathsome Couple*, with its allusions to the Moors murders. Elaborate, murky panels like soiled etchings tell the story of the unspeakable but also pathetic pair, not without black comedy: we see them collapsed and far too overdressed for the legend, "When they tried to make love, their strenuous and prolonged efforts came to nothing." Instead they begin their dreadful "life's work", of which I only say that no detail is shown ... the horrors are always delicately offstage and your imagination is left to throb.

The crime fans' favourite is the infinitely sunnier *The Awdrey-Gore Legacy*, whose frame story about vanished novelist Miss D. Awdrey-Gore (one of many similar anagrams in the works) parodies Agatha Christie's famed disappearance and encloses a devastating set of "rough notes" for a Golden Age mystery. It's all here: the panel-by-panel evolution of the Great Detective from blandness to a seething mass of quirks ("His deductions concerning each case are given in the form of a linked series of haiku in Gaelic of his own composition.") ... the picture-gallery of suspects ("Heroine. If she turns out to be the murderer, have a second with different hair colour.") ... possible scenes of the crime and classified murder-weapons ("GRADUAL: arsenical buns. INSTAN-TANEOUS: boulder. INEXPLICABLE: confetti.") ... maps, clues and alternatives for What The Murderer Failed To Realize ("that yellow stitchbane is not yellow at all, but a pale mauve") ... the great revelation scene, and after. All very funny and allusive. Meanwhile the frame story has tantalizing links with the internal "novel notes"—what *is* the all-pervading significance of the condiment Cad's Relish? It ends in cryptic yet almost meaningful postcard clues and a message to chill any mystery-lover's heart: "And what if then we don't find out / What all of it has been about?"

> *Ligament, exequies, spandrel, chandoo,*
> *Gehenna, etui, anamorphosis, glue....*

Gorey excels at dry wit, teasing cross-references and period gloom; it is entirely in character that his merchandising company should be called Doomed Enterprises Inc. A self-taught artist, he's a master of both elaborately overdone backgrounds and the layout and balance which make a very sparsely populated drawing look satisfying. (Though his characters' faces always look a bit skimpy or scamped, except for those chaps lost in splendiferous beards.) The few words of caption he allows himself are carefully selected. I treasure the kitchen scene of *Les Urnes Utiles*, depicting an ornate urn evidently about eight feet high, labelled in beautiful script: "Hundreds & Thousands".

His eye for words is most peculiarly evident in a personal favourite, *The Nursery Frieze*. No cuddly "C is for Cat" animals in the Gorey nursery: this is an endless strip of dreary, monochrome landscape, enlivened only by the odd desolate tower or blasted oak, whose foreground shows a procession of mournful, black and vaguely tapir-like animals (another Gorey speciality. Some weirder relatives of these creatures fill his cover for Frank Belknap Long's supernatural collection *The Dark Beasts* ... which 1964 Belmont edition must now be quite rare). In scroll-like speech balloons, each beast utters a single word for the edification of the child audience: most are obscure, few are cheerful, but they do form a little rhyme. Extracts appear above, and on the following merry note the frieze concludes:

> *Wapentake, orrery, aspic, mistrust,*
> *Ichor, ganosis, velleity, dust.*

Dust to dust.... Macabre themes? The artist protests: "I write about everyday life." In the same self-interview (in *Gorey Posters*, 1979), he explained: "The books are about something, not what they seem to be about ... but I don't know what that other thing is." Nor do I, but I recommend them and collect them assiduously. Does anyone have a copy of *The Other Statue*? Seriously, now.

1992

9: THE REST OF CHESTERTON

One of my bright but doomed ideas for publishing projects was a fat detective-story omnibus titled something like *The Rivals of Father Brown*, to hit the stands when G. K. Chesterton dropped out of copyright in 1987. It was to contain all Chesterton's *other* detective tales ... which, going by a generous definition of "detective story", would just outnumber the 49 stories in the well-loved Father Brown omnibus.

It nearly worked. The publisher was enthusiastic. I collected a fee for assembling the text (six volumes and some oddments), loaning priceless first editions and writing the introduction; and then a long silence fell. Abruptly it was explained that the book was to have been part of a new line of "classic crime" (news to me; I thought it was going to be just, you know, a book), which had for mysterious reasons self-destructed and taken my Chesterton anthology with it. Publishers! By then it *was* 1987, and before I could start again I discovered the brand-new *Thirteen Detectives* by G. K. Chesterton, edited by Marie Smith, a slim volume containing many of "my" best stories. I recommend it through clenched teeth.

The doomed book would have featured some very odd pieces, I must admit. Chesterton was a genius, but an incredibly slipshod one, producing most of his fiction in blazing haste between one "important" matter and another. Dazzlement and hilarity alternate with trivial quibbles and numbing anticlimaxes. A thing worth doing, the author liked to say, is worth doing badly....

Thus *The Club of Queer Trades* (six stories, 1905) starts with "The Tremendous Adventure of Major Brown", lapsing into a rather weak coincidence to explain the splendid melodrama of its hero finding **DEATH TO MAJOR BROWN** spelt out in pansies across a flower-bed, or being taunted by the disembodied voice that cries: "Major Brown, Major Brown, where does the jackal dwell?" These are anti-crime stories, using Chesterton's patent trick of the Happy Surprise—the black riddle whose answer is radiantly innocent, as in Father Brown's cases "The Honour of Israel Gow" or "The Absence of Mr Glass".

Prattling here about unlikely clubs and societies, Chesterton inspired a later story when he wrote darkly: "Of the Ten Teacups, of course I dare not say a word." The Carter Dickson impossible-crime novel turning on the existence or otherwise of this sinister group is, of course, *The Ten Teacups* (1937) ... wetly retitled *The Peacock Feather Murders* in the USA.

Next comes *The Man Who Knew Too Much* (eight linked stories plus four others, 1922), displaying the remarkable spectacle of our century's most bouncy and flamboyant optimist trying to portray a world-weary cynic in amateur detective Horne Fisher. What Fisher knows too much about is politics and the wicked ways of how England is really run, based on Chesterton's own horrified encounters with plutocratic *Realpolitik*. As usual, extravagant language and sweeping ideas carry the thing off, and clues stand obediently on their heads. The broad scatter of bullet-holes in a target tells mere experts that the gunman is a duffer, while Fisher knows he must be a deadly sharpshooter, to place his shots so they form a passable caricature of the intended victim....

Eventually the stench of politics becomes too much for Chesterton, and Horne Fisher's career ends in a fictional war. *Tales of the Long Bow* (eight linked stories, 1925) eventually goes further to show a revolution in England, but mainly consists of daft fables which are more howdunnits than whodunnits— the "how" concerning the bringing to reality of various figures of speech. A man eats his hat. Pigs fly. In a scene with a curiously prophetic feel, the contamination of a river with industrial effluents allows an apparently doomed protester to ... set the Thames on fire. H'mm.

The Poet and the Lunatics (eight linked stories, 1929) is the best-loved of these "unknown" Chesterton collections. Several critics praise it and its detective Gabriel Gale above even the Father Brown stories. They have a point. Gale is an intuitive, psychological detective, like the "philosophical policemen" of *The Man Who Was Thursday* (1908): "The ordinary detective discovers from a ledger or a diary that a crime has been committed. We discover from a book of sonnets that a crime will be committed."

In one memorable case, Gale detects the onset of madness in a man who is coming to believe he is God—and leaves him lashed to a tree overnight through howling rain, to save his sanity by *proving* to him that he can't control events. (Martin Gardner has wistfully suggested that such treatment might be good for other mystical dabblers who like to imagine the universe is all in their minds ... beginning with Shirley MacLaine.) Is this detection? Gale's detective reasoning is brilliantly convincing and brilliantly written; what more can you ask? Another story's clue points to a thoroughly modern madness: "the man who broke the bowl merely because he thought it a prison for the fish..."

Four Faultless Felons (four stories and framing text, 1930) takes us back to the Happy Surprise plot and is full of rumbustious fun. "The Moderate Murderer" half-kills someone to save him from something worse; through sheer doubletalk "The Honest Quack" has his intended father-in-law locked up as insane, with highly generous motives ... and so on. Most melodramatic of all, "The Loyal Traitor" sets up a wild Ruritanian conspiracy complete with a mystic, prophetic verse which betrays the whole secret of the hero's ludicrous impersonations, if you're quick enough to spot it.

Lastly, *The Paradoxes of Mr Pond* (eight stories, 1937) has a detective of the Aged Civil Servant persuasion, who is frankly a bit of a bore—he says these *jolly paradoxical* things all the time, usually without the profundity of Gale or Father Brown. But it contains several fine pieces. Jorge Luis Borges's personal favourite opens the book: "The Three Horsemen of Apocalypse", where deadly plans go astray and somehow get lost in a maze with no turnings or branches, a single road stretching in a mathematical line through otherwise impassable marshes. Vintage stuff, hard to begin again without reading right through.

So many of these quirky stories remain impossible to find that I'm tempted to take my omnibus proposal to some more publishers. Wish me luck.

1992

10: Notes & Queries

The Case Book of David Langford is crammed with odd little items noted down in a lifetime of reading pop-fiction when I should have been working. Here is an almost random selection....

• What is the most damaging possible typographic error? P. G. Wodehouse put his finger on one of the commonest with a verse tirade against the printer who inserted "not" when he had written "now". My personal favourite comes in the 1970 Corgi paperback of Anne McCaffrey's science-fantasy *Dragonflight*, a romance of hero dragonriders on their telepathic, teleporting steeds. Towards the climax the heroine and (of course) her dragon prance off on an impossibly dangerous errand; the worried hero's own dragon telepathically searches the entire world for the missing pair, and after a long, dramatic pause reports: *I cannot bear them.* Quite a few readers already felt that way about the almost dementedly wilful heroine, and took a while to realize that the word must have been "hear".

• Since the golden-age days when she could do no wrong, Dorothy Sayers has been given a hard time by critics for snobbery and like crimes. To redress the balance on one point: Colin Watson's generally excellent *Snobbery With Violence* sneers at Harriet Vane's unnatural cool when (in *Have His Carcase*) "she searched with absolute impassivity the pockets of a corpse whose neck has been hacked through to the backbone with a razor." In the actual text she spends a long paragraph feeling sick, takes several queasy and self-recriminating pages before so much as fingering the corpse's jacket, and can't bring herself to touch its bloodstained breast-pocket at all. Critics need to check that their prejudices haven't been quietly rearranging their memories....

• It's notorious that T. S. Eliot was a Sherlock Holmes fan who modelled Macavity the Mystery Cat on Moriarty, pinched a chunk of "The Musgrave Ritual" for the Second Tempter scene in *Murder in the Cathedral* (there are other Sherlockian echoes in the play) and puzzled academics with the bit in "East Coker" about being lost "in a dark wood, in a bramble, On the edge of a grimpen, where is no secure foothold...." Those who'd searched at length and in vain for the Old English root of the obscure word were not best pleased to hear it was merely the great Grimpen Mire from *The Hound of the Baskervilles*. A further micro-reference that I've never seen mentioned in print is Eliot's arrangement of *A Choice of Kipling's Verse* (1941), where unrelated poems from

1902 and 1897 are carefully placed together. They are titled ... "Sussex" and "The Vampire". Nudge, nudge. You know my methods, Watson.

• All this Sherlockiana reminds me that Fr. Ronald Knox was a wittier fellow than his dull detective novels indicate. He began the joke of studying Holmes stories with solemn rigour, making deduction after amazing deduction from Conan Doyle's slapdash inconsistencies and so parodying the loons who deciphered Bacon's signature everywhere in Shakespeare. (Unfortunately, too many of those who followed his example took the thing seriously—though not Rex Stout, who scandalized the Baker Street Irregulars club in 1941 with his argument that Watson was a woman: in fact, Irene Adler Watson.) Look for Knox's 1928 *Essays in Satire*, containing his famous proof by Baconian analysis that Queen Victoria drafted "In Memoriam" for Tennyson—who confessed this by adding numerous lines like "A potent voice of Parliament", a palpable anagram of "Alf, poet-pen to Victoria. Amen."

• Kyril Bonfiglioli's splendidly witty and nasty *The Mortdecai Trilogy* (out at last in one volume from Black Spring: buy at least a dozen) teases us another way by taking chapter epigraphs from noted poets—Browning, Tennyson, Swinburne—but adding one forgery per book, each acrostically signed by its author. The same hallowed literary technique allowed Robert Robinson, in *Landscape With Dead Dons*, to cheekily hand readers the vital clue *before they actually started the book.*

• Speaking of minute textual nitpicking, did you know that every edition there has ever been of Chesterton's *The Innocence of Father Brown* has the stories in the wrong order? "The Honour of Israel Gow" contains one of the series' very rare references to an earlier tale, as amid a hellish atmosphere of night, wind and madness the characters dig up the dead man's grave and Flambeau confesses: "I'm afraid of his not being the right shape." Whereupon Father Brown says: "Nor was that piece of paper, you know ... and we survived even that piece of paper." This malformed paper appears in "The Wrong Shape", the *next* story in the book. I gleefully mentioned this to Martin Gardner, who was preparing *The Annotated Innocence of Father Brown*, but he'd spotted it already and saved me the work of looking up the original dates: "The Wrong Shape" was published in January 1911 and "Israel Gow" (as "The Strange Justice") in April 1911.

• Writers are always peculiarly irritated by petty censorship—in particular, the prohibition in an adult magazine (usually by an ordinarily foul-mouthed editor) of realistic swearing for fear of offending a readership which habitually uses the taboo words every day. A few favourite examples... *Astounding Science Fiction* used to have a fanatically prudish editorial assistant who cut out any trace of "smut". SF writer George O. Smith finally sneaked one past her in his story "Rat Race" (1947) with a throwaway gag about "the original ball-bearing mousetrap ... a tomcat". In the swinging 60s, things were looser but it remained hard to get the F-word published in American SF magazines: less fiery epithets like "gosh-darn" might be substituted. Robert Silverberg managed the big one in "Going Down Smooth" (*Galaxy*, 1968), which starred an insane computer spewing out obscenities thinly concealed in binary code. "1000110 you," it would say, and a great deal more besides.

• Even more subtle is Rex Stout's story "Instead of Evidence" (1949), which features some unusually zany material about a joke-and-novelty company—largely, I suspect, so the chief suspect can try to sell Nero Wolfe on the idea of a novelty pot of orchids. "Whoever you send it to, preferably a lady, she will lift the pot, suspecting nothing, and your own voice, the voice of Nero Wolfe, will say to her, *Orchids to you!*" It's a very silly scene ("Probably she'll drop the pot," muses the entrepreneur; Wolfe actually flees his office to escape this hard sell), and the choice of recorded words seems odd. Was Stout, who loved playing with language, tempting us to substitute a word etymologically very close to "orchids" and fitting much better into that phrase ... i.e., balls?

1992

11: The Missing Bits

I went on holiday with—and rather enjoyed—an advance proof of Patricia Craig's *The Penguin Book of British Comic Writing* (Penguin 460pp £15.99), acquired by the devious route of opening parcels addressed to me by our editor. Unlike the Frank Muir *Oxford Book of Humorous Prose*, this one doesn't give you a sprained wrist: huge drifts of biographical, critical and transatlantic material are omitted, and funny fiction (as opposed to, er, funny stories) left to the 1990 companion volume *The Penguin Book of British Comic Stories*.

In brief: sixty-odd items, twenty-three already familiar to me. Familiarity doesn't have to breed contempt; old favourites are often cheering, and sometimes old unfavourites look better out of context—A. P. Herbert's babbling "Topsy" monologues are off-putting at book length ("Trix darling I've made the *most* voluminous error I've *alienated* the editor of *Undies* and...") but succeed in small doses. There are mild surprises from noted humorists, like Wodehouse's essay on thriller clichés; slightly unexpected inclusions like Dylan Thomas being parodic and Germaine Greer polemical (a bit from *The Female Eunuch*); and a sprinkling of "yes, very worthy but not actually nor even intendedly *funny*" items, such as Orwell's much-reprinted "Boys' Weeklies", V. S. Pritchett going on about the ever-hilarious writings of Dostoevsky, A. J. P. Taylor's diary entries on his droll broken leg, etc.

I thought of putting Bernard Levin's assault on pretentious concert programme notes into this category, but eventually concluded that his silly anagrams of the offending note-writer's name are supposed to be mirthful. Considered as humour, taking advantage of an easily anagrammatized name seems on a par with the side-splitting childhood discovery that the phone book contains people called Bottom, Bugg and Smellie....

Overall it's a good collection. Traditionally reviewers are expected to whinge over missing items which should have been included, and to deplore book extracts torn raw and bleeding from their context. But in one "familiar" extract, what caught my eye was a passage I'd never seen before.

This was from Gerald Durrell's *My Family and Other Animals*, with the author's extraordinary family arriving in Corfu, the dog Roger widdling at inconvenient length on the nearest lamp-post, some rancid repartee about which family stomachs have been misbehaving: all very characteristic, but I knew the book fairly well and was convinced this must be a spurious interpolation by some unknown hand. How peculiar! But research in second-hand shops produced an old Penguin edition, which agreed with *British Comic Writing* and utterly refuted the Langford memory.

After my holiday the mystery solved itself. I never buy *Readers Digest* condensed editions or suchlike, but my perfectly respectable-looking 1964 hardback of *My Family and Other Animals* proved to be sixty pages shorter than the Penguin paperback despite larger print, with 17 and not 18 chapters, and on its title page the dread words "Edited for Schools by W. G. Bebbington, MA".

Blimey. W. G. Bebbington certainly made sure no whiff of corruption could reach innocent schoolkids. At one stage the entire Durrell family moves house in order not to have room for Great-aunt Hermione, "that evil old camel, smelling of mothballs and singing hymns in the lavatory" (in brother Lawrence Durrell's phrase). This whole description is another of many, many censored bits. In the introduction, accounting for four offspring and no visible father: "My mother also insists that I explain she is a widow for, as she so penetratingly observed, you never know what people might think." W. G. Bebbington has sternly blue-pencilled all the words after "widow"....

(Paul Fussell has an essay on the 1965 reissue of Booth Tarkington's sub-Twain novel of US boyhood, *Penrod*, in which episodes like the proper punishment of an offensive racist have been made meaningless by the toning-down or removal of his racist abuse. All this years before "Political Correctness", in a volume claiming to reprint the "complete text" of the 1914 original!)

It's weirdly disconcerting to find that a well-known book is incomplete like this. I felt wrong-footed a few years back when a science fiction line reissued Eric Frank Russell's wisecracking thriller *Wasp*, and some damn-fool editor had taken peculiar pains to reproduce "the original magazine serialization" ... that is, a version that had been savagely cut to fit, with the fun and wise-cracks suffering most.

Then there's A. P. Herbert and *Uncommon Law*, the omnibus volume of the three classic Misleading Cases collections. (There are further collections without "Misleading Cases" in the title—*Codd's Last Case* and *Bardot MP?*) This is a splendid and very funny omnibus, with many improvements and added silly footnotes, but it omits several items collected in the original trilogy of small books. Some omissions seem to be to avoid repetition (for example, yet another go at the awfulness of the Inland Revenue and its forms), some because the spoof cases are unusually weak (a curious Coroner's Court item about a dog which is maddened by political broadcasts into killing its master) and one because ... well, could there have been some tiny trace of censorship?

This case, lost since its appearance in *More Misleading Cases in the Common Law* (1930), is a joke libel action against the British publishers of the Catholic *Index Librorum Prohibitorum*, of which Mr Justice Wool querulously asks: "By whom have these books been prohibited? Who has judged them to be blasphemous or obscene?"—and declares that British law provides no special privilege to "a religious body which has its headquarters in Italy" allowing it to libel authors by calling their books corrupting and harmful. "Who is the Pope? He has not been called in evidence...." Ho ho, very satirical.

This is all happily out of date, since the Index (a thorough pest since 1559) was finally abolished in 1966—though the Irish government seemed not to notice. But *Uncommon Law* was assembled in 1935. Had someone leaned on Herbert to omit this contentious piece? Is it a coincidence that 1935 was the year he entered Parliament and started pushing through his Marriage Bill (to ease the unfairness of Britain's divorce laws), a task requiring tireless diplomacy in the face of strong Catholic opposition? I wonder.

But I have more urgent worries—such as searching my library for *other* cut books. Only yesterday I found that my copy of John Cleland's *Memoirs of a Woman of Pleasure* (better known as *Fanny Hill*) says on the title page, in tiny print, "Edited for Schools by W. G. Bebbington, MA". What else have I been missing all these years?

1992

12: Owl Stuffing Time

It's 63 years since the first edition of *The Stuffed Owl: An Anthology of Bad Verse* edited by D. B. Wyndham Lewis and Charles Lee. (Various expanded editions followed.) This must be among the most popular anthologies of all time, full of one-line brilliancies like Wordsworth's invocation "Spade! with which Wilkinson hath tilled his lands ..." However, the *Owl* is avowedly incomplete since it spares "eminent living English poets" of 1930. Later anthologists offer updated collections—most recently Nicholas Parsons with *The Joy of Bad Verse* (1988)—but contemporaries still get off lightly.

The cat leapt from the bag in *Pegasus Descending: A Treasury of the Best Bad Poems in English* ed. James Camp, X. J. Kennedy and Keith Waldrop (1971). "A letter to Exposition Press, asking permission to reprint lines from one of their authors, and pointing out that it would seem no shame to keep company with such immortals as Keats and Tennyson, was returned with the superscription, 'Who are you kidding?'" Robert Frost's publishers said approximately the same. Bad-verse anthologies are doomed to incompleteness. Even, I suppose, the one I've never seen but covet for its title: Richard Walser's *Nematodes in My Garden of Verse* (1959).

This issue I offer a tiny personal anthology, beginning with the anatomically explicit Emily Dickinson lyric unearthed in *Pegasus Descending*:

> A Dying Tiger — moaned for drink —
> I hunted all the Sand —
> I caught the Dripping of a Rock
> And bore it in my Hand —
>   His Mighty Balls — in death were thick —
>   But searching — I could see
>   A Vision on the Retina
> Of Water — and of me —
> 'Twas not my blame — who sped too slow —
> 'Twas not his blame — who died
> While I was reaching him —
> But 'twas — the fact that He was dead —

Somehow the argument of the last verse is even more vaguely worrying than the double-take in the second. But onward, with further thrilling categories of verse to be described (for Political Correctness) as "differently good"....

Anticlimactic. Inspired by *The Stuffed Owl*, G. K. Chesterton wrote an essay on bad poetry (in *All I Survey*, 1933) ascribing the Brontë sisters' depression to the acute torment of listening to the poems of their father the Rev. Patrick (actually printed alongside the sisters' in one edition of their works). The Reverend had patented his own maddening verse form, a near-limerick in which the last word *invariably lets you down*:

> Religion makes beauty enchanting;
> And even where beauty is wanting,
>   The temper and mind
>   Religion-refined
> Will shine through the veil with sweet lustre.

Plonk!

Political. In the early 80s King Fahd of Saudi Arabia had his Court Poet eulogize the Briton who most awed him:

> Venus was sculpted by man,
> But the far more attractive woman, Margaret Thatcher,
> Was sculpted by Allah....

Possibly it loses in translation. Further lines, including "Her figure is more attractive than the figure of any cherished wife", appear in John Julius Norwich's anthology *More Christmas Crackers* (1990).

Mathematical. Frederick Soddy the Nobel-winning chemist went bananas in 1936 and published formulae for the radii of mutually touching circles and spheres as deathless verse, in *Nature.* A brief extract:

> Four circles to the kissing come.
> The smaller are the benter.
> The bend is just the inverse of
> The distance from the centre.
> Though their intrigue left Euclid dumb
> There's now no need for rule of thumb.
> Since zero bend's a dead straight line
> And concave bends have minus sign,
> *The sum of the squares of all four bends*
> *Is half the square of their sum.*

Self-Confessed. W. H. Auden admitted an early line he'd wisely suppressed but which, he pointed out, would have made a perfect Thurber cartoon caption: "And Isobel who with her leaping breasts pursued me through a summer." (Little did she know.)

Evolutionary. Another forgotten epic poem is Victor Purcell's *Cadmus* (1944), which indicates that when creating life on Earth, God was at risk of going blind:

> The shallow threshold of the sounding sea
> Was floored with crumbled layers of debris,
> A liquid mass of silicates and lime,
> And with this mud was other mud, a slime,
> A viscous ooze, a dimly vibrant plasm,
> A pungent, flowing mass — Great God's orgasm!

Edmund Wilson quotes lots more of this in *The Bit Between My Teeth*, 1965.

Science-Fictional. Many SF authors are under a false impression that they can dash off incidental verse. Damon Knight records a stanza from the tautologous *Starship Through Space* by Lee Correy, which Sums Things Up:

> We who have tasted alien stream
>   And done what others only dream;
> We who with earth-dirt on our shoes
>   Have walked the path the sunbeams use;
> We will trod the Milky Way.

Royal. The thuddingly sycophantic paean to Elizabeth II called *Lilibet* (1985) is by "a loyal subject of Her Majesty" whose anonymity is strictly guarded and whose alleged relation to A. N. Wilson must be a thing of mere fantasy. Of its 1,000 lines the most grimly memorable are perhaps:

> Delay and disappointment could not flatten
> The ardour of Lieutenant P. Mountbatten.

(Who also rhymes with "hat on"—and Bernard Levin claims to have traced the rhymes "piano"/"manner", "novelty"/"duty", "sins are"/"Windsor"....)

Lipogrammatic.

> 'Twas a night, almost Christmas,
> And all through that room,
> A warm joy is stirring;
> No sign of a gloom....

This "translation" of Clement Moore's "'Twas the night before Christmas" limps along for much the same reason that sprinters would if their legs were manacled. It's from one of the century's least probable novels, *Gadsby* by Ernest Vincent Wright (1938), which for 50,000 words avoids the most common English letter. "The entire manuscript of this story was written with the E type-bar of the typewriter *tied down*...." After all that you'd think the author would have adopted an E-less pseudonym (such as David Langford) rather than sully the cover with his name.

Vignettes. "Who prop, thou ask'st, in these bad days, my mind?" (Matthew Arnold). "Is this, ye Gods, the Capitolian Hill?" (Wordsworth). "He viewed the uncovered bottom of the abyss...." (Dyer). "I love the dead!" (Tupper: an opening line). "Mother of God! no lady thou..." (Mary Elizabeth Coleridge). "Irks care the crop-full bird? Frets doubt the maw-crammed beast?" (Browning). "The press restrained! nefandous thought!" (Matthew Green, "The Spleen"). And we conclude with the great McGonagall's moving description of what followed "The Albion Battleship Calamity": "Her Majesty has sent a message of sympathy to the bereaved ones in distress, / And the Duke and Duchess of York have sent 25 guineas I must confess, / And £1000 from the Directors of the Thames Ironworks and Shipbuilding Company, / Which I hope will help to fill the bereaved one's hearts with glee."

1993

Me and Whitley and the Continuum

1: MUDDYING THE WATERS

Towards the end of 1989 I heard the rumours. In 1990, confirmation came in the form of a big, fat and much-hyped hardback. Yes: I, humble and obscure Langford, had been selected from millions of other SF authors as an influence on that god amongst men, Whitley Strieber. It is a proud and lonely thing...
It is time for a flashback to 1978.

The original daft suggestion came from Paul Barnett, now better known as the author John Grant but then my editor at David & Charles Ltd, and struggling to break free of this publisher's relentless specialization in trains and canals. Constantly editing things called *201 Interesting Stretches of Canal Visible from Norfolk Railway Lines* can make you yearn for new horizons.

His brief to me was: write a spoof book about a nineteenth-century UFO encounter. "Examine" the "evidence" as a physicist would. Lambast modern ufology for its lack of scientific rigour. Make the Victorian UFO sufficiently over the top that no close reader could believe it. What larks, what larks!

More than one sceptic has been tempted in this way to exert the happy irresponsibility of the SF writer, only to find the resulting satire embedded (like a fly in ointment) in the pseudoscience which was supposed to be satirized....

For the antique UFO report, Paul lent me a period style-book in the form of Thackeray's *Adventures of Philip*. My wife Hazel searched her family tree for an impeccably documented ancestor: William Robert Loosley, undertaker and craftsman of High Wycombe in Buckinghamshire, and provider of posh furniture to Disraeli. Unearthed from the dusty recesses of my typewriter, Loosley's first-person narrative (in tone oddly reminiscent of Thackeray, with a random larding of Biblical phrases) had, it seemed, been miraculously preserved for more than a century, just handily for publication in 1979.

A surrounding commentary by that little-known savant David Langford proved quite inconclusively that during his carefully recorded encounter in the Buckinghamshire woods, Loosley was exposed to advanced knowledge of nuclear physics, quantum mechanics, general relativity, black holes, and indeed everything else his impartial editor could remember from an Oxford physics course.

I heard a whisper that Whitley Strieber was most upset to find he had an entry in The Encyclopedia of Science Fiction. *This was because he does not write and has never written sf. Also, the Pope is a scientologist.*

No, this isn't a plug for the book, long out of print despite its snappy title of *An Account of a Meeting with Denizens of Another World, 1871* (David & Charles, 1979; St Martin's Press, 1980). I come to bury it, not to praise it, and as usual my publishers had the same idea. There was an abrupt change of editors, and the new chap combined integrity with economy by omitting two key elements of the original plan—simulated pages from "Loosley's manuscript", and a non-zero publicity budget. Instead he wondered whether the book could make its own way as a jolly good SF novel. In the face of this rampant indecision about how and whether to promote it, my squib passed away quietly to that remainder shelf from whence no traveller returns.

Nevertheless, *An Account* had made its mark. The grottier sort of newspapers and magazines ran Amazing UFO Proof stories, their devotion to investigative journalism being amply shown by the fact that not one asked the obvious question, "How about giving us a look at this 108-year-old manuscript, then?" Enshrined in many a footnote, plus two pages of the doubtless deeply scholarly *The World's Greatest UFO Mysteries* [1], Loosley has passed into history—at least, that peculiar alternative history beloved of so many ufologists [2]. My finest hour came when I was attacked for the excessive caution and scepticism of my own commentary on Loosley's narrative.

Later I found that I wasn't the only SF writer to have gleefully muddied the waters of research. John Sladek, as "James Vogh", had gone to the extent of inventing the lost 13th sign of the zodiac. His books on the sign Arachne, he told me, "were conceived as jokes, but very quickly turned into moneymaking enterprises. Only they didn't make a lot of money, either. So finally they turn out to have been a gigantic waste of time." I probably picked a slightly better market. Astrology already has its fact-proof theories and doesn't require more, while ufology seems prepared to assimilate any odd incident whatever, declaring it to be further conclusive confirmation of something or other.

(And as we all know, an explained or exploded incident never attracts the same attention as the original enigma. Even the *Skeptical Inquirer* displayed no interest in an offer to confess my own folly in their pages—though they did condescend to report the revelation when, instead, I published it as an essay in *New Scientist* [3].)

The moral seemed to be that SF authors writing with tongue in cheek should stick with SF. In offtrail phenomena as in bodice-ripping romance, the book market sniffs at jokesters but rewards sincerity, even misguided, self-deluding and totally barmy sincerity. (I do not, at this juncture, mention Whitley Strieber and *Communion*.) It felt vaguely depressing to have contributed another snippet of disinformation to the already over-large folklore, without even the compensation of getting rich. I ended my first confession with apologies to all, most especially my bank manager.

Now, the sequel.

Personally I still incline to the opinion that any true first contact with alien thingies will be as clear and unequivocal as the message beamed Earthwards in my and John Grant's harrowing disaster novel *Earthdoom*: "YOU EARTHLING SCUM ARE THE DREGS OF THE UNIVERSE. WE COME TO ANNIHILATE YOU PAINFULLY AND RAPE YOUR PLANET." However, I do admit that there are ufologists of integrity ... which according to me means a readiness to entertain the wild supposition that UFO does not *necessarily* stand for Alien Space Vehicle Piloted By Little Putty Men With Enormous Eyes.

One such researcher, Jenny Randles, contacted Paul Barnett with the glad news that the story of *An Account* had been incorporated—without any visible criticism of its content—into the latest work by no less than Whitley Strieber.

(Later, still rocking with laughter, she passed this on to the even more noted ufologist Jacques Vallee, who is supposed to have very slowly said: "Oh. God. You mean that *An Account*'s a spoof, then?")

For the first time in my life I became frantic to get hold of a book by Strieber. Luckily, before I could do anything terminally rash such as part with money, his British publishers sent me a copy of *Majestic* (Macdonald, London, 1990; 318pp £12.95 hardback). This I skimmed avidly until I found the good bit, which is on pages 46 and 47.

In what some might call a dramatic break with his former practice, Strieber presents this as a novel, though one very closely based on truth. This allows him to tinker a little with his source material, and indeed to omit source references which might be checked. Although his two good pages are a direct condensation from *An Account*, there's no mention of the book itself, or of its being copyright in my name. Perhaps being a major bestseller puts you above things like literary ethics.

Again, because Strieber is going on about the purported UFO crash in New Mexico in 1947 [4], he carefully backdates the discovery of William Robert Loosley's fabulous manuscript from the 1970s to 1941. (The 1979 edition of *An Account* says that it was found "only a few years ago", which by no stretch of the imagination includes 1941. Internal evidence is arranged to indicate a date later than 1975. Of course it had been, as it were, found in 1978.)

Even in this book's brief summary, Strieber's keen critical intelligence can be shown by his rendering of a rather carefully phrased comment about this hard-to-locate MS:

> "I can only declare that the manuscript has so far withstood every test of authenticity to which it has been subjected."
> (*An Account*, 1979.)
> "The ms. has been authenticated by British antiquarians."
> (*Majestic*, 1989.)

Exercise for the beginning student: which of these sentences admits the possibility that the number of "tests of authenticity" might have been less than one?

Exercise for the advanced student: how closely based on "true incident" can be a book whose reconstruction of 1947 US Intelligence documents incorporates a text which I didn't draft until 1978? Come to think of it, why wasn't the Loosley story publicly expunged from UFO legend after the appearance of my 1988 *New Scientist* article?

Exercise for a weary reviewer: do I really have to struggle on to page 318 and its plea for me to rush in a letter telling Strieber about all the occasions on which I've been abducted and/or offered little yellow flowers by passing aliens?

Exercise for you all: if someone reproduces a story and believes it to be factual, does he perhaps have a responsibility not to tamper with the facts? Conversely, if someone does so while believing it to be fiction, might the word "plagiarism" not conceivably apply? [5]

I suppose that I should at least be cheered by the prospect of reaching, for the very first time, a readership numbered in the millions. Surely this is every pure-souled author's dream. Before long I will learn not to chafe at anonymity, and to stop making the obsessive calculations which begin: "two pages out of 318, that's ... that's ... I wonder how much 0.63% of Whitley Strieber's royalties would be?" [23/1/90]

NOTES

1. Nigel Blundell and Roger Boar: Octopus, London, 1983.

2. It still goes on. For example, the Plymouth *Western Evening Herald* for 30 January 1990 carried a piece by the "mystic" Marilyn Preston, which links the flattening of grass by Loosley's mothership with the recently famous phenomenon of "crop circles". Tra la.

3. 26 May 1988. No need to look it up; the important bits are incorporated into the above.

4. You have to be a pretty hard-line ufologist to put much credit in an incident chiefly attested to by documents—the MJ-12 or "Majestic-12" records of a supposed US government investigation—which appear to be such embarrassingly bad forgeries. See for example Philip J. Klass's "New Evidence of MJ-12 Hoax" in *Skeptical Inquirer* (Winter 1990), the latest in a sporadic series about these dubious papers. Now you know where Strieber got his title.

5. The extremely general and hypothetical phrasing of this paragraph has no connection with a certain author's alleged fondness for lawsuits. Well, not much.

As a remoter spinoff of the book I later received a number of letters from crop circle enthusiasts, proving in irrefutable terms that the complexity of observed patterns was clear evidence of some directing intelligence. For some reason they tended to get upset when I enthusiastically agreed with the bit about directing intelligence. The day of reckoning for crop circles was yet to come.

The mention in these notes of the Octopus book turned out to be prophetic, as will emerge.

2: Letter to Putnam (USA) and Macdonald (UK), February 1990

Dear Sir or Madam,

Majestic by Whitley Strieber

Looking into this novel recently published by you, I find that two pages are devoted to a detailed condensation of my book *An Account of a Meeting with Denizens of Another World, 1871*, published by David & Charles (UK) in 1979 and St Martin's Press (USA) in 1980.

This is also a work of fiction, though presented tongue in cheek as an account of a Victorian UFO. It is entirely my own work and is copyrighted in my name. (Its fictional nature is a matter of public record, by the way—see for example "Myths in the making" in *New Scientist* for 26 May 1988, to which the attention of American UFO researchers was called by an abstract in the Fall 1988 *Skeptical Inquirer*.)

Pages 46 and 47 of *Majestic* are chiefly occupied by what amounts to a brief adaptation in *Reader's Digest* fashion of the central narrative in my book, the difference being that *Reader's Digest* would routinely ask permission and pay a substantial fee. In this case, no permission was asked nor fee offered.

At the very least, normal professional courtesy surely requires that future editions of *Majestic* should carry an appropriate credit for the use of my original creation, as the present one does for a few lines of Rilke. (Was a permission fee paid for this?) Using this existing acknowledgement as a guide, I would suggest something along the following lines:

> The condensation from *An Account of a Meeting with Denizens of Another World, 1871*, as by William Robert Loosley, edited by David Langford, appears by permission of the copyright holder. Original version copyright (c) 1979 by David Langford.

Since *Majestic* purports to be firmly "based on fact", I don't ask that such an acknowledgement should stress the fictional nature of *An Account*, or the backdating of the "Victorian" narrative's supposed discovery from the 1970s to 1941 in order to make it fit Mr Strieber's plot.

It is possible that I might write at greater length about the repercussions of *An Account*, and with this in mind I also ask formal permission to reprint in its entirety the version of my story which begins on the third line of page 46 of *Majestic* (British edition) and extends through most of page 47. Under the circumstances, I do not think that such permission can reasonably be refused.

I look forward to your reply.

Note

Macdonald was subsequently taken over by Little, Brown. Who in 1993 published the awesome John Clute/Peter Nicholls *SF Encyclopaedia* under their Orbit imprint. I was delighted to discover that good old Whitley's fling with my story is documented therein....

See also the copyright page of any paperback of *Majestic*.

3: Secrets of UFO Research

Out of the depths of his experience as an author and agent, my friend Chris Priest suggested the above knife-twisting request for reprint permission—as a result of which I can now confirm that Whitley Strieber and his US publishers will *not* grant me permission to quote the version of my original story which he and they used without permission from me. One can lie awake at night meditating on the sublime beauty of this.

Paul Barnett chimed in with a gratifyingly fiery "To whom it may concern" letter which it's perhaps as well that I didn't spread around. "I am shocked that another novelist, Whitley Strieber, should have gutted the plot of David Langford's novel and pretended that it was his own.... I hope that Mr Strieber has sufficient integrity to issue, at the very least, a public apology." No, Paul, Mr Strieber has no intention of doing any such thing.

Jenny Randles comes in here because I nervously sent her the Part 1 article, in case she objected to my dropping her name. She didn't, but suggested some rephrasing to avoid the original implication that dear old Whitley had "swallowed the spoof hook, line and sinker". This would have suggested that he was a gullible and incompetent researcher, and might thus have been an actionable remark.

Oh, surely not, I thought. I then heard about the great Strieber lawsuit threat. Apparently, even if you have written the book whose account of an "abduction experience" first inspired WS to remember being abducted by anally fixated aliens (*Science and the UFOs* by Jenny Randles and Peter Warrington), and even if this massively profitable inspiration or influence is acknowledged by Strieber (see *Communion*) and his biographer (see *Report on Communion* by Ed Conroy), it is still most unwise to make jokes about it all on the radio. Jenny was required to publish and broadcast an apology, but escaped an actual libel suit because, in Strieber's compassionate words, "she has no money."

At this point I had a few bad nights myself. After all, although I might have dull truth on my side, WS had a very expensive firm of Mayfair lawyers. For example: could I, if it came to the crunch, *prove* that I'd made up the story? In 1984, when *Private Eye* was carrying correspondence on *An Account* and how it had been ripped off by Nigel Blundell for his potboiling UFO compilations, Paul Barnett had naughtily written in to observe that although I might have supposed myself to be inventing the tale, he personally believed that Langford was the mere channel for alien intelligences who wished the facts to be known. (He also accused me of naughty indiscretions with one of his female pseudonyms ... but I digress.)

A month after I'd written to Macdonald (UK) and Putnam (USA), responses started to arrive. The faceless manipulators on this side of the pond proved to be old publishing acquaintances, Peter Lavery and Nick Webb, who wrote in friendly terms and promised a credit to me in the British paperback. They also enclosed a faxed copy of Whitley Strieber's non-apology to Putnam, which explained much and had me rolling around in merriment.

It turns out that Whitley Strieber, the most famous UFO pundit in the known universe, actually does his research in such quick-buck compilations as *The World's Strangest Mysteries* (Octopus UK and Gallery USA, 1987). This contains the exact text and typography of "my" recounted story in Nigel Blundell's and Roger Boar's *The World's Greatest UFO Mysteries* (Octopus, 1983); I seem to remember from *Private Eye* gossip items that Blundell was not above recycling his own as well as others' material.

Strieber also explains that he wrote to Octopus, not of course bothering to ask permission since as a Victorian story this was antique and out of copyright, but merely to check whether the tale could have been available in 1947 and usable for his book. (The Octopus text mentions the date 1871 and begins: "For nearly 100 years, the secret of what undertaker William Robert Loosley saw in an English wood remained locked away in his desk drawer." Add "nearly 100 years" to 1871, and ... well, at the least you get a non-antique date on which the MS was first published and, one might infer, acquired copyright protection.) Receiving no reply, he simply went ahead regardless. Ho hum.

It would be asking too much of any researcher to suggest that he might have tried looking up the person whom Blundell/Boar called "science fiction expert David Langford ... [who] later wrote a book about it"—in, say, the 1986 *Twentieth Century SF Writers*, which gives my and my agents' addresses.

So. Farewell then, Whitley Strieber. I retire with a chuckle slightly soured by the final, icily legalistic letter from Putnam/Berkley. I'd have been content with the offered credit in future editions plus a nice letter of apology. I'd have been delighted with this plus a nominal $100 permission fee. But any such further gesture would, it seems, be an Admission of Liability, and they're not risking that. Bloody lawyers.

FINAL NOTE, DECEMBER 1993

I was informed much later that the great and good Mr Strieber had been reported in *Locus*, the American sf newsletter, as having apologized. Exactly to whom remains a mystery, for it certainly wasn't me.

Apparently I do get a tiny credit in the paperback editions of *Majestic* (but no complimentary copy, and I decline to buy the thing). This represents a moral victory, i.e. a totally useless and unprofitable one....

In a final bit of wish-fulfilment I published a short UFO-related story called "Encounter of Another Kind" which the discerning may find in *Interzone* magazine (December 1991).

1990-1993

Tell Me the Old, Old Story

Hello, and thank you for having me....

Here is the secret background of what I'm going to say today. Not long ago I was a guest at Boskone 29 in America ... and when I heard that the convention's theme was to be "Storytelling", I thought this would be a nice, easy talk to prepare. Just a matter of digging out all my favourite horror stories about science fiction and publishing, many of them so old that they're recorded on bricks in cuneiform—and all of them so nostalgically familiar to British audiences that when I repeat them everyone stands up as a mark of respect for the elderly, before giving the ultimate British gesture of appreciation ... taking the form of a headlong rush to the bar.

Unfortunately, my master plan to recycle the old stuff had been sabotaged by the diabolical machinations of Boskone, which had collected all my most venerable pieces into a special Langford fanzine sensitively called *Let's Hear It for the Deaf Man*. Meaning that, as their legal advisors politely told me, if I quoted *either* of the jokes from this copyright publication, I'd have to pay a large permission fee. Bah.

It's a pity really, because being unoriginal is one of the great themes of modern sf and fantasy. The old ones are the best ones, as H. P. Lovecraft used to say. Publishers know this all too well, and can always make us writers laugh heartily at their latest retelling of grand old stories like Gutenberg's "Thy cheque is in ye maile", or the Victorian publisher's famous line, "We must apologize for the sixteen months' delay in calculating your royalties, Mr Dickens, but there is still a slight bug in the Analytical Engine."

For writers, of course, the most exciting way of not being original is to write novels that use somebody else's background. I've recently been reading the sourcebook for a new British shared-world venture, to be called "J. G. Ballard's Disaster Area". Participating writers are given a completely free hand, except that all stories must include a crashed car, a drained swimming pool, a reference to Marilyn Monroe, at least thirty-five litres of spurting arterial blood and *no plot*. Another team of authors headed by John Clute is working on a grand series of space operas set in the wild and wacky world of the *Oxford English Dictionary*. Forthcoming titles include *Etymology of Doom*, *Lexicographers of the Blood Asteroid* and *Invasion of the Obsolete Pronunciation from 61 Cygni C*.

Well, I needed to come up with another convention talk (for Boskone 29) and had just written a long article about recent sf plot devices for New Worlds *magazine. One thing led to another.*

Well, I suppose I'd better talk a bit about storytelling and pass on some of the literary insights which have made my name a byword in the international remainder market. One useful discovery is that fantasy and sf can now be interchangeable—astute authors are able to sell the same novel twice, thanks to Piers Anthony's handy word processor macro that converts the entire vocabulary at the touch of a single key.

This interchangeability follows naturally from Arthur C. Clarke's Third Law, which goes, "Any sufficiently advanced technology is indistinguishable from a completely ad-hoc plot device." Thanks to developments in science, for example, the technology of sf weather control no longer needs gigantic fusion-powered space-platforms to modify the output of the solar photosphere. You can now do it all with the flapping of a single butterfly's wing, provided this happens on a sufficiently distant continent. This high-tech insight is in sharp contrast to the mere fantasy writers who insult readers' intellects by waving magic wands.

Here's an example drawn from what we shall have to call real life. Does it make that much difference whether Jack Chalker achieves his special effects by scientifically rewriting the reality equations (as in his **Well World** series) or magically pronouncing spells (as in his **Soul Rider** series, and all too many others)? Either way, he is able to proceed rapidly to his recurring literary pastime of subjecting female characters to grotesque and humiliating transformations. You know, the lucky ones get to become compulsive brothel slaves; the rest end up with crippling deformities, embarrassing problems of incontinence, or even become scientologists. Of course, since Chalker himself is such a genial and cuddly author, this can say nothing about his personal fixations and must result from shrewd marketing analysis of what's enjoyed by the general public. Speaking as a member of the general public, I sometimes wonder if I should sue.

If you don't opt for one sweeping and all-encompassing plot device, you needn't be afraid of introducing a huge number of lesser ones. In the light of present-day fantasy, Tolkien's famous expedition into Mordor was ludicrously under-equipped, with only one cursed ring and one magic flashlight. Hadn't he even heard of backup copies? To see how it should be done, aspiring authors are recommended to study the latest books in Roger Zelazny's **Amber** series, whose hero makes the Gulf War forces look seriously under-equipped.

For those who don't know the series, I should explain that the current hero Merlin is the son of Corwin, whose adventures filled five earlier volumes of seething complexity, involuted flashbacks and labyrinthine family relations. A picture of the family tree was in fact considered for inclusion in *The Fractal Geometry of Nature* but rejected as being too complex.

Now this is how to equip a modern hero. Merlin begins by getting born right, as a Lord of Amber (the *good guys*, roughly corresponding to the American Republican Party). He has walked the maze-like Pattern of Amber, gaining various powers such as pedestrian travel between worlds. (When you can't find the basic and practically unique Pattern to hand, there's always the underwater anti-Pattern, the alternate Pattern in the sky, the miniature Pattern in the magical Jewel of Judgement, and a whole slew of more real, less real, metaphorical, shop-soiled and remaindered Patterns.) Owing to mixed parentage, Merlin is also a Lord of Chaos (formerly and perhaps still the *bad guys*, roughly corresponding to the American Republican Party). This provides innate gifts of shapeshifting and other handy magic, leading to good lines like "My Concerto for Cuisinart and Microwave spell would have minced him and parboiled him in an instant". Some of these interesting little abilities we don't learn about until the second Merlin book, where a nasty Lurker at the Threshold explains rather too smugly that none but a shapeshifting Lord of Chaos can pass this particular dread portal, and shortly afterwards adds "Shit" as our hero does an impression of the Incredible Hulk.

As well as the Pattern, Merlin has mastered its Chaos equivalent the Logrus, which confers added skills of tactical nuclear weaponry, remote handling and magical apportation (useful and indeed much used for summoning beer and pizza). He also possesses Amber's inevitable pack of Trumps, the local occult teleportation and radiophone service. Plus a sentient, self-propelled and chatty strangling wire, and some arcane blue stones whose properties escape my memory but are no doubt pretty boggling. Furthermore he has constructed Ghostwheel, a vast, innovative, magic-powered computer complex (no kidding) which is more or less omnipotent in his service whenever it happens not to be sulking. Surveying all this at the end of the fourth volume, Zelazny obviously feels the lad Merlin is still lacking in worldly resources, and issues him with an enchanted ring controlling immense new powers and offensive weaponry. Just what he needed! This plot turn took me completely by surprise—I'd been thinking the only possible new gift for this man who has everything would be one of those gold buttons with the message, "I've Got Everything".

By now it seems rather difficult to provide this guy Merlin with any credible opposition, especially since he also has many sorcerous pals, sisters, cousins and aunts of awesome talent to help him out of tight spots. You feel that the second golden rule of the bad guys must be, "Don't ever tangle with that bastard Merlin." The first, I'm told, used to be "Don't lend money to that bastard Maxwell." So ... unlike inferior works which keep disturbing the reader's tranquillity by offering serious threats to their lead characters, the new Amber series looks set to continue indefinitely as one of the most reliable insomnia cures on the market. Strangely enough after all these years, I'm *still* waiting for the volume called *Forever Amber*.

Of course, if you're writing hard or hard*ish* science fiction there is a limit on the number of amazing gadgets and astonishing innovations you can credibly stuff into the plot. Or is there? A fine-tuned example of getting slightly carried away is David Brin's *Earth*. This includes whole thickets of perfectly legitimate extrapolation which we can take on board as a mere part of consensus future number 27, subtype IV: eco-doom, UV hazards, extinctions, pollution overload, data-net hacking, clunky writing, all that sort of thing. Along with this come the unexpected developments which are so much to be expected unless you're a really cautious futurologist—strange quirks like a bloody war fought in the name of Freedom of Information against Switzerland's oversecretive bankers. Personally, considering that one of the tallest buildings in London, the 619-foot Telecom Tower, is classified and does not appear on official maps, I can't help wondering which side my freedom-loving British government was on.

Back to the book. Against this teeming background, our author duly slips in his big sf innovation, which looks to be quite a cunningly plausible extension of gravitational physics as we know it. Microscopic black holes, rather than suffering the quantum-thermodynamic decay predicted by dear old Stephen Hawking, can here be "knotted" into a kind of stability and thus last long enough to threaten the Earth by nibbling at its core. On top of this is piled a (to say the least) highly unlikely theory of gravity lasers, whereby the hungry singularities can be manipulated by surface-mounted detectors or probes, with all manner of weird anti-gravitic side effects—such as portions of the landscape bounding into orbit with an accompaniment of visual effects by Industrial Light & Magic. This particular plot-line devolves into a sort of global ping-pong game as the good guys try to nudge the unpleasantness out into space while others, many of them anonymous, prefer to keep it in there for their own nefarious purposes. Bad guys, who can figure 'em? They just *like* living on a planet that's being eaten away from within.

All right. The story is indeed good clean fun, exciting to read. But meanwhile, in another part of the hypertext, a more familiar computer-net war is being fought. Here the climactic action comes when a revered ecological prophetess and Nobel laureate is up against the ropes thanks to viral assault programs *and* gravitational mayhem. So she manages with her dying keypunches to do what no one has ever done before and download her entire personality into ... well, I have neglected to mention the subtle plot point that those orbiting singularities within the Earth had been leaving funny tracks behind them in the planetary mantle. From the book's description it's hard to believe that these could have anything like the connective complexity of an ordinary, dumb, personal computer, but nevertheless our politically correct Green Lady (plus *just possibly* the whole of the world data net) is electronically translated into these dubious circuits. She instantly becomes the formerly hypothetical world-spirit Gaia and assumes control over gravitational physics—being able by unexplained means to exercise veto power over whether or not the gravity-laser effect works. This includes using it to literally rip to shreds "a few hundred" persons who somehow get judged as Evil (no trial; no hope of appeal; organic, holistic Gaia knows best).

By this time the symptoms of sf indigestion are getting quite agonizing.

Whatever next? I will tell you. The Tunguska "meteor" explosion of 1908 was in fact the arrival of an ultimately life-enhancing singularity.... Too much, cries the bloated reader, too much. But the irresistibly readable Mr Brin still has his funnel down your throat and eases in one last little delicacy, like that final wafer-thin mint which detonates the very fat man Mr Creosote in Monty Python's *The Meaning of Life*. Perhaps, Brin hints excitingly, this unlikely farrago of events was not mere chance, but was choreographed throughout by *aliens working amongst us for our own good!*

At which point, the reader's brain explodes messily. Well, of course that's what hard science fiction is all about....

And if you want to study the all-important sf technique of causing grey matter to emerge in twin, high-pressure streams from your readers' ears, I can recommend several recent sourcebooks. One of them is Orson Scott Card's *Xenocide*, the sequel to *Ender's Game* and *Speaker for the Dead*. For much of its length, *Xenocide* is cunningly disguised as a gripping drama of hard science fiction and realistically intractable problems. Then something very strange happens....

The plot elements go like this. Forgive me if you know it all by heart. We are on a distant planet with human colonists, natives sensitively called "piggies", and a truly revolting virus that makes AIDS look like a pussycat. In fact the virus is so uningratiating that a large human spacefleet has just arrived on the scene after decades of slower-than-light travel, equipped with heaps of ultimate planet-sterilizing weaponry. Fortunately our hero has this good friend Jane, a tame artificial intelligence who can intercept the instantaneous ansible communications and stop the fatal order getting to the fleet. Less fortunately, the background contains a world of super-geniuses who are kept under control by genetic crippling ... one of these great brains is soon on the case and is expected to nobble Jane at any moment. Meanwhile, a counter-agent to the intelligent and self-adapting virus seems absolutely impossible to synthesize. In addition, a bunch of the sensitively named "buggers" exterminated in an earlier book are loose on the same world and have developed spacecraft on which the piggies, egged on by their relatives the rogue sentient trees, can spread the plague through the galaxy. It sounds a trifle daft in synopsis, but actually it's all rather tense.

Then, with a loud noise of anticlimax, the *deus ex machina* is lowered on creaky pulleys. Suddenly, the nicer characters in the plot get together and solve these awkward problems by inventing a New Physics which produces all the solutions out of a single hat. The result is faster-than-light travel, plus a means of creating a self-reproducing anti-virus simply by thinking about it, plus a similar quick fix for the genetically inherited obsessive-compulsive disorder suffered by all those superbrains, plus an instant cure for a hitherto hopeless physical cripple who conjures up a brand-new body in the blink of an eye while the old one crumbles tidily away just like an old Dracula movie ...

and a final useful side-effect of the new discovery is the resurrection of the dead. Almost, one would think that Orson Scott Card had become religious or something.

As a method of sorting out awkward plot tangles, this does seem a bit sweeping and hard for vile unbelievers like myself to swallow ... but if it wins Card his usual Hugo it is no doubt just what the readership wants and what all we aspiring writers should imitate. Since I think I can see a small delegation from Tor Books preparing tar and feathers at the back, it must be time to move hastily on.

Though I must say that I'm picking on Orson Scott Card only as one representative of the Great Sf Escape Clause, the plot device that solves everything. In fact they're all over the place. Another example which I perversely enjoyed is Storm Constantine's *Hermetech*—a book full of zany, wacky applied sex. This has two of my favourite phrases of 90s sf so far ... the description of a super-transsexual who acquires, dotted all over his or her stomach, "a fleet of sphincters"—and another line which in a world of radical cosmetic surgery is just a shade ambiguous, where as a quick health check someone prods this skinny kid, and: "He could feel the bones through her spare buttocks."

At what I can only call the climax, it is discovered that Storm's world can be put right by climbing into bed and tapping the unlimited, earthquake-like potential of the female orgasm. Sort of "Drop your pants, Luke, and use the Force!" (I wonder if Margaret Thatcher ever tried that one. As the famous blues song goes, "She was only a grocer's daughter, but she taught Sir Geoffrey Howe.")

It was our very own British critic Nick Lowe who invented the useful term "plot coupon". This identifies a great tradition of post-Tolkien fantasy, the idea being that these coupons are scattered widely over a large and geologically unconvincing map full of things like square mountain ranges and names that only the author can pronounce, so that it takes three fat volumes before the characters can collect the full set of coupons and send off to the author for the ending. Another labour-saving idea identified by Nick is to cut down on the tiresome mechanics of plausibility by writing the plot itself into the book as a character, under some such name as Fate, or the Force, or the Hitch-Hiker's Guide to the Galaxy, or Seldon's Plan.

How does this work? Well, one of the things I enjoyed about Dan Simmons's grand space-operas *Hyperion* and *The Fall of Hyperion* is that this author has gone one better than Nick. There are *two* characters who instantly become comprehensible once you realize they are thinly disguised aspects of the Plot.

Diligent readers—meaning of course you lot—will all know about the *Hyperion* story's major, all-purpose plot device the Shrike, an invincible killer machine with mysterious control over space and time, whose hobby is carrying people off to eternal torment on its Tree of Pain. Sounds rather like a British fanzine reviewer. This unfriendly practice is eventually explained as quite logical and practical, being the baiting of an empathic trap for the ultimate, autonomous principle of compassion, that is, God. (By which Simmons means only *one* part of *one* God. Real space opera doesn't stop at just one.) The Shrike is acting on the basic principle my mother told me at the age of three and which I started to distrust at the age of six ... that if you're wicked enough, God will come along in person to disapprove.

Unfortunately, having finally grasped that this is what the Shrike is up to, one does begin to wonder at its habit of buzzing helpfully through just about every subplot, smoothing transitions, precipitating climaxes and generally doing things unrelated to its supposed purpose. Surely some hidden guiding force must lie behind this behaviour, some ultimate Author? Then of course you realize that Nick Lowe's principle applies. The Shrike is in fact the executive arm of the book's plot ... and by keeping things moving like this, it saves Dan Simmons all sorts of effort in motivating his characters to go to the right places and do the right things. It's really extremely cunning.

The other manifestation of the plot is needed to pump vital information into the reader. Finishing off this mini-series in *The Fall of Hyperion*, Simmons makes a brave attempt at putting across his bizarre metaphysical rationale for everything that's been happening. But he has certain problems. One is that the revelations are all so totally, gob-smackingly cosmic that no ordinary character except the omniscient author is really in a position to know them. Let alone explain them. And what's worse, they tend to read as excessively mind-boggling or even plain ridiculous if spelt out in clear English.

The fiendishly clever answer is to filter this apocalyptic stuff through a thinly disguised mouthpiece of the Plot ... a super-brained but maddeningly quirky Artifical Intelligence who talks a weird, high-entropy mixture of Zen koans and Keats quotations, laid out as blank verse and festooned with funny punctuation symbols to evoke computer meeps and bleeps. You get cross-eyed just trying to read it. The author surely deserves a special Signal To Noise Ratio Award for this triumph of style over content.

By the way, I wondered if Simmons might be getting a trifle carried away when after vast amounts of physical and metaphysical exposition he revealed that his other major plot device—an instantaneous communicator curiously similar to Orson Scott Card's—operated on the private wavelength of God. Eventually, displeased at being made a vehicle for insurance salesmen and naughty chatlines rather than prayer, God concludes the book by announcing the withdrawal of this facility until further notice. Which is indeed jolly mind-wrenching, and it's a good thing He didn't get so annoyed as to take away our more frequently misused privileges like gravity or the strong nuclear force.

(The main problem with this scene is how badly God's prose style seems to have deteriorated since the King James Bible. Yet another elderly sf writer trying and failing to make a come-back.)

The ingenious way Dan Simmons managed to stretch a few embarrassingly over-the-top disclosures into pages and pages of high-entropy woffle brings me to an aspect of creative writing sadly neglected by teachers. When did you last hear of a Milford or Clarion workshop which discussed the important technique of padding? This is a true essential for those of us who mean to break into the highly-paid genre of Enormous Great Fat Books. Here is a classic brief example:

> She looked on him. Never before in her life had she seen such a male. He made even Gunther seem a lesser man. Her imagination had not even dreamed that such a man could exist. The men she had known earlier, even Gunther, had been no intimation that there might be males such as these. Such men, she thought, could not exist in her time. In her time there was no place; there could be no place, for such men as these.

Yes, that was from *Time Slave* by the fabled John Norman. Wash your ears out at once with soap and water.

A much more common ploy that I can recommend is technological padding, with lots of code numbers and brand names. It only takes about one minute's in-depth research to construct a macho paragraph like this, suitable for insertion into any military epic:

> Slowly, lovingly Arnie unslung and hefted his favourite automatic gun, the weapon that shared his bunk and which he valued above any mere woman, an idiosyncratic VK 155 L/50 Swedish equalizer with 155mm calibre and a taut 865m/sec muzzle velocity. Sometimes his buddies scoffed at its bulk, but the squat, chunky 14-round magazine and blockbusting 25km range made it his kind of weapon, tough and mean.

You can throw in this sort of thing more or less at random and be sure that only a tiny percentage of the audience will actually look it up in *Brassey's Artillery of the World* to discover that that this particular gun is in fact a self-propelled model weighing 51 metric tons.

But, you are asking, those of you who aren't heading off to ask the barman instead: do any of today's really successful sf authors rely on the magic ingredient of padding? Some of you may have heard of the late Isaac Asimov. Groundbreaking experiments show that the typical Asimov blockbuster of his final years can be processed with solvents which leach out all that disfiguring, unsightly fat, leaving behind a zippy little novella which is very nearly up to the standards of *Astounding* in the 1940s. Incredibly, the reverse process is also true, and Asimovian short stories can be inflated into hefty novels using the expensive silicone injection process which is a jealously guarded secret of the multi-national Silverberg Laboratories.

At this point, by way of example, I meant to lull you all into a deep, relaxing slumber by reading some chapters from a recently published Isaac Asimov novel ... but I found that to perform such a public recitation I'd need to pay a large permission fee, to Robert Silverberg. Instead, I must thank Charles Platt for pointing out that Asimov was quite open about the, er, low density of his recent stuff. In *Robots and Empire* one of the characters suddenly sees it all in a blinding burst of insight:

> Solaria, Aurora, the other Spacer worlds that she had visited
> or had viewed on hypervision, all seemed filled with people
> who were unsubstantial—gaseous.
>
> That was the word. Gaseous.

An honest author, I must admit: he takes the word right out of my mouth.

Of course science fiction has just one supreme master of padding, and having researched some of his most keenly felt and philosophically daring passages, I don't see why you shouldn't suffer too. Silence, please, for *Galaxy 666* by Robert Lionel Fanthorpe writing as Pel Torro, at the moment when— it is important to remember—he's two pages short of the contracted wordlength and has run out of plot:

> "This crazy galaxy is the price that the universe pays for or-
> der. 666, eh? By the seven green moons, it was well num-
> bered! There's something strangely capricious about this place.
> Just as our universe is a motivated universe, this one is mo-
> tiveless. The real universe, the universe to which we belong,
> has purpose; this one is whimsical, fanciful and fantastic. This
> is a temperamental galaxy, an hysterical galaxy, a mad galaxy.
> This is an insane, freakish, wanton, erratic, inconsistent gal-
> axy; it's a completely unreasonable galaxy. It's undisciplined,
> refractory, uncertain and unpredictable. It's a volatile galaxy,
> a mercurial galaxy. [...] It's a frivolous galaxy; it's inconsis-
> tent and inconstant; it's variable; it's unstable; it's irrespon-
> sible and unreliable."

At which point, and not before time, the speaker sums it all up by falling over. This is the sort of masterly use of the thesaurus which led to the Fanthorpe Lightbulb Joke: "How many of his pseudonyms does it take to change a light bulb, to replace it, to reinstate it, to substitute for it, to exchange it, to swap it, to put another in its stead ...?"

Now all this literary research of mine had a central purpose. Frankly, it seemed about time that I wrote a major sf novel and became obscenely rich. Having learned my lesson from all these succesful books, my planned ideal storyline contains brilliant flights of unoriginality, hordes of off-the-wall plot devices, a stream of ludicrous *deus ex machina* revelations, some radical feminist insights borrowed from thinkers like Jack Chalker and Piers Anthony ... and thanks to brilliant use of padding, the work will extend over many fat volumes while requiring only 2 cubic centimetres of actual invention. And then, tragically, after outlining this sure-fire scenario, I was crushed to find that my whole concept had already been stolen—and I'd certainly sue the fellow responsible, but it turns out that this L. Ron Hubbard is dead.

So it's back to the word processor again ... and thank you all.

1992

Foodies of the Gods

Ladies and gentlemen,

I'm here now to provide a soporific moment between the Helicon banquet and the extreme gastric excitement of the coming awards ceremony. As you recline bloated in your chairs, your eyelids are permitted to droop.... I asked the committee if they could provide me with a witty opening anecdote, but all they'd offer was what they claimed to be an important announcement: FLASH PHOTOGRAPHY IS NOT PERMITTED IN THE GENTLEMEN'S TOILETS.

Looking around at these appalling scenes of gluttony, I've been trying to think of resemblances to famous banquets in fantasy and science fiction. It's been more fun than in *Dune*, where noble desert people are liable to pop in and spit all over your floor as a sign of respect; or in *Titus Groan*, with a one-legged fanatic marching up and down the table stamping in the porridge— please don't anybody get ideas; and of course if this were a C. S. Lewis banquet the speeches would end with us all being torn apart by wild beasts as a punishment for approving of science and reading nasty agnostics like H. G. Wells.

And then there's the nostalgic memory of countless stories where that whole meal would have been a single compressed food pill, containing enough energy to give you the runs for a week. I've always meant to look into the physics of those high-energy pills ... they must be so crammed with calories that if your spaceship's fuel ran low, you'd just chuck a day's rations into the propulsion chamber and zoom off again at $10g$ acceleration. Some scientists believe those power pills must be chemically identical to baked beans. Anyway, this seems a much better emergency drive than in Poul Anderson's famous beer-powered spaceship, whose operation has always bothered the keen scientific intellects of sf fans. This is because it violates the First Law: "A fan must not waste a pint of beer, nor through inaction allow beer to go to waste, unless of course there is a handy Scientologist to pour it over."

Food is a wonderful subject, and there's not nearly enough about it in science fiction ... although I remember that at one of the UK Milford writers'

Wild horses were required to make me speak after a banquet (at Helicon, the 1993 British Eastercon held in Jersey), owing to heady memories of once doing this at the Birmingham SF Group's Xmas dinner. "We'd like you to talk for about twenty minutes," they said. In the event, dinner was delayed and concluded with the encouraging announcement: "Dave Langford will now talk hilariously for twenty minutes. Oh, and the bar closes in five minutes." Everything went black and I don't remember any more.

workshops, Josephine Saxton was bitterly accused of writing *food pornography.* We cosmic-minded sf people seem very conservative about our eats, which is why we were all so shocked by that terrible revelation in a certain movie with its famous line, *"Soylent Green is breakfast at the 1992 Eastercon hotel!"*

You meet more interesting recipes in Jack Vance's books: a typical Vance hero remains totally cool when informed that item 3 in column B of the menu is "parboiled night-fish, fresh from the bogs".[1] Sometimes the Vance menu gets a trifle too interesting; I remember his inn where all the food, right down to the bread rolls and the HP sauce, has the same acrid flavour. When asked about this, the waiter points to a large black insect scuttling across the floor and helpfully explains that since these creatures have a terrible stench and get into everything anyway, they are deliberately included in all the recipes to help you get used to the taste.[2] Try one when you get home.

Only Lloyd Biggle Jr seems to have investigated the awesome sf possibilities of typing in the wrong order codes at an alien fast-food outlet. After doing this, one of his characters ends up with "a segment of dinosaur bone, stuffed with what was obviously large insects and covered with a rubbery-looking sauce. Her vegetable dish was grass in an advanced state of decomposition."[3] After experience of British fast-food places, you may be wondering what is supposed to be so alien about this.

Some sf writers have tried to imagine new kinds of food. In one of William Tenn's futures, for example, a popular dish is this purple spaghetti-like stuff which actively squirms up from the plate towards your mouth and wriggles about cosily once it's inside. As an gourmet explains: "... In addition to flavour, texture and aroma, you'd experience *motility.* Think of it: food not just lying there limp and lifeless in your mouth, but food expressing eloquently its desire to be eaten."[4]

Robert Sheckley had a vaguely similar thought in "Untouched by Human Hands", the one whose unfortunate heroes are starving to death in an alien warehouse, surrounded by tins covered in slogans like VIGROOM! FILL ALL YOUR STOMACHS AND FILL THEM RIGHT! and VORMITASH—GOOD AS IT SOUNDS! In desperation they decide to try VALKORIN'S UNIVERSAL TASTE TREAT, FOR ALL DIGESTIVE CAPACITIES, but in the end can't bring themselves to take a bite because, as one of them definitively states, "I don't eat anything that giggles."

I distinctly heard a giggle from our own good taste expert Iain M. Banks as he explained the future etiquette of cutlery, whereby you put on a special set of steel teeth for stripping the meat off a nice snack of tasty raw finger-on-the-bone.[5] The Banks Guide to Social Deportment explains that it's very bad manners for the owner of the finger to scream while this is happening. Gives a whole new meaning to those Indian menus that offer Meat and Ladies' Fingers.

But speaking of haute cuisine mutilation, there's a Maurice Richardson story which points out a little-known advantage of one notorious sf situation—being a decapitated head connected by lots of tubes to a life-support system. The great thing is that *you never get full up*. I quote: "On shellfish day, last [Gourmet] Club Meet, I scoffed a hundred-weight of assorted Dublin Bay prawns, scampi, langoustes, écrivisses, durian-fed Venusian landcrabs, and those delicious giant Martian lobsters."[6] This sort of snack goes on for a month or so, washed down with several whole crates of wine, until everyone's jaw muscles finally need a rest. The only snag about this utopia of endless throughput is the decapitees' constant suspicion that they may sometimes be getting food they've already eaten.

Which brings me at once to Samuel R. Delany's idyllic notion of taste as an artform, in *Stars in My Pocket like Grains of Sand*.[7] Here, instead of just looking at ancient, historic carvings, you go right up to them and experience their taste with a long, succulent lick. And sure enough, as the author points out, you can just detect this faint, haunting flavour of cinnamon and sandalwood through the thick layers of slime and dribbling mucus left by all the alien-reptile tourists who were in the queue ahead of you. This is called sharing the experience.

After which, the only possible dessert is the "monster slobby yellow cheese" described by Brian Aldiss in *The Eighty-Minute Hour*,[8] which he tells us "tasted as if it had been whipped together from hippopotamus smegma". Few other sf authors would have taken the trouble to carry out the necessary research at Jersey Zoo.

At this stage in my foodie reminiscences I think it's time for a little Robert Lionel Fanthorpe, who summed up all our feelings after the long trip to a convention when he very nearly wrote in his famous novel *Restaurant 666* ... "Food. He needed food. Food was his need, for he was hungry, empty and famished, desirous of sustenance, and avid for nutrition. Yes, he felt esurient and voracious, ravenous, insatiable of appetite, eager for aliments, edibles, foodstuffs, comestibles, victuals, viands, provender and nosh."

All right, I'm lying. But here is a genuine Fanthorpe food simile which beautifully sums up the feeling of excitement that must be already throbbing through your veins at the thought of the coming award presentations:

"[His] strangely treated blood rose like the aroma of ancient Chinese culinary eggs."[9]

And I'm sure we all feel the same. Thank you all.

SCHOLARLY REFERENCES

1. *The Face*, 1979.
2. *The Dirdir*, 1969.
3. *Watchers of the Dark*, 1966.
4. "Winthrop Was Stubborn", 1957.

5. *Consider Phlebas*, 1987.

6. "Way Out in the Continuum", date not to hand; collected in Richardson's *Fits and Starts*, 1979.

7. 1984.

8. 1974 ... my thanks to Steve Rothman for reminding me of this essential pivot in any account of sf delicacies.

9. *Nemesis*, 1964.

1993

You Do It With Mirrors

Fourteen Months Before. It was one of those incautious moments. I was at Boskone 29, enjoying the heady sensation of being a guest and looking forward to liberal supplies of bourbon, groupies, contracts and coffee. "We can get them all for you," Ben Yalow explained, "except perhaps for the bourbon, groupies and contracts."

The Boskone newsletter (*Helmuth ... Speaking for Boskone*) had just been impressing me with its deeply professional policy of printing anything I submitted. After a few too many beers in the hotel bar I heard my mouth say, "British con newsletters are usually so boring and stark and functional." Interested in what I would declare next, I began to pay attention and found my lips issuing the statement, "What they need is better production, and traces of literacy, and more funny bits so fans will read the whole thing including the tedious programme changes." My tongue went madly on to utter, "In fact I could—"

Suddenly I found that even here in kindly America I was surrounded by committee members of Helicon, the 1993 British Eastercon, all wearing wide, fanged smiles. "You're on, Dave," someone cried.

"Glmmmmmmpf," said my nostril as I choked on the beer.

The Langford theory of newsletters was no more than a few vague prejudices at the time. Keeping it simple seemed a cunning plan: no elaborate DTP systems that encouraged the priests of the inner mystery to spend hours at a time laying out perfect paragraphs like exquisite corpses in satin-lined caskets. An independent survey of what I was already using for *Ansible* favoured WordPerfect, into which any fool can type text.

(*Technical Bit Which May Be Skipped:* a non-Windows WordPerfect 5.1 with Bitstream FaceLift fonts, if you really must know. The committee's weird idea that we could move stuff between the computers using Laplink was rapidly superseded by my own high-tech solution known as Hurling Floppy Disks Across The Table.)

What was the thing going to be called? Helicon was named for its site, St Helier in Jersey, and the last con newsletter there had been called *Jersey Yarns,* which made me gently puke. Helicon used a "sun" logo. Sun ... writing ... *Heliograph.* "I am not afraid," I wrote to the con committee, "of the totally bleeding obvious." Harry Bell drew a newsletter logo and we were in business.

Some months in advance I started writing news items. Editorial policy regarded any white space as a tacit admission of failure. And no matter how boring the lists of programme changes, I wanted the whole thing larded with funny bits to ensure it got read from end to end.

Strange anniversaries were ruthlessly researched (with help from Andy Porter's *SF Chronicle* birthday list, to remind the revelling fans that time's wingèd chariot was parked outside the door and blowing the horn). Besides the complete new edition of the *Encyclopaedia of SF*, which I luckily had on disk, I consulted that useful reference *The Perpetual Pessimist: an Everlasting Calendar of Gloom and Almanac of Woe* (by Daniel George) ... so the first issue on 8 April 1993 not only had birthday messages for E. J. Carnell, S. P. Meek and Ralph Milne Farley but also revealed that Helicon was auspiciously beginning on the anniversary of a failed prediction of worldwide deluge in 1524.

Thus, helped by the fact that the convention was also a noted fictional birthplace, we were ready for the traditional First Issue of Newsletter problem (i.e., no news)....

> WELCOME TO HELICON. And welcome to *Heliograph*—the newsletter which we understand is pronounced something like "Heliogrrraph". As noted by Helicon's most famous native, "I have the Heliconian stress on the letter 'r'." (Harrri Seldon, in *Forrrward the Foundation* by Isaac Asimov.)
> BICENTENNIAL: in April 1793, the New England inventor Eli Whitney did a huge service to all sf professionals by inventing gin. (*A Pedant Writes:* That was the cotton gin, you fool. *Heliograph:* There's no pleasing some fans.)

The first item duly provoked an outraged response in #2, for the benefit of esoterica fans:

> COMPLAINT: "What's this in issue #1 about some parvenu called Seldon being the most famous person from Helicon? What about us, then?" *Signed:* Calliope, Clio, Erato, Euterpe, Melpomene, Polyhymnia, Terpsichore, Thalia and Urania.

But I'm getting ahead of events. All too many thrills and spills lay between the hapless editor and the first printed copy of *Heliograph 1*. I flew to Jersey days early, leaving Hazel to enjoy herself at home ... our different attitudes can be detected from the phone call when I got there. *Me:* "It was great fun, I had a window by the landing gear and the plane stopped at Guernsey on the way so I got to go up and down twice for one fare!" *Hazel:* "Oh! Oh, that must have been so *horrible* for you...." Being paranoid about electromagnetic damage to disks, I had one set in my pocket, another in my suitcase and a third travelling with Martin Hoare on a Channel ferry. *Martin:* "It's great fun, the crossing lasts hours and hours, and you can drink yourself silly all the way over and watch other fans get seasick and vomit all over the bar!" *Me:* "What a pity that I foolishly booked a plane."

After the usual adventures I was introduced to my newsroom, which in the interests of total security had a combination lock on the door. Fortunately this didn't block traffic too much, since vast numbers of British fans remembered the unchanged code from previous conventions. (Later remark by Chris O'Shea, quoted in a post-final *Heliograph:* "The secure store isn't, Ops doesn't and the newsletter hasn't.")

As it finally took shape, the awesome newsletter production equipment consisted of a couple of IBMs as I'd requested, a late-arriving laser printer (with an interesting scar on its drum that led to exciting black marks in every left margin and regular hotel-wide searches for Liquid Paper), and the Chris Suslowicz Museum of Industrial Archaeology. Yes, after each master sheet slid smoothly from the 1990s DTP system it was carried across the room and backwards through yawning gulfs of time to an ancient, rickety electrostencil cutter and a Gestetner mimeograph that had seen service with the Panzer corps.

While I first stared in awe, the committee broke it to me that Chris Suslowicz, the owner and understander of all this heavy-metal hardware, wouldn't be arriving until—according to my timetable—about half-way through issue three. I retreated to the bar and don't remember any more that day.

Next morning, with large tracts of the newsroom still commandeered for dynamic, last-minute badge production, I and all-round technical supremo John Dallman cut two dozen electrostencils of a dummy front page I'd brought with me. Or, to be precise, we cut or failed to cut the same one two dozen times, fiddling with all the controls (and wincing at the tactless comments of badge-makers who evidently hadn't enough work to do) until in a blazing burst of Null-A insight John noticed that the stylus was bent and changed it. Sparks flew and the characteristic atmosphere of the *Heliograph* newsroom immediately made itself felt: a billowing mix of ozone and random carcinogens as the cutter burned its way through acres of vinyl. The fine black dust that rapidly accumulated on the computer screens was a useful index of the state of one's lungs, and to conjure up a Lovecraftian vision of nameless, blasphemous ichor you had only to blow your nose.

Then came the mimeograph, which after an hour or two I decided had not after all seen service with Rommel but with Torquemada. Let us draw a veil over this, mentioning only the anguished cries of "Can we fucking ink it from side to side, not up and down?" ... the discovery that, Roneo men all, we none of us knew where you put ink in a Gestetner ... the ransacking of countless hotel rooms for complimentary packs of tissues after agreeing that we certainly knew how to make ink come *out* of a Gestetner.

(By happy chance we'd picked the right electrostenciller. Con chairman Tim Illingworth had provided a second machine out of the goodness of his heart, having bought it in a junk shop and being sublimely unaware of whether it worked—he thought we could have fun finding out. To add to the "Lady or the Tiger" excitement there was also a second mimeo which, days later, proved to be utterly unusable owing to damage in transit....)

As the first, interestingly tilted and blotchy issue hit the stands, a part-blind fan labelled as "Blind Pew" popped in with a request that all issues of *Heliograph* be clearly printed in black ink for the benefit of those with dodgy vision. "Gladly," I cried, and as an afterthought went to check the huge pile of ink-tubes thoughtfully provided with the hardware. One was red and the rest were green.

IAIN BANKS perpetuated a noble sf tradition by breaking his bed on the first night of Helicon. (As Bob Shaw discovered after Brian Aldiss broke a bed during a party there, Tynecon '74 was "a five-bed convention". Go for it, Iain!)

AFTER cruel treatment by the Style Police, the *Read-Me* authors promise never again to write about "medias" (see *But What Can Replace a Fanzine*, 1100 Monday). "We have now been told correct datas and rethought our criterias," said a spokesman. "There will be no more such erratas."

ARCTOPHILES "are warned that the note on an exhibit in the Art Show *means* it. Do Not Open The Box if you *care* about cuddlies!" *(Chris Bell)*

BREAKFAST NOTES. *Q:* What's red and invisible? *A:* No tomatoes.... The Action Committee for Mushrooms At All Con Breakfasts wishes to thank Helicon for ... sorry, *what* was the message?

HOW TO WRITE GOOD. Jane Barnett (aged 15), when told by her father that her writing showed poor control of nuance: "I wouldn't recognize nuance if it came up and gently brushed my leg."

... But most attempts to give the flavour of *Heliograph* as it turned out run slap into the "You had to be there" syndrome. Famous author Iain Banks is a reliable source of eccentric news at British conventions, and later provided us with another fascinating snippet by crawling around underneath the carpet in the hotel bar. The "arctophiles" item heralded a running gag about Tom Abba's bear-in-the-box in the Helicon art show, which was shielded from unwary eyes because this unfortunate teddy-bear had been strung up with ghastly torture-hooks inspired by *Hellraiser*. ("BEAR HORROR SHOCK," began a later item. "A copy of *Eon* was sold....") Jane Barnett's father Paul writes as John Grant and under this name was technical editor of the new *SF Encyclopaedia*: he realized what a paltry and trivial job that had been when he came to work more or less full-time on *Heliograph*.

JOHN JARROLD becomes President of the World! Well, of World SF. Interviewed by *Heliograph*, the new President prised a beerglass momentarily from his mouth and said, "I didn't know what was happening, I wasn't even there, don't blame *me*."

BRIAN ALDISS demonstrated his mature technique for persuading one of Jenny and Ramsey Campbell's offspring to go to bed, culminating in a stentorian cry of "FUCK OFF!" (It worked.)

STOP PRESS UPDATE: Matt Campbell wishes to announce *Very Loudly Indeed* that Brian Aldiss's amazing Getting-the-Little-Swine-to-Bed technique (*Heliograph #2*) DIDN'T ACTUALLY WORK.

This was our first taste of controversy, when Mr Aldiss put a mildly stroppy note under the newsroom door complaining of "anti-Aldiss material" and asserting that "I told no kiddies, not even Brian Burgess, to 'Fuck Off'." Assured by unreliable witnesses that the first report was accurate, our protagonist having been a trifle off-sober at the time, we contented ourselves by printing his rebuttal prefaced by "BRIAN ALDISS, Sci Fi author, corrects..." Meanwhile he'd given the newsroom a new euphemism, heavily used for the rest of Helicon whenever alleged abuse was to be recorded: "Go to bed!"

QUESTION. Why exactly did *Lawrence Watt-Evans* think that he was Brian Aldiss and that John Brunner should go to bed?

Trying to make every item at least a bit amusing was a continuing policy. One slight hitch was noted.... Helicon had an influx of 52 Romanians, who all arrived in suits and strange tall pointy hats, like a delegation of heavily politicized garden gnomes. My idle fingers recorded the figure and on impulse (the line looked as if it could do with a bit more text) made it "52.02". Well, at least I didn't add "plus or minus 0.06", but the newsroom had a procession of puzzled visitors. "We have bad trouble with newsletter. Here it says *[etc, etc]*. Is special meaning or" (in tones of deepening menace) "your Western sense of humour?"

Strange tongues were heard everywhere at Helicon, and to aid translation a complex system of colour-coded ribbons and little spots on con badges was supposed to indicate who could interpret between what. Fandom soon reduced the system to chaos. The "I speak Romanian" ribbons ran out within 52.02 nanoseconds, and others lasted only a trifle longer; soon the committee was running round trying to clip bits from the over-long and generous ribbons issued on the first day. Meanwhile one heard explanations like: "And that one-quarter of a tartan spot on my badge stands for how much Gaelic I know...." Your reporter confirmed himself to be deaf in seventeen languages.

My biggest linguistic mistake on *Heliograph* was in allowing my eyes to glaze over each time I tried to read a contribution from Colin Fine which appeared to be an essay on the artificial language Lojban. "Too long," I kept saying. "Maybe *next* issue." Colin had neglected to hint in his headline that, just after the point at which I invariably fell asleep, this piece announced a new and imminent programme item in which Lojban would be discussed. Oops.

Besides Romanians there were Russians, who were doing a roaring trade in obsolete KGB credentials at their dealers' room table....

RED SALES IN THE SUNSET: 30 people had joined the KGB at last count. Beware the midnight knock on the door from *Brian Aldiss*, the entire *Family Harrison* and *Anne McCaffrey* (who will be carrying a small, monogrammed flame-thrower).

TRICENTENNIAL CYBERPUNK. In 1693 Gottfried Wilhelm Leibniz of calculus fame invented the first mechanical calculator that could multiply and divide, thus heralding an exciting new era of arguments over the restaurant bill. ("Fie on you and your Engine, *ſir*, I had only a *ſmall ſalad* and a *Pepſi*.")

JOHN CLUTE tergiversates: "Text is terrifying!"

OVERHEARD: "If this were a normal con all you'd have to do would be to find someone...." *[And then you'd know where they were—Ed.]* • In Ops: "We printed out all the programme participant letters and A. N. Other's was three pages long...." • Programming subcommittee irregular verbs: "I reschedule, you slip, he runs late."

TRUTH SHALL BE TOLD. The spellcheck on the mighty *Heliograph* computer, confronted by "committees", suggests "comatose"....

TEN DAY WONDER TANDOORI. The *Taj Mahal* appears to work on the Lovecraftian approach to cuisine: "I am excited not so much by the actual *presence* of mysterious Bengali dishes before me as I am by the eldritch *rumour and suggestion* that these exotic apparitions might one day appear." Be warned.... *(Ramsey Campbell)*

EROTIC SF panel: "The French are suggesting installing teledildonic machines in hotel rooms...." *Mike Cule:* "I'm not sure I would want to put anything of mine into any such orifices." *Dave Clements:* "What about your credit card?" *Mike Abbott:* "By barcoding suitable portions of anatomy you could pay at the same time." *Brian Ameringen:* "Surely, when you cross a teledildonics machine with a cashpoint you get someone coming into money?"

DISCRETION. We are not allowed to reveal the number of the room in which GoH *Karel Thole* and *Jean Owen* broke the bed.

In a more serious and scientific vein, the Hotel de France venue has a built-in chocolate factory and shop, leading to a blitz of useful information:

HELICON STATISTICS! We have filled 7 Jersey hotels and drunk 1,600 pints of real ale, as at 1300 Saturday. Chocolate sales: 2,500 champagne truffles, 55 of the 5kg blocks, 7 large rabbits, 82 Easter eggs, 1 lifesize Tim Illingworth, and 20 people have taken the behind-the-scenes tour. (Still 3,000 truffles and 8,500 other chocs to go. Must Try Harder.)

Quite a respectable team of *Heliograph* newsroom regulars had somehow coalesced out of all this insanity.

I dutifully credited them all, one of my own favourite ideas being to end each issue with a credits box using linked literary "job titles". It was sheer luck that, having picked *The Hunting of the Snark* for the first such theme, I needed to credit Amanda Baker:

Heliograph 1, 8/4/93. Bellman: Dave Langford. Baker: Amanda. Boots: Dave Clements. Boojum: Caroline Mullan. Snark: John Dallman. Ocean Chart: Harry Bell. Strange Creepy Creatures: John Stewart, Mark Young.

I hugely enjoyed watching fans in the bar turn to the end of each newsletter to find what daft link the credits had this time. The sequence went on through Niven (Thrint: Dave Langford. Grog: Paul Barnett. Speaker-to-Duplicators ...), Asimov (First Speaker: Dave Langford. Emperor: John Dallman. Mayor: Bob Webber. Mule: Chris Suslowicz. Encyclopaedists: John Grant, John Clute. Prime Radiants: Amanda Baker, Pam Wells. Second Foundation: sshh!), Dick (Glimmung, Kipple, Conapt, Pink Beam, Vugs), Wolfe (Autarch, Hierodules ... the large person who got to be the Group of Seventeen was unamused), Ballard (Drained swimming pool, Spinal landscape, Marilyn Monroe, Traven, Talbot, Travers, Talbert, Travis etc) and more. The real mind-burster that no-one could guess was based on an obscure passage of Aldiss's *Report on Probability A*: Impaler of Distortions, Impersonator of Sorrows, Suppressor of the Archives, Wandering Virgin—"Thank you for making me a virgin again!" cried Lynne Ann Morse with mixed feelings, and was duly quoted out of context in the upcoming issue.

Incidentally, *The Hunting of the Snark* also gave us Rule 42: "No one shall speak to the Man at the Helm." This, alas, was not rigorously applied despite all my efforts, and urgent stints of *Heliograph* typing were apt to be interrupted by arcane queries in strange international accents. Once, overwhelmed by too many satirical birthday congratulations (I was 40 on the Saturday of Helicon), I must admit that the editor rose up and told all the chatterers present to "Go to *bed*."

> CLOSING CREDITS. *Heliograph* could not have been brought into existence without the help of very many people, but nevertheless it was. (*Chorus:* "Start again, Langford!")

Newsroom madness grew more and more uncontrollable. Short quotations aside, I'd resolved to rewrite every single story until it was maximally terse, funny and comprehensible, or at least the first two. Meanwhile Paul toiled over increasingly excruciating headlines.... Helicon had a crowd of weird emaciated punk Finns with nose-rings and things ("Differently intelligenced ... or differently nostrilled?" I mused) who claimed to be zombies and sent in countless bulletins on their rotted state: at one point I found Paul unable to decide between ZOMBIE FACTOID—IT'S DEAD TRUE! and DEATH IS NOT THE FINNISH, and could only break the impasse by using them both.

And then there was Thog the Mighty.

Although we dutifully recorded programme changes, *Heliograph* production was more or less incompatible with seeing any of Helicon's programme. (The exception in my case was the banquet, which I had to attend because I was giving a speech, on particularly revolting meals in sf. Later in *Heliograph*: MARY CELESTE MYSTERY SOLVED BY IAN SORENSEN! "Dave Langford did the after-dinner speech.") One item, however, spread all over the convention and newsletter like some rampant fungal growth: the scabrous "If I Ruled the Universe" election campaign.

This featured various mighty beings attempting to sway an ultimate audience vote and thus become Universal Ruler. The candidates were Sir Edmund Blackadder (Neale Mittenshaw-Hodge), Boadicea/Boudicca (KIM Campbell), Genghis Khan (Mike Cule, whose cheerleaders' chant of "*Yak Fat! Yak Fat!*" still haunts me), Tim Illingworth (Chris O'Shea), Ming the Merciless (Alison Scott) and Stupendous Man of *Calvin and Hobbes* fame (John Richards with mask, cape and of course Hobbes—a battery-powered growly tiger which remorselessly crept along tables and fell off the end). Helicon was duly plastered with campaign posters, mostly vile lies from Blackadder ("ILLINGWORTH plays with Barbie dolls!") illustrated with grossly libellous Sue Mason cartoons. In the end the audience vote for Universal Ruler went to a last-minute write-in ... Hobbes.

My favourite silly moment in all this came when, after talking to a press photographer and coming away muttering that the bastard wasn't interested in sf but just wanted pictures of weirdly dressed fans, John Richards found a particularly insulting Blackadder poster in the hotel foyer. He faded into the secure store and, seconds later, the awesome masked figure of Stupendous

Man lumbered along the corridors. With heroic and theatrical gestures the offending poster was wrenched from the wall; our superhero turned majestically away to discover that same pressman with mouth hanging open, fumbling frantically for his camera. After one ghastly frozen moment, Stupendous Man demonstrated super-speed.

This is where Thog came in. Idly filling out a paragraph in which potential world rulers abused each other, Paul remembered a bit-part character from his own fantasy novels and typed: "*Thog the Mighty* doesn't *want* to rule the world.*" This could have been a mistake. From commenting on the hustings ("Thog the Mighty spells universe '*gllb*'."), this brutish entity rapidly overran the whole newsletter with fire and the sword. Even my carefully researched birthday lists sprouted addenda like: "*Every* day my birthday—*Thog.*" If towards the end of Helicon there was a *Heliograph* gestalt, a newsroom group mind, it was undoubtedly named Thog the Mighty. Wrestling wildly over the semicolons, grown men found themselves talking in Thog. "Stop nitpicking and let's print the thing." "Hah! When Thog the Mighty nitpick, nit *know it have been picked.*"

Somewhere out there the convention was reeling along out of control: "Oh God," cried a passing committee member, "the organization's a shambles, we're just about managing to paper over the cracks, and that's *not for the newsletter.*" There were fewer and fewer programme changes to record, and the news items that filtered in grew sillier. When soft toys start sending in contributions, you know it's time to stop:

> Lewis P. Bear complains formally about the anti-bear and bearist artworks in the Art Show. Arnold Schwarzenbear ... *[aw, go to bed—Ed.]*

One can even be reduced to raiding the newspapers:

> The Independent's article on Helicon today catches the subtle, elusive flavour of fandom: "*Otherwise it is unclear who these people are. They could be someone's neighbour or relative....*"

But the manic *Heliograph* staff made the dangerous discovery that news items from "outside" were hardly necessary. Desperately witty things—well, they seemed witty at the time—were constantly being said in our own fume-filled room, and could instantly be quoted. If Helicon had lasted a few more days the newsroom might have become a self-perpetuating news vortex, feeding madly on itself and generating endless one-liners to be listed in our ever-longer sections titled Overheard, Vox Pop and the like.

> "You mean I'm—wow!—a cross reference in the *SF Encyclopaedia*?" • "Are *you* claiming to be nubile?" • "Some-

one bit me last night and I don't know whom...." • "Isn't it sad when the snappiest dressers in fandom are the soft toys?" • "Even Iain Banks doesn't know why he crawled under that carpet...." • "If I turn the Gestetner up to full speed I can make it to the Banq—oh dear." • "I want to complain! You didn't credit my comment!" *(Anon)* • "A *draft* of artists?" "An *acquisition* of publishers?" "A *whinge* of writers." "A *spittoon* of *Heliograph* staffers." • "Why Thog not in *Heliograph* credits?" • "I have a Complaint. Too much *chit-chat*; not enough news."

I actually sought out the one aged fan who complained, in the hope of making soothing noises. The conversation went something like this.... *Aged Fan:* "Yes, your newsletter is full of in-jokes and I'm not an 'in' person." *Me:* "But that 'bear' stuff is about the Helicon art show...." *AF:* "Never go to art shows." *Me:* "And *this* is all to do with the *Read-Me* booklet—" *AF:* "Couldn't be bothered with that." *Me:* "And 'Tim Illingworth' is the convention chairman—" *AF:* "Never heard of him." *Me:* "And this credits line is actually an sf reference to **The Book of the New Sun**...." *AF:* "Like I said: all *in-crowd* jokes."

Suddenly it was Monday evening. Helicon was miraculously over. I could start eating again, and perhaps even sleeping! To hammer home the message, I changed the subtitle box of the ninth issue from *Helicon's Newspaper* to *The Last Dangerous Heliograph* and made sure that all subsection titles referred to sf stories about entropy or the closing down of universes ("Travellers in Black", "The Voices of Time", "Running Down"). The final, post-closing-ceremony item was typed ... since nothing hugely newsy had happened, this merely offered an "AT-A-GLANCE SUMMARY OF THE CLOSING CEREMONY. See pages 94-146." It was all over.

(Actually there was no room to write up the full horror of the closing multi-channel slide show based on 1,000 embarrassing snaps taken at Helicon itself. 45 minutes after the ceremony was due to start, Martin Hoare and his team of ace technocrats carried in the projectors and began to set them up. The audience thrilled as the very first slide that actually appeared read: "That's All Folks!" Every possible permutation of the guests' pictures and names was shown, with John Brunner labelled as George R. R. Martin and artist Karel Thole as fan guest Larry van der Putte ... then Brunner as Martin and Thole as Brunner ... and so endlessly on, to a stream of esoteric technical remarks like "Now John Brunner's head's in the way of the *side* screen." Afterwards Mr Hoare exulted that the committee had confessed they'd never believed he could put on the slide show at all.)

It was, as I said, all over. Unfortunately several people said interesting or appalling things at Monday night's final party, and on Tuesday, as the convention was being dismantled around me, I found myself typing up a supplementary *Dead Dog Memorandum*. Our mimeo experts were not in evidence; the laser printer glowed white-hot as hundreds of copies churned out to meet the delirious demand. Then I went home.

But *Heliograph* was the newsletter that would not die. Chris Suslowicz and Cathryn Easthope had a hotel room full of computer gear, and two more ersatz issues rolled out of my fax machine, the *Undead Dog Memorandum* and *Embalmed Dog Missive*. Excerpts follow, as tidied up by myself for the unbelievably rare *Heliograph Souvenir Edition:*

> IT IS TUESDAY, the newsletter office is deserted and the equipment has been packed for its eventual return to the mainland. *Thog the Mighty* has discovered that his transportation (Horde, one, for the use of) has been misbooked for the previous day and is sharpening his sword. (*Alex Stewart:* "Thog say, plane for wimps. Thog swim.") Langford has departed for the mainland to avoid the likely bloodshed, pausing briefly to Blu-Tack™ 5,271,009 copies of the *Dead Dog Memorandum* to various walls. "Stop that man and nail his feet to the floor," screamed an enraged *Martin Easterbrook*, engaged in convention poster removal. Too late—the denuded corridors had been fetchingly redecorated....
>
> FOOD CORNER. There are no restaurant reports because with typical selfishness all the reporters are still in the restaurants. There is also an absence of newsroom—the final wording on the door was "go away in a huff and never return", so copy is not arriving, and the Alternative Newsroom is making it all up from a secret location. Stay tuned.
>
> *Heliograph 10-ish*, 13/4/93. Wook: Dave Langford. Clattuc: Chris Suslowicz. Chilke: Thog the Mighty. Tamm: Cathryn Easthope. LPFers: BSFA Council. Yips: Ops.

And then it was really over. The egoboo was tremendous (as editor I probably got an altogether unfair share, but that's life). The physical and mental debilitation lasted three weeks. I wonder what it would have been like to attend Helicon?

Three Weeks After. It was one of those incautious moments. I was at Jean Owen's and Martin Hoare's wedding party, reduced to a slithering moral jelly by heady speech-making and champagne cocktails, and Caroline Mullan was telling me what she thought of *Heliograph*. "All right for a mere Eastercon," she allowed grudgingly, "but your approach just wouldn't work for a Worldcon newsletter like ours at ConFiction."

"Oh, I don't agree ..." my mouth began to say, until I suddenly noticed we were surrounded by a horde of feral, red-eyed 1995 Worldcon committee members, licking their lips and closing slowly in. For once my brain managed to insert a few words of its own. "Er, I mean, you're *absolutely right,* Caroline."

1993

The mighty Thog newsletter team—as described in this piece—rode again at the next Eastercon, held in the Adelphi Hotel (Liverpool, England) with a vaguely nautical theme. It was therefore the work of mere hours for me to recall an old gag of John Brunner's and christen this newsletter The Adelphi Coracle.

The Great Con

It is a story that they tell, of how a great Convention Organizer sought to build a convention which should be a monument worthy of his incomparable love for science fiction. A convention it should be of perfect grace and beauty, more marvellous than any other convention had ever been or could ever be, so that to the end of time it should be a wonder, and fans would treasure it and speak of it and delight in its celebration of his love. And this convention he said was to be, because the pearl is lovelier than the most brilliant of crystalline stones, *Pearlcon: The Ultimate Science Fiction Convention*.

Year followed year as he devoted himself to preparing and adorning Pearlcon. A great hotel was chosen in a place of beauty, amidst snows and hills and valleys and winding rivers and convenient access by road, rail and air. Here was planned a Guest of Honour speech of cunning workmanship; and about it grew programme strands of strange and lovely originality, and a promised 24-hour bar as exquisite as a jewel.

With every month of effort the Organizer learnt new possibilities, new interests, new features of holistic and multi-streamed appeal. "Those were pretty things," he said of his early plans for quizzes and panels and Women In Science Fiction; and had them put aside into special interest rooms where they would not hamper his main design. Greater and greater grew his cosmopolitanism. With awe and amazement fandom saw the Pearlcon progress reports sweeping up from their specialist beginnings to a superhuman breadth and height and catholic magnificence. They did not know clearly what they had expected, but never had they expected so sublime a thing as this. "Wonderful are the miracles," they whispered, "that love of science fiction can do."

From the central thread of the main programme the Organizer now looked out into a vista of marvellous branching alternatives soaring and floating on either side, of tea parties and soft toys and body-painting and computer workshops and silent movies and self-defence classes and obsolete printing equipment and marshmallow interest groups and mediaeval smithcraft and community singing and Regency history and corporate management strategy and Logan's Runs and construction of orbital lasers and raffia-work, all perfect and unobtrusive in their balance.

Very often would the Organizer look on the planned flow-chart of that vista, deeply moved and yet not fully satisfied. The Ultimate Science Fiction

---

This one naturally comes with profuse and necessary apologies to H. G. Wells and his atypical short story "The Pearl of Love".

185

Convention had still something for him to do, he felt, before his preparation was done. Always he would order some little alteration to be made or some recent alteration to be put back again, a Coca-Cola special interest display or an exhibition of dragons in fretwork. And one day he thought that Pearlcon's multiple appeal would be clearer and simpler without the heavy emphasis of the main programme; and after regarding it very steadfastly for a long time, he had the main programme dismantled and removed.

At the next committee meeting he said nothing, and the next and the next. Then for two more he stayed away altogether. Then he returned, and as the subcommittees again stood awed by the serene vastness of their achievement, he saw that only one thing there was to mar the absolute harmony. There was a certain disproportion about the centre of things, the dear immortal cause of all this beauty. A little blot of crudity and bias and parochialism lay incongruously in the glorious expanse of Pearlcon's celebration of the entire universe. It was as if the total summary of human aspiration were labelled, "Made in Taiwan".

Long the Organizer mused, but no one knew the thoughts that passed through his mind.

At last he spoke. He pointed to the phrase that jarred, enshrined in Pearlcon's very name, the phrase "science fiction".

"Take that thing away," he said.

1988

The Arts of the Enemy

My dear fellow, don't you think it's for *you* to be apologetic? Consider your position. You burst uninvited into the most strenuously forbidden vault of Thousand Doves Monastery, and lie there hurling abuse at a simple artisan who's never done you any harm. I mean, do you make a regular habit of flinging yourself over precipices and cursing whoever comes to pick you up?

Oh well, I take the point. Losing a leg is so apt to strain the temper. A hand too, I see. Ribs. Spleen. We'll do something about all that presently. Would it be naive of me to assume that you're a visiting Hero, out for loot? Evidently you came via the dummy flagstone in the long cloister ... there's no mistaking the marks of the Grinder on that particular route. Spider bites, too? Yes. But you were too quick for the fire-blast trap. Mostly. Well, never look a gift cautery in the mouth, ha ha.

One simply has to rely on such tiresome precautions to retain any shred of privacy in an age like this. A pity, speaking quite impersonally, that you didn't try the secret passage from the refectory hall. There are some tolerably ingenious little safeguards there that could use testing, including a squad of killer were-orcs.

Good question. Were-orcs are tricksy: all the time you're fighting them, they keep shifting shape into *different* orcs. Very confusing. Throws a swordsman off completely when the wart he was aiming for leaps six inches to the left. Oh, do please stop bleeding over things. Here ... um ... amulet of serendipity, periapt of good digestion, rune of resistance to the clap ... *here* it is. Philtre of implausible healing.

If you say "foul villain" again I shall grow seriously bored. I am no miserable poisoner. Only *good* things get manufactured here. See, I'll sprinkle some on my hand. Reassured? And now on you.

Shush. Yes, I should have mentioned that your injured limbs would dissolve painfully into thick pools of evil-smelling slime. All a normal part of the healing process. They'll reform in an hour or so, good as new.

There is no effect on me because my health is already perfect. It is customary for me to have a single red eye. I detest personal remarks.

The British editorial collective "Midnight Rose" (Neil Gaiman, Mary Gentle, Roz Kaveney and Alex Stewart) sold a number of shared-world anthologies which Penguin/Roc published in Britain only. This was my contribution to Villains, *set in a generic Fantasyland whose sole special premise was that the stories focused on the bad guys—who were even allowed to win.*

Now, what have we here? Your shield will never be the same again; you must have used it to jam the rotating knives in the fourth traverse, very resourceful. Iron rations from somewhere near Ombrifuge in the Twenty-Four Kingdoms: a poor bargain, that stuff, it gives you the trots. Good, well-worn sword. "WHOSO PULLETH THIS SWORD FROM THE STONE IS RIGHTWISE KING OF ALL ..." From Blind Odo's smithy, of course. He puts that on all his swords. A sort of trademark. And this interesting opal ... dear me. I must consult the speculum for this.

Thank you. Indeed, I've misjudged you. You are an idealistic fool of a Hero, and it is, as you say, a charm of detection of evil, and one can hardly deny that it's led you to me. More precisely, to this plain golden ring I'm wearing.

I can explain everything. First, though, have a look at your jewel in the speculum. See the triple fracture plane there? I'd guess the thing was enchanted by old Antigropelos of Sorcerer's Isle: he rather runs to defects like that. The wretched charm could equally well have led you to, let me see, either a lode of cinnabar or a shoal of phosphorescent jellyfish. Depending which was nearest. I'd like to see you trying to rid the sea of jellyfish. Because you came, didn't you, to rid the world of me?

I have always been misunderstood.

Since you aren't going anywhere just at the moment, you might as well hear a little more. One so rarely has an audience. It's not merely the need to work in private; there is such dreadful prejudice abroad. If the jolliest, kindliest fellow in the world should happen to have a black-glowing complexion and shifting features, things get said in the back rooms of taverns ... and before you know what it's the crowd of peasants with scythes and torches, and yet another tiresome search for a new house. I've never even claimed to be a Lord, only a simple researcher.

Of course, you must have some trifle of talent yourself, I mean the only Talent that counts. You worked that opal charm quite successfully, and its spell needs an active operator. I could teach you things. My own work is based on the concept of a fundamental balance of impersonal forces called Good and Evil, or Light and Dark, which ...

Oh, this silly, superstitious fear of mere knowledge! You should join the good brothers upstairs in Thousand Doves. Gardening, loud piety, eight daily prayer sessions, invincible ignorance, and just enough side interests to fend off the boredom. You know. Gluttony. Lewd women. Highway robbery. Nipping the buds of each other's fruit-trees on the sly. The usual things that monks go for.

Naturally they "tolerate" me. They rely on me. Who do you think keeps up the charge on their famous Holy Healing Stone? Gods don't stoop to fiddle around with that sort of routine maintenance: one quick miracle and you never see them again, and probably the miracle was a county-wide rain of boiling pus rather than anything friendly. But me, I do good works.

No, I've never so much as killed anyone—more than you could say, I'm sure. And since you're not saying, what does the speculum reflect about you? Seventeen dead. Ho hum. You can't have been heroing very long. No champion ever got his own song cycle without a body count in the high three figures....

Well, in strict justice I must confess to a very few, but arguably they were accidental, or in self defence. Funny coincidence, in fact, with you lying there in that wobbly state. Brings back memories.

It was after the unpleasantness surrounding my last little place, where I'd been making some real progress with the accumulator—the ring. All of a sudden there was a huge upsurge of that prejudice I've mentioned. Wild stories about a foul black lord (which was very rude and unflattering), and the sky of the kingdom being darkened by enormities (much exaggerated and no more than a temporary side effect, as I explained at the time), and an epidemic of monstrous births ... to be utterly fair, it did occur to me later that there could have been some slight leakage from the alembics, and I resolved to take precautions in future. Which is one reason why I'm now established under a monastery.

Anyway. To cut a long epic short, I was roughly treated without a fair trial. Have you ever seen anyone struck simultaneously by two spells of Invincible Fulguration, together with Galligaskin's Convenient Macerator and the Cantrip of Remorseful Earache? All that remains, I can tell you from personal experience, is a shallow depression in the rock containing traces of thin, weeping fluid. I thought at the time that I deserved better. Earache, oddly enough, is even worse without ears.

The amusing coincidence is that I was carrying a phial of the same healing stuff you're now growing so familiar with. My own invention. It faithfully preserved what little was left of me....

As I reconstruct it, the aggressors fled the ruins of what they credulously regarded as a cursed land (I'd really meant to investigate why the wheat had started coming up black), which was declared forbidden and taboo for ever and ever. So it wasn't more than a week before the usual party of adventurers equipped themselves with the usual talismans—weapons, torches, flasks of oil, multi-sided dice, all that—and started combing the ruins. Of course they homed in on the ring where it lay in the middle of this broad patch of ooze.

(Look, if bubbling slime and naked prongs of reforming bone are such a bother to you, don't *stare* at yourself like that.)

Why hadn't I finished healing before then? Nothing comes of nothing. Magic as I see it is governed by all sorts of conservation laws. Raw materials are needed. You might have noticed how your tunic and hose and that silly leather harness are being, er, used up to replace the bits you left behind in the corridors. Just so, and entirely inadvertently, I dissolved the greater part of one dwarf, one elf and one small being with hairy feet. Quite a little morality fable about rushing incautiously to grab valuable-looking rings. You never know what you might stumble on. In that case it was me.

But it's my work I'd really like to talk about. Magicians are absurdly secretive and I never got far with my little notion about the free community of knowledge, the Open Conspiracy as I liked to call it. But you have only to look at the Grimoire—here. Don't touch, now: it's bound in the skin of a trained were-porcupine. Any unauthorized browser soon gets the point, ha ha.

Look. Here's Nicanor, going on about how all enchantment is illusion, deception, glamour and sleight: he bases his entire shifty philosophy on that. Here's Stevegonius, who reckons it's pure force of naked will. And Gowlais, with his texts and incantations that are supposed to work of themselves, without knowledge or understanding—even, as far as I can see, without anybody needing to read them. Faustus, reducing it all to a dismal chaffering with demons, as though the proper trappings of the great Art were a merchant's bench and stool. Bülg and the doctrine of compelling living and unliving things by their True Names. Rather irritatingly, the whole lot of them got results.

The message is that there is no one message. Magic is how you see it. Truth is what is true for you.

So my own perception of the Balance...

Oh, but I must tell you about this disciple of Bülg who came across the most fascinating problem. She practised in the dwarf lands somewhere down south of here, and her experimental Naming cantrips would keep going wonky. In the end she found she'd run into a tribe of were-dwarves. One of the most subtle examples of weredom on record. They could change their nomenclature at will, and an enchantment that collectively Named the *dwarves* of the area would founder on the ones who were currently being *dwarfs*. She had to tackle them one by one in the end. A most singular discovery.

Now mightn't that account for some part of the notorious dwarvish, or dwarfish, resistance to magic? It could be a useful thing to bear in mind.

You look improved enough to take a little wine. Would you ...? Of course it's black. Sable and ebon are nicer words. Or fuliginous. Everything down here goes that way sooner or later, usually sooner; I think there's a spot of trouble with the furnace and the air shafts. I hope.

My own crucial experiment used a minimum of material. Two precisely matched swords and a very, very long incantation, nineteen thousand stanzas with one eye on the steel, one on the scroll (yes, I had two then). To me the stuff of the world is light and dark, mixed up together like black draught stirred into milk, most exceedingly hard to separate. On a tiny scale, I did it.

When I'd finished that first exhausting effort, one sword radiated the faintest tinge of black, and I knew it would deal a just measurably nastier wound than before. The other had healing properties of exactly the same order of feebleness. I had established a principle, the conservation of light and dark.

Then out of curiosity I touched the swords together, and the balance restored itself with a blinding grey flash that left them fused, twisted, ruined. Which had to be the end of the work and the beginning of travel for a while, as I could think of no convenient means of explaining to a Master Swordmaker that his matched creations, ordered on approval, had furthered the cause of knowledge in a final sort of way. But I'd begun.

Imagine, after that, what a really high concentration of Light or Dark might achieve!

In my next research I gained further wisdom at a traditional cost. Yes, that's right. You see, the substance of this world is too feeble to sustain much added load of the black *or* the white energies: it gives way, bursts, vaporizes. Sometimes my skin still burns like fire at the memory. Oh, you noticed?

For an impersonal researcher, though, the discovery shed an exciting illumination on the old legends of saints. Think about it: these alleged holy men worked without apparatus, healing away, promiscuously spreading sweetness and Light. They put forth this power from their own bodies. What had to be the consequence?

Clearly they needed to get themselves back in balance by blowing off their excess of Dark in very unholy acts. And indeed you all too often hear of such sainted ones blasting people with unearthly fire for quite trivial differences of opinion, or committing pointless acts of vandalism like burning bushes or withering perfectly innocuous fig-trees.

After all, what was the alternative for them? When matter gives way under the terrible burden of a whopping imbalance of Dark, it's a hot business. For sorcerous reasons which I've not wholly fathomed, the resulting fireball tends to rise high in a spectacular column of smoke and flame. Compare this observation with the many tales of saints snatched up to heaven in fiery chariots, and you will surely...

But I digress.

What a good question. You're brighter than you look. Yes, this ring is a huge focus of one energy—and of course you know which. No, it's not composed of matter. Matter couldn't stand the strain. What looks like gold is a toroidal system of containment spells ... there are the formulae, written on it in fiery letters. Meaningless, of course, without some knowledge of high-energy thaumatics. The spells form a perfect shield.

Well, nearly perfect. One tries to keep one's distance from people, but when I brought over the grimoire and the wine I forgot. I meant to advise you: after you leave, try not to sire any children for a little while. Say a year. You know it makes sense.

(Speaking of which, the speculum should no doubt be able to reflect something of your activities in that area. What, ninety-three? You must have been heroing for a trifle longer than I'd assumed. A rest will do you good.)

And *why?* Come now. The disinterested enchanter pursues knowledge because it is there. Onward, ever onward. Just by moving my remaining fingers a hair's breadth I could topple this monastery and set it surfing through glowing lava down Slawkenbergius mountain and into the Kingdoms. But that would be a mere party trick. I must accumulate far, far more energy for serious work. The gates between worlds! The secrets of the stars! The reason why cockatrices cross the road! I have to know it all.

Meanwhile, that vulgar prejudice I talked about remains a problem. As one's non-Light reserves grow, more and more busybodies sniff them and start to pry. (No personal offence intended.) You do begin to see why, merely for the sake of some peace and quiet, a reasonable fellow might reluctantly contemplate—just contemplate—overriding the minds and free will of a province or two. Or even building one of those square countries with the huge, unneighbourly mountain walls, like that reclusive chap out east.

These bad impressions have only ever once worked in my favour, when I first presented myself to the Abbot upstairs for a talk about sanctuary, and he genuflected most disgustingly at my feet. Drivelling on about O Baphomet, O Black One, O Master. Our monks do like to keep a cautious foot in either camp, just in case. (There's at least one were-layman among them ... first touch of full moon and thick hair sprouts all over his tonsure.) I think it must have been a great disappointment when I devoted myself to good works. At any rate, Father Abbot looked distinctly hopeful when one day someone embraced the Holy Healing Stone and threw his crutches away so enthusiastically that he broke the Dean of Novices' nose. Thought I was showing my natural cloven hoof at last, you see. By their fruits....

Yes, that's the way of it. As the years go by, I work down here at the long, slow business of enchanting this and that amulet or potion with a measure of Light, enough to be useful and not so much as to rouse suspicion ... and the balancing by-product of Dark gets pouched in the ring for my own use. It's a neat system. The monks sell the amulets and things, and people carry them off rejoicing. Impoverished but rejoicing. Naturally it wouldn't do to have the charms pile up here, straining to discharge into the ring in one grey blaze of cancellation. Oh no. By now, after a blow like that to the sealing spells, the blast could level the Kingdoms and sink the Archipelago. The common folk don't realize the care I take to protect them.

Certainly you could do it yourself. I'm happy to teach anyone the rites. The more the merrier: after all, when someone else stores up what looks to be a really valuable charge of Dark, I can always come and take it away from them. All's fair in love and thaumaturgy, eh? Many hands make dark work, ha ha.

That should have been time enough for the healing. Let's see. Dear me, your leg's come back all funny-shaped. Sometimes I begin to think the air in this chamber isn't altogether healthful. Another ventilation shaft, perhaps, some day. I do try not to encourage visitors, you know. Can you walk? In a way, yes. You'll master the extra joint in no time, and perhaps the, as it were, ebon or sable appearance will wear off after a while. I do have some well-tried receipts for simple cosmetics....

As for the hand, it's better than new. Bigger, at least. You could wear a glove. A gauntlet, then.

What?

There's no need to phrase it so rudely. I suppose I should never have expected gratitude from a blasted Hero. Anyway, the answer to that one's surely quite obvious. If I'd gone down the other path and accumulated the energies of Light, think of the counterbalancing work that would have been needed then. Sending out an endless stream of cursed blades, baleful potions, charms of malignity and decay ... I couldn't bring myself to do that.

It's a matter of conscience, don't you see?

1992

Wisdom of the Ancients

The works of Lewis Carroll are not the likeliest source of advice to aspiring writers—apart possibly from "Take care of the sense and the sounds will take care of themselves". But while browsing through his copious volumes of less famous stuff, I rediscovered a poem which remains instructive, didactic and desperately relevant. Full of dubious advice, it takes a poke at contemporary "formula" poetry; it's called *Poeta Fit, Non Nascitur*, which I immediately translated as "I really must base an article on this."

> "Then, if you'd be impressive,
> Remember what I say,
> That abstract qualities begin
> With capitals alway:
> The True, the Good, the Beautiful—
> Those are the things that pay!"

Straight away you think of today's bog-standard fantasy novel, in which the Fell Sword bearing the Great Rune of the White Gods is raised by the One King against the Dark Bane of the Chaos Lord in the Black Tower of the Inner City, etc. Yes indeed, isn't it easy to make all your stage-props seem more important by allotting them capital letters?

Three problems do follow. This is such an effortless, clichéd gimmick that assiduous use no longer achieves much beyond proclaiming you a lazy and formulaic writer. Worse, enough repetition of such low-budget spotlighting may make the Fell Spell or, for that matter, the Black Hole seem progressively more trite and silly. And sooner or later, plot requirements will force several of the capitalized phrases to cohabit in the same paragraph, producing a clotted and reader-resistant mess like my sample above. Spurious Capitals (to pinch a phrase of Christopher Priest's) need to be used with enormous caution.

Carroll's tongue-in-cheek mentor would draw a second moral from that spoof fantasy sentence: he advises that

> "... there are epithets
> That suit with any word—
> As well as Harvey's Reading Sauce
> With fish, or flesh, or bird—
> Of these, 'wild', 'lonely', 'weary', 'strange',
> Are much to be preferred."

The budding writer is quick to seize on the possibilities:

> "And will it do, O will it do,
> To take them in a lump—
> As 'the wild man went his weary way
> To a strange and lonely pump'?"
> "Nay, nay! You must not hastily
> To such conclusions jump."

It's sadly true that—again in fantasy more than SF—the all-purpose epithets have become devalued. If you take a long view, the beginnings of the rot are visible in the poetry of Swinburne ... alternately praised as "the supreme master in English of the bleak beauty of little words" and disparaged (by Edmund Wilson, no less) for his "generalizing visageless monosyllables". Tolkien was rather fond of such handy words, like "dark" or "cold" or "grim", which to the uncritical eye produce a vaguely evocative effect irrespective of sense.

Over-use of the trick (besides making you look like yet another bloody Tolkien imitator) leads to poorly focussed writing. One has to supply one's own associations when no precise image emerges from the text. Lazy readers actually tend to find the result soothing, since there's no need to give the prose any particular attention when it merely pushes standard, familiar buttons. This characteristically woozy, monochrome fantasy style recalls Edmund Wilson's nasty suggestion that Swinburne had invented a new genre—"alcoholic poetry". For example:

> And the high gods took in hand
> Fire, and the falling of tears,
> And a measure of sliding sand
> From under the feet of the years,
> And froth, and drift of the sea;
> And dust of the labouring earth;
> And bodies of things to be
> In the houses of death and of birth....

Anyone identifying that as more Carroll loses sixty points. The sounds are nice but the sense ("take care of the sense ...") has grown somewhat hazy and diffuse. The analogous breed of Tolkien imitation, all rolling empty cadences, slips down with far less effort or memorability than something quirky, knobbly and individual by (let's say) Mervyn Peake.

When writing a computer program to generate cod fantasy titles for nameless and shameful reasons, I made up a shortlist of terse "epithets that suit with any word". Here's an edited version: black, blind, bright, chaos (this seems to have become an adjective, don't ask me why), chill, cold, dark, dead, deep, dim, dire, doomed, dread, false, far, fell, fire, foul, great, grey, grim, high, iron, lone, long, lorn, lost, mad, old, one, pale, sea, stark, stern, strange, tall, true, vast, vile, white, wild. Yes, I know, a couple are nouns, legitimized like "chaos" by years of Fire Dragons and Sea Changes. You will doubtless be able to think of more, you clever person.

Obviously, many of these are liable to turn up naturally from time to time. But if you find you're addicted to using them a great deal, especially in generalized or indiscriminate contexts ("dark" forever referring to baddies or forebodings rather than illumination, "cold" to matters unconnected with the thermometer) or in capitals, you should perhaps be worried. Or you should perhaps be a best-selling sword and sorcery author. I forget which.

All writing is a tightrope-walk, and when trying to avoid the pitfall of easy generality one can effortlessly fall off on the other side....

> "Next, when you are describing
> A shape, or sound, or tint;
> Don't state the matter plainly,
> But put it in a hint;
> And learn to look at all things,
> With a sort of mental squint."
> "For instance, if I wished, Sir,
> Of mutton-pies to tell,
> Should I say 'dreams of fleecy flocks
> Pent in a wheaten cell'?"
> "Why, yes," the old man said: "that phrase
> Would answer very well."

You can't add much to an example like that. Old Norse and Anglo-Saxon poets went in a lot for "kennings", allusive phrases which didn't cause confusion because everyone understood the code; when the skald said "bone-house" people knew he meant the human body and not the local crypt. (Or at any rate they pretended they did, and asked furtive questions later.)

The terror of being obvious leads to ad-hoc kennings, euphemisms and neologisms which all too often misfire. Tennyson gave us "ocean-spoil" because it seemed too downmarket to write "fish". Boxers used to "tap" each other's "claret", to save past centuries' sports-page readers from the ugly sight of printed blood. Patricia McKillip's "Riddle-Master" fantasies irritated me by talking for some reason about a riddle's "stricture" instead of meaning or moral ("And the stricture of *that* is—" said the Duchess). Stephen Donaldson ... but enough. I could go on and on.

So you write "It was getting dark and cold", and feel dissatisfied with the phrase, possibly because the Dark Ruler with his Cold Spells has already been endemic in the narrative. You scratch your head and laboriously substitute: "An inspissated squid-ink photonlessness of Cimmerian intensity commenced to permeate the environs, whose calorific ambience now recalled the supernal frigidity of Cocytus itself." I am naming no names, but some writers think this sort of thing is posh. It must be what Quiller-Couch had in mind when he gave his basic rule of style:

> Whenever you feel an impulse to perpetrate a piece of exceptionally fine writing, obey it—whole-heartedly—and delete it before sending your manuscript to press. *Murder your darlings.*

Throw away your Roget, and walk again!

How, then, is the hapless author to convey a bit of fairly banal information? Indirection is a favourite literary tool, blending the facts into the narrative flow. "Bloggs peered ahead, finding it harder to see the track in the failing light; he found himself shivering." Ultimately, all writers have to feel their own way. A plain "The forest ahead could no longer be seen" implies darkness, but might allow the possibility of fog, sun-dazzle in Bloggs's eyes, temporary obscuration by land contours as Bloggs shambles onward, the dissipation of an illusion or mirage, or even (though the calmness of the sentence does rather tell against this) that Bloggs has just been struck blind by a passing Dark Lord.

There are always two questions worth asking. Does the reader actually need to know that it's getting dark and cold? And if so, dare one stake everything on the hazardous chance of simply saying (especially if a lot of fine writing has been perpetrated just lately), "It was getting dark and cold"?

If this sounds like a morbid level of concentration on a puny six-word sentence, remember Samuel Delany's extremely nifty essay which spends two and a half pages discussing a sentence of eight words, with a whole paragraph devoted to the opening "The". (Which he instinctively visualizes as "a greyish ellipsoid about four feet high that balances on the floor perhaps a yard away". Try to imagine his inner pictures of words like "concatenation", "molybdenum" and "gleet".) It's another trap, of course: if you burst your brain over every definite article you'll never finish anything, whereas—I do believe I feel an epigram coming over me—if you never think about words you'll never write words worth thinking about.

How to bring a story, an article or indeed anything else to a close? The poem points the way:

> "First fix upon the limit
> To which it shall extend
> Then fill it up with 'Padding'
> (Beg some of any friend);
> Your great SENSATION-STANZA
> You place towards the end."

Oh, Mr Carroll, they're still doing it. Because *The Lord of the Rings* ran natu-rally into three volumes, this has become the limit to which a fantasy must extend, because the publishers demand it (say the authors), because that's what authors produce (think the readers), because that's what the readers insist on (loudly assert the publishers).

So Book 1 of the trilogy establishes the characters and the problem. "Un-less the Scrotum of Pulverulence is joined with the Chaos Runefork at the Blue Moon's Latter Eclipse, Plotdevice the Foul will triumph and introduce VAT on books."[1] Book 3 sees lots of rousing battles and the ultimate, sensa-tional nobbling of the Dark Lord. "What Plotdevice the Foul failed to realize is that by triumphing over us so utterly and frustrating all our noble designs, he inevitably brought about his own defeat!" Book 2 inserts a suitable narra-tive delay between introduction and resolution, and fatally tends to consist of padding—usually in the form of an interminable journey which advances the plot by approximately as far as the average glacier gets between breakfast and elevenses.

But they get published. God, how they get published. I sometimes won-der whether every aspirant's secret desires are met by the literary-workshop aim of coaxing you to write originally and well. Is this an ivory tower attitude? If the earnest student of this collection is consumed with impatience to get into print, and the ephemeral, identikit junk on the bookstands seems to show that working hard at good writing isn't necessary, is it kind to preach about long-term damage to one's talent and reputation; about Cyril Connolly's mini-mal definition of a successful book as one which lasts ten years? It all depends on whether you take writing seriously and personally, or whether...

> "Now try your hand, ere Fancy
> Have lost its present glow—"
> "And then," his grandson added,
> "We'll publish it, you know:
> Green cloth—gold-lettered at the back—
> In duodecimo!"
> Then proudly smiled that old man
> To see the eager lad
> Rush madly for his pen and ink
> And for his blotting-pad—
> But when he thought of *publishing*,
> His face grew stern and sad.

---

1 The British government intermittantly threatens to stimulate our ailing publishing industry by ending books' exemption from Value Added Tax, a sales tax which would boost prices by a healthy 17-1/2 %.

REFERENCES

Lewis Carroll: *Phantasmagoria and other poems* (1869)

Cyril Connolly: *Enemies of Promise* (1938)

Samuel R. Delany: *The Jewel-Hinged Jaw* (1977)

Patricia A. McKillip: *The Riddle-Master of Hed* (1976) etc.

Sir Arthur Quiller-Couch: *On the Art of Writing* (1916)

John D. Rosenberg: introduction to *Swinburne: Selected Poetry and Prose* (Modern Library, 1968)

Algernon (he is called Augustus only in the epigraphs of Charles Sheffield novels) Charles Swinburne: *Atalanta in Calydon* (1865)

Alfred, Lord Tennyson: *Enoch Arden* (1864)

J. R. R. Tolkien: *The Lord of the Rings* (1954-55)

Edmund Wilson: *The Shores of Light* (1952), *The Bit Between My Teeth* (1965)

1989

Leaks

It had been a definite mistake to spend so many hours last night practising. Making his way up the street, Ken struggled not to think of that obscene grey bladder in the local baker's window, which inflated and deflated in a miraculously unconvincing simulation of dough being kneaded. His own brain seemed to be doing much the same. Small wobbling flaws, perhaps UFOs or fragments of detached retina, floated through his field of vision, and that solitary spoonful of cornflakes lay in his stomach like a cluster of leaden dumplings.

What a wonderful thing it was to be talented. He could sympathize two hundred per cent with that bloke in the Bible who hid his talent in a napkin rather than stick out his neck.

Even the green double-decker buses exuded an alcoholic dread as they ground slowly past. Crisp packets leered mockingly from the gutter, sharing some terrible knowledge with the passers-by who so very pointedly ignored the moral leprosy stumbling in their midst. And how had he managed to get beer in his *hair*? Did it just ooze through one's pores from the foetid jellies inside? In every way it was a typical morning.

Behind the offices' grimy Victorian facade, a lift which doubled as a municipal convenience heaved Ken up through Social Services, Housing and Consumer Advice, Traffic Planning.... This Department branch shared the fifth floor with the town council's nerve centre for co-ordination of cemeteries and crematoria. Ken thought longingly about a nice co-ordinated coffin as he steered himself past death's door.

It had been many unpaid months since he'd last been called for temp work at the DPR office; going by appearances, their cleaners followed roughly the same schedule. In a familiar display of method acting, the receptionist behind the desk managed to convey that Ken's own Paranormal Resources included uncanny powers of invisibility and inaudibility. Air molecules of superior importance had passed through her door, Marcia's posture made it clear,

---

Another story written for a Midnight Rose shared-world collection, Temps *(motto: "Not At All Based On* Wild Cards, *Honest"). The British twist on the superhero idea was of low-budget "wild talents" being paid a pittance by the incredibly bureaucratic Department of Paranormal Resources—a lowly branch of our Civil Service—and sent on occasional tedious missions for the good of the state. That's all you need to know ... except that this is also a multiverse crossover story, since the Robinson Heath setting is from my own non-shared-world nuclear farce* The Leaky Establishment.

and likewise bluebottles with greater social charm. She continued to apply nail-varnish.

Ken peered at notices sellotaped to the dingy cream walls (THE SEC-TION PRINCIPAL WARNS THAT DISCIPLINARY ACTION WILL FOLLOW IF THERE IS ANY FURTHER REPETITION OF THE UN-AUTHORIZED RAIN OF FROGS IN CONFERENCE ROOM 2) and wondered about his chances of drawing on Departmental resources in the shape of paracetamol. Time passed.

"Mr Vanrey? You're *late*," said Marcia severely and without prior warning. Her nails glowed iridescent purple.

"That's Varney."

"Oh. It says here.... Mr Vanrey, the Department's time is very valuable. I have a travel warrant for you, and a briefing sheet, and you're to start at once." She sniffed. "And the Senior says he hopes you remember something from your college work about enortpy."

Kenneth Varney, BSc. (Physics) (3rd), stared. "About what?"

"Enortpy." She pushed a slim, puke-coloured folder at him. The typed label said CONFIDENTIAL * ENORTPY RAY.

"... Entropy, maybe?"

"I *spell-checked* it, Mr Clever. Now, you're to be a Departmental observer at the nuclear place, whatsisname, at Robinson Heath. Special investigation. I suppose the physics made them think of you." She sniffed again. "It's only an S-H job. Don't go getting above yourself."

His head gave a particularly vicious twinge. Stalking horse. You heard about these things in a theoretical kind of way. When the DPR had only half a mind to intervene, they'd try stirring up the situation by sending half a talent. Just knowing a quote specialist unquote was on the case could be enough to make your criminal or enemy agent show a detectable break in behaviour patterns. Such as, for example, staying late at the lab and dropping Ken Varney into a convenient swimming-pool reactor.

He asked the question uppermost in his mind.

"No," said Marcia, "but I can do you a Fisherman's Friend if that's any help."

With a groan Ken tucked the folder under his arm and turned away ... then back again. "One thing. Um, your word-processor, you use one of those spell-checkers where you can, you know, add new words ...?"

"To the built-in luxigon? Yes, that's right."

Leaving, he felt ever so slightly cheered. Clearly he had some talent for investigative work after all.

Somewhere out west of Paddington his spirits made the significant leap from whirling dread to mere powerful unease. Could he really be sitting legiti-mately in First Class No Smoking? Ken Varney with his second-class denims and designer stubble? The ticket inspector had also had obvious difficulties with this concept, but in the end had stalked away baffled.

Feeling a return of the eerie power to tackle words of more than two syllables, he studied the file on entropy (or enortpy) rays. They were hypothetical, and statistical, and saved from nonentity only by a communication written on a sheet of headed A4 [classified] with a worn HB [classified], intercepted by [classified] at location [need-to-know status insufficient], and reading:

MIKHAIL. ENTROPY BEAM DEFINITELY EFFECTIVE ON TRANSPORT HERE. CONTINUE TRIALS SAME LOW LEVEL. TROJAN.

As he hacked his way through the surrounding layers of soft, clinging, wet-strength officialese, Ken gathered that this note would have been dismissed as a rollicking jape if it weren't for the transport pool of the Nuclear Utilization Technology Centre on Robinson Heath, which when examined with a keen statistical eye had detectably [classified]. Only a little bit—"LOW LEVEL", he thought, feeling momentarily clever—but most definitely [classified].

Stalking horse. Marcia had wanted him to feel humbled, but actually his usual assignments for the Department were humbler still and consisted of helping move office, rearrange filing cabinets, fill out the numbers for manpower inspections ... any little job where payment at his sub-competent talent level was cheaper than contract labour. As paranorms went, he rated as the kind of small change it was easier to stuff in the charity box than count. Everyone remembered the Monty Python sketch where Ken's grade was rated just below penguins, though just above BBC programme planners.

And now he was roaring towards NUTC, a place so high-powered and high-security that paranorms weren't normally allowed within a mile of it, just in case of [classified], or even of [need-to-know]. It was a famous quirk of the civil service that, like the Home Office forensic unit, the Department's research lab was attached to NUTC—presumably meaning that they could conduct research on anything but paranorms.

"dS," he mumbled painfully, "equals dQ over T." There, he still knew the definition of instantaneous entropy change. A few more hours' recovery time and the information might even start making sense.

Gasometers bulged like fungi outside the carriage window, succeeded by plastic-faced office blocks in contrasting shades of liver, lights and spam, and then a grimy expanse of station. Ken shouldered his bag and was soon shuffling down the platform, cautiously swivelling his head in slow motion and wondering whether a quick hair of the dog would be advisable just for the sake of practice. This gambit was blocked by a small placard saying MR K VANREY, held up by a uniformed driver of few words and one implacably pointing finger. Score another first for Talent Grade Z: he'd never before been chauffeured in an official car, even one that banged and wheezed through Reading and the countryside like this.

"Ducts!" was his first thought when the heart of Britain's defence industry lurched into view, as though with incidental music from *Brazil*. Huge silvery ducts ran inside the miles of high wire fence, rearing up in triumphal arches to allow traffic at each gate. Smaller, black-clad ducts linked the square buildings, whose inner walls and ceilings were threaded by narrow pipes painted in Civil Service cream: they circled the security office where he was photographed holding a prison-style number, they paced him and his escort along endless two-tone corridors, they clumped companionably in the bare room where briefing was supposed to happen. The Robinson Heath installations had clearly been designed by some perverse lover of spaghetti.

The briefing group...

Dr Fortmayne from Weapons Physics had thick grey hair, a glittering eye, and bounding excitement. It seemed he must be strapped in place, otherwise he'd vibrate off his chair. "Let me make one thing clear: I want this gadget. I want it very much. I disagree with our whole approach. We shouldn't be piddling around, we should be going through the site and surrounds with a tooth-comb." He frowned. "Whatever a tooth-comb is."

Sergeant Rossiter of MOD Police/Security mumbled something and was understood to be saying that tooth-combs came expensive these days. His raggled moustache and furtive manner evoked memories of the least reputable of Ken's occasional employers, Greasy Mal from Highbury, the man of a thousand fiddles.

Someone called Brownjohn, large, bland and moist, represented Transport. "Run of bad luck. Could happen any time. Obvious hoax by one of our bright lads. And when we catch him—"

There was a wrangle between Theoretical Physics ("An entropy projector is a plain and simple impossibility."), the DPR Lab Principal ("So is he," with a nod towards Ken: "Six impossible things before breakfast.") and NATO Liaison: "I don't care whether it's impossible or not: if it's available it'll make a nice bargaining point to squeeze some more counterforce goodies out of the bloody Americans. Since we can't seem to develop our own." At this, Fortmayne leapt upright in sputtering outrage, and the decibel count rose sharply.

Theoretical Physics turned out to be the sort of man who could in cold blood say words like appertaining, tantamount and even predicated.

Ken's head had reverted to full throb-level, but he gleaned that the entire NUTC transport pool was suffering mysteriously accelerated decay. Vehicles wore out naturally but too fast, as though spending all their nights in loud clubs burning the carburettor at both ends. It might have passed unnoticed, but then the message to "Mikhail" had turned up in a routine check of outgoing site mail, addressed to an empty house in the nearby village of Bogley....

"If I had a contraption like that," said Brownjohn, "know what I'd do? Get rich beaming the thing at whisky. Twelve years aged in cask, only take a few months. Why waste it on our vans? Why not Trident?"

Fortmayne pointed out with heavy irony that NUTC transport was serviced every other week, that economics did not permit Trident warheads to be detonated quite so frequently, especially in the Home Counties, and that it was entirely credible that the same insidious influence was indeed being directed against the British deterrent. "And what do they send us? This person Mr Vanrey." (Marcia's spelling was now immortalized within the sealed plastic of his new security pass.) "Possibly he'd like to tell the committee in a few words what special talent he brings to this critical situation? An unnatural gift, perhaps, for turning his face pale green?"

"Touch of 'flu," Ken lied.

"I have Mr Varney's dossier and can vouch for him," said Dr Croll, the DPR Lab Principal. "I think the details of our operation should remain on a need-to-know basis. Our watchword is security." Ken gazed at him admiringly. What a wonderful human being.

"I don't agree with what you're saying," Fortmayne said reflexively, but people were looking pointedly at their watches and Rossiter rubbed his beer-gut with slow significance. Lunch was declared and Ken found himself annexed by Croll.

"We call it the Mushroom Cloud," said the DPR researcher, in the tones of one apologizing for a tedious family joke. Ken agreed that once you'd regarded the local pub's sign in that light, it became impossible ever again to see it as a Wheatsheaf. They entered.

This Croll seemed a cheerful fellow, rotund and bouncingly bald, and deeply untroubled by entropy rays. Ken felt distinctly less lichen-coloured as he contemplated an imminent hair of the chihuahua, if not of a full-scale St Bernard. Pints and curly sandwiches arrived at the table.

"To your success," Croll said with mock formality. "Had we but world enough and time ... but I have to talk a little business. It is really very simple. You will wear *this* and move around NUTC, observing and sometimes taking sinister notes, and we shall see what is stirred up."

This was a conspicuous lapel badge in day-glo lime, about three inches across, carrying a single bold character. Drawing on the Dead Sea Scroll remnants of his physics, Ken said: "Greek. A capital *psi*, right?"

"Very good. Yes, like a pink triangle or a yellow star. You will be noticed. Good. But I must admit that I brought you here for another reason, because I am professionally interested in your abilities."

"Ability. With a very, very small A."

"No modesty, now. You can't imagine how much, as a researcher, I truly envy any genuine paranorm. The gulf between us is narrow but it is deep."

Ken was embarrassed. "Honest, it's nothing, like being able to wiggle your ears. I used to send off to the small ads in *Knave* and *Private Eye*, you know, Dr Farrell's Famous Cerebral Enhancer Tonic, a guaranteed forty-four-inch talent within two months. Wore my fingers out, rubbing the damn stuff on my temples every night before retiring. I think it was oil of wintergreen actually."

It wasn't something he cared to talk about, especially in a pub. But Croll quizzed him further with the unblinking earnestness of a Scientology interviewer closing for the kill, and at last said: "Perhaps, you know, we can help. Measure your mind's height by the shade it casts. First, though: show me."

Ken had gulped half his pint and Croll was lagging, so it was straightforward enough. He concentrated on the beer mugs and thought parched thoughts. For some reason it always helped to clench his teeth askew and close one eye. Potentials shifted and his mental thumb pushed down hard on the balance of Nature. Quite rapidly, though without any fuss, his own beer-level rose two inches.

"That's it. I mean, that's all there is to it. It has to be alcoholic and it has to be my glass, I don't know why."

"What about conservation of mass? No, don't tell me, I think I see." Croll slid the two mugs together for comparison. "Beer finds its own level. My loss is your gain. But, hmm, what about range? Could you perhaps tap that whisky-bottle up behind the bar?"

"Well, I have to want it, and I don't much like whisky in beer. And I'd have to stand up and look all conspicuous: otherwise, there's a three foot drop from the Teachers optic to this table here, and the potential energy gets a bit frisky. You know, fountains, waterspouts. Whisky and splash."

Croll clicked his tongue. "It is not exactly 'that one talent which is death to hide'. From the dossier I had imagined that, with training... Just imagine the scenario. A hostile spyplane flies low over Robinson Heath; you glance upwards, narrow your eyes, and vital hydraulic fluid leaks disastrously away!"

"Gallons of it, into my beer mug, with a horizontal velocity vector of seven hundred miles an hour? I hate getting barred from pubs."

"With training, much is possible. You seem to have made room in your glass already. Do please show me again. There, the owner of *that* one is in the lavatory."

Ken clenched his teeth askew and closed one eye. This time Croll kept his attention on the unattended drink twelve feet away. "Excellent. The glass is falling hour by hour, the glass will fall forever...."

"But if you break the bloody glass you won't hold up the weather," Ken quoted.

"A man of culture, I see."

"Oh, you meet a lot of big brains with degrees down at the job centre and Social Security. The word is 'overqualified'. Which is why—" On second thoughts, this was no place to discuss hauling anonymous clinking boxes off the backs of lorries for Greasy Mal.

"Nevertheless a Department spotter recruited you. Nature's handmaid Art makes mighty things from small beginnings grow—Dryden. I would like you to visit our laboratory later today. You have potential."

"And I have a bloody drink problem. Every time I try to practise what I can do..." Ken tried not to remember his unwelcome reunion with last night's Chinese takeaway on this morning's pillow. He made a queasy toasting gesture, drank, and convulsed disastrously. "... Oh *shit*, it's lager and lime."

"Fortunately this is only an old suit," said Croll a little coldly.

For the next couple of hours, Ken prowled within what he'd been told was ten full miles of wire-link fence around the Robinson Heath site. How much area was that? About eight square miles if it were a circle, which it wasn't, or six and a quarter for a square, which it wasn't either. Now the average size of a typical entropy ray projector would be...

Much of the area seemed about as derelict and useless as this statistical line of thought: grass and gorse, decaying tarmac, rabbit droppings, marshy expanses harbouring only a few far-flung ducts. It must be out of sheer embarrassment that the MOD insisted on maps showing the site as a blank white patch. Clearly, when you passed at last through the secret door of the inner circle and walked the throbbing corridors of power you'd envied all your life, the most earth-shattering revelation was how even more boring than the real world it could be.

The beer buzzed in him, and he hoped Croll's own several pints would be interfering with the fellow's afternoon study of the dictionary of quotations. Meanwhile, nobody started back from Ken with cries of guilty alarm.

Instead: "Aagh!" he said in guilty alarm as a hand clamped on his shoulder.

"Just a word in your ear, mate," murmured Sergeant Rossiter. "Just one word. The word is ... pathetic."

"I'm doing my job."

"No, you've already done that, so why arse around? ... Oh dear, all new to you, innit? We leaked it two days back about this dead unusual visit from a DPR weirdo, pardon my French, special talent. Anyone acts funny here *today*, they must be small fry because every big-time guilty conscience is already going to be off sick or taking leave. They're the names we'll feed in for correlation. And where does that leave you, sunshine? Having you here at all's just the follow-through, not the job."

Feeling shrewd and acute, Ken said, "I suppose a really bright villain wouldn't risk acting suspiciously like that, and he'd come in today just as usual."

"Maybe, squire, maybe. So you reckon we should keep an extra close eye on all the ones who stay home suspiciously, *plus* all the ones who suspiciously don't, and that narrows it right down to our entire workforce of lemmesee 11,676 suspicious characters."

"All right, I get the general idea."

"Less a few who went sick or was already off to Benidorm before we let out the rumours. Of course they could be double-bluffing, couldn't they?"

"All *right*."

"Lighten up, now. Enjoy the sights if you like. Nifty little badge you've got there with the wossname, Greek for 'piss'—ask me nicely and I'll get you another with the Greek for 'off'."

Pausing only to call him "chummy", Rossiter drifted away and left Ken thinking dark, entropic thoughts. He prowled on.

At one stage he loitered as suspiciously as he could by the north gate and watched Ford Transit vans accelerate smoothly past security guards who seemed unconcerned about possible stacks of nuclear warheads being smuggled out in each. At another he found the fire-door of a concrete blockhouse flapping its EMERGENCY USE ONLY lettering in the wind, slid cautiously inside, and left in haste when threatened by a big wall sign lurid with trefoils and the interesting rubric PURPLE RADIATION ZONE.

This must be part of Fortmayne's plutonium-infested playground. If I were a great detective, Ken thought, I would see right through all that stuff about tooth-combs, and say "Fortmayne doth protest too much" (no, that would be Dr Croll's line), and thrill the assembled suspects in the library by asking which of all these characters was most likely to be the proprietor of a fiendish entropy ray? The number one weapons physicist, of course: Fortmayne. Gesturing grandly to the imaginary inspector closing in with the handcuffs, Ken snagged his finger against the rusty barbed-wire shroud of a passing duct. Ouch. All this, and tetanus too?

The huge ducts and pipes, he decided grumpily, represented the government cash-flow into this unpromising hole in Berkshire. Vast sums surged down the MOD arteries, while the DPR pipeline would be a hair-thin capillary, subject to continual leaks. Billions for defence and about fifty pee for Ken Varney.

Sucking his finger, he shadowed an ailing and consumptive minibus into what turned out to be the Transport yard. Here government vehicles were being subjected to artificial respiration, intensive life-support and major transplant surgery. The stench of petrol was too thick to cut with a knife, and would have required industrial lasers. Entropy lay around in almost visible pools, like the local lake system of sump oil. From an office window two floors up a fat white blur that might have been Brownjohn watched him narrowly.

Who could be a more logical choice for the inside job, playing the dreaded entropy ray across the NUTC service and garaging areas? On the other hand, wasn't Fortmayne the most plausible villain? And hadn't Rossiter more or less warned him off? At this rate of detection he'd soon have a strong circumstantial case against every single bloody member of the briefing committee. We are all guilty. All the world's a symphony orchestra, with some on woodwind and most of us on the fiddle.

Something clicked then in Ken's mind, as though a fruit machine were signalling *nudge nudge*. Hadn't someone in a smoky pub in Highbury once winked and mentioned what they called the car pool fiddle? He thought again about the precepts and philosophy of his very occasional employer Greasy Mal, and quite suddenly laughed out loud. Then he wished he hadn't: jarred by the noise, the inspirational light-bulb flared out and left his skull a blackened, smoking socket. Never go boozing with a hangover *and* a parapsychologist. Which reminded him...

The DPR laboratory was an unassuming wooden shack, propped up by the more opulent Home Office Forensic Unit. Both were liberally spattered with what might have been red-hot evidence in the form of semen stains, but after some thought Ken placed the burden of guilt on pigeons, especially the one which had dropped its burden on him.

"Welcome!" said Dr Croll, buttoning a white lab coat. "The raven himself is hoarse that croaks your fatal entrance under my battlements, if I might put it like that."

Ken flicked without success at the shoulder of his best denim jacket. "It was a pigeon actually; it just looks like it must have been a horse."

"Come in, come right in."

Inside the sanctum, the old familiar laboratory smell attacked his nostrils with a wire brush. Dull green tiles covered the floor. High-tech things with screens and digital readouts jostled on the benches with archetypal brass instruments that might have been used in the early experiments of Faraday, or Newton, or Torquemada.

For a moment, Ken felt disoriented by the feeling that this place was more like a lab than any real lab could be. Something movie-like about it, perhaps, along the lines of exploding control panels or Dr No's art-deco reactor.

"If you could just sit here," said Croll, indicating the electric chair. Yes, that was the subtle anomaly. University physics labs were always short-changed when it came to important equipment like electric chairs.

"Er..."

"Oh, yes, I suppose it must look a trifle intimidating. I am very interested in physiological readouts, in trying to map what the body *does* when paranormal abilities come into play. There's no art to find the mind's construction in the face. And so we need all these sensors."

Somehow Ken found himself gently crowded into the chair. "Trust me," said Croll. "I'm a doctor."

What he had in his bulging scientific mind was both simple and deeply irritating. Not content with borrowing Ken as an experimental subject, Croll wanted to play social worker and do him a bit of good. He'd nipped out to the village grocer for test materials in the shape of countless Tetrabrik litre boxes: orange juice, grapefruit juice, pineapple juice, mango juice, and worst of all tomato juice.

"I can't possibly. It only works with something boozy, I told you."

"My snap diagnosis, Ken, is that you are too permanently fuddled ever to transcend your talent's limitations. What you do at present... It provokes the desire, but it takes away the performance. However, if this will console you in the slightest, we do first need one control reading."

The last of the chilly disk electrodes, slimed with something like KY jelly, had been taped in place. Croll handed Ken a plastic cup, the sort guaranteed to translate coffee directly into scorched fingers, and took a hopeful-looking brown bottle from a cupboard.

"Would, ah, light ale provoke the desire sufficiently?"

"You bet."

"Now good digestion wait on appetite," said Croll in his special quotation voice, "and health on both." Recorders were whirring and displays dancing with a sinuous EEG jiggle.

Ken clenched his teeth askew and closed one eye. The universe duly moved for him, and he raised the suddenly full cup. There was an outraged pause. "Fuck me, what's this?"

"Nothing but cold civil service tea, I'm afraid. My secretary always used to say they brewed it from old tights. Personally I would not know. ... So, Ken, it has to be alcoholic, does it?"

Croll had him there. It was the lager-and-lime effect all over again.

"Let me tell you an anecdote. There was once a fellow called Logan whose talent seemed even more spectacularly useless than yours. He was able to incinerate individual dust motes, no more than one at a time. They filed him as a micropyrotic for want of a better word, and then wrote him completely off the useful list with a grade of, well, your grade. Years later he made the imaginative breakthrough all by himself and emigrated to glory in America, the land of vigilantes and handguns."

"Oh yeah, I saw a Day In The Life of him in one of the colour supplements. Local clod makes good. Learned to focus it on gunpowder or something, didn't he? Mr Misfire, The Man Whose Adversaries Shoot Themselves In The Foot. He looked a right sight in those puce leotards."

"Pre-cisely. I am convinced that I, here, could have developed his ability much sooner: but our beloved masters, after first building this laboratory at Robinson Heath to save money, had a security scare. They became paranoid about letting wild talents anywhere near the nuclear work at NUTC ... unless they happen to be in Security or Intelligence, and by definition too lofty, too busy to spare *me* one miserable afternoon. You know that today is the first time in a year that I've been able even to calibrate the psychotronic readouts?"

He added, with dreadful inevitability: "We all know Security is mortals' chiefest enemy."

Ken writhed in the hard seat, which at the seat of his jeans also felt oddly cold and damp. Being wired up was even more uncomfortable than it had looked, but being wired up *and* lectured at...

"Ow!" he said. Croll had sneaked up behind him with a needle.

"This will help make you more suggestible. No, no, don't move now, it might affect the sensors. The instruments of darkness tell us truths, but not if you wiggle the wires. Let me just tighten this strap; and this one. Now I want you to try for some juice. Just one small change in your talent. You know you can do it. Tip the tea out in this beaker...."

Open wide. Rinse. Even the bloody dentist never strapped him in. Ken made his miracle-working face again, staring with concentrated loathing at the box of grapefruit juice; and, almost at once, nothing happened. Except that his head hurt even more.

"Look," he said patiently, "it's as though you convinced me to walk across this dark room, and then showed me that I'd been on a narrow plank over a sodding great crevasse a mile deep. And there you are saying 'you can do it, just walk back again now.' It's not the same."

Croll beamed, and hunched himself over a small console to one side of the EEC soft-drinks mountain. "I had not yet mentioned that we can provide a counter-stimulus." His hand pounced.

What followed was a mixture of red-hot needles and severe cramps in each buttock, as though the dentist were mounting a surprise attack from the rear. Ken made loud appropriate noises, and added: "Stop that!"

"You cannot imagine how irritated I am by the sheer waste when a potentially fine talent is bestowed on someone like—" A sort of visual *ugh* passed over Croll's face. "A giant's robe upon a dwarfish thief. What a cheap, sleazy use you make of your priceless gift. Now, if I were in your place..."

Ken offered to change places (and even robes) immediately, but this cunning ploy got only the response it deserved: a second and hotter dose of National Grid. No wonder the blasted hot-seat had been damp. Croll was going to do him good even if it killed him. The after-twitches felt like sitting in a bowl of small, muscular and hyperactive eels.

"Look. I can't concentrate when you do that. Just give me a minute. Did I tell you about what I worked out this afternoon? Only bloody solved the entropy ray business, that's what." In just such a way, when in the dentist's chair, Ken always found himself able to deliver frighteningly voluble monologues, without hesitation, repetition or deviation, on subjects like drizzle or bus tickets. "It's all a load of rubbish, it's just someone doing the old car pool fiddle over in Transport. The only thing I don't understand is ... oh."

Oh no, he thought. What hadn't made sense was why, with a nice little con going, anyone should be so yoghurt-brained as to draw attention to it by sending open letters about entropy beams. Who in this business was several protons short of a nucleus? Well...

"That is doubtless very interesting and rewarding for you, but as an attempt at distraction it is childish. I ask you to focus your mind, Ken. Focus on that one small change. Present fears are less than horrible imaginings, and the voltage dial can be turned up a great deal further."

Yes, it really stimulated the mind, this sitting in the seat of power. "You sent that letter, didn't you? The one from TROJAN to MIKHAIL, and very funny too. I bet you sent dozens till they intercepted one. You'd spotted the con and you moved in."

Croll's hand wavered over a particular red button, as though it were a fat beetle he didn't quite want to squash because of the mess. "Why should I do a thing like that? What possible motive could I have?"

Dominoes were still falling with a painful *click click click* inside Ken's head. "It got *me* down here, that's what. Your first bloody guinea pig in, what did you say, a whole year? Of course you suggested the stalking-horse game to that committee. Come clean, chummy." Oops, that had slipped out.

By now Croll had whitened to the point where the dome of his baldness looked like a peeled hard-boiled egg, awaiting the descent of some teaspoon of the gods. He closed his eyes and said, apparently to himself, "Screw your courage to the sticking-place." Then, mostly though not perhaps wholly in Ken's direction: "I will complete my experiment. What's done cannot be undone. Afterwards I think there will have to be an unfortunate accident. This high-voltage equipment does not receive nearly enough safety inspections. There may be an enquiry and even a sharp reprimand."

Of course, Ken was brooding, after spending my life reading all those thrillers I should have thought that when you're strapped to an insidious torture machine in the arch-fiend's secret den, it is not the best time to gloat out loud that you've got the goods on him.

The red button went down. This time the shock to his tormented buttocks included overtones of jagged teeth, killer vindaloo and barbed wire.

"Just a reminder," said Croll. "I *will* see you prove my theories by overcoming your petty self-imposed limits. If even on pain of death you can't bring yourself to love fruit juice, then think of hating me. The labour we delight in physics pain. Look there on the shelf: concentrated sulphuric acid. If some of it were transferred to your cup, you could try to throw it over me. Think of that."

Ken studied the flimsy cup and rather thought the stuff would burn instantly through to irrigate his groin. He pointed out with irrefutable logic that offing Ken Varney was bound to cause more embarrassment than explaining a mere, um, late April Fool letter. Croll retorted even less refutably that the one was a temporary inconvenience while the other would be Wasting MOD Police Time and therefore meant a security downcheck for unreliability, leading by steady logical steps to the dole queue. Unfortunately this made sense.

It was time, Ken decided, to panic. If only this were a sci-fi story he would, around now, discover an unheralded new talent for causing entire crates of whisky to materialize in the air three feet above his tormentor's head. Small delirious details loomed at him, like the particularly important-looking blue-bottle buzzing up the window. He noticed for the first time that Croll was wearing a copper bracelet bulging with magnets, the sort that small ads claimed would help against rheumatism, warts and telepathic intrusion. At any other moment this would have brought him a cheering rush of superiority.

Then he looked at the bright new scab on his finger where the wire had snagged it, and thought: ducts. There were plenty running under the wall benches or slung from the ceiling, but those weren't the ones. No, but if, if you just concentrated in the right way, made that one small change in emphasis...

With a shudder he clenched his teeth askew, and closed one eye, and after a long moment drank. It was every bit as horrible as he'd expected.

"Tomato juice?" said Croll, looking up and peering, white with excitement. "Excellent, my dear Ken, excellent! By this move to abstinence you have significantly extended your lifespan, by numerous minutes." He scribbled a note.

Ken's stomach was already making urgent distress signals to him, but he ignored them. Spilling one damned spot on the floor might give the game away. He drank, and watched one-eyed as the cup refilled, and drank again, and again. And again. How much more could he take?

"Excellent. I think we might have a few minutes ... to examine some other aspect ... before ... time and the hour ... terminate this experiment...." Croll was even whiter now, positively cream-faced in fact, but his brain still seemed to be working. "Wait. Why have ... none of the ... tomato juice ... boxes ... collapsed? Liquid should ... be gone...."

He turned, swayed, and to Ken's enormous disgust slumped over the console and its red button. Evidently the voltage had been turned up yet again, to the extent of simulating a gigantic fire-breathing dragon with teeth like Cleopatra's Needle that bit you in the bum. Ken lost control of his consciousness and stomach more or less simultaneously.

... Someone, somewhere, had for quite a long and drawn-out time been trying to wake him with their knocking.

"Are you all right?" A uniformed MOD policeman was shaking his shoulder. It had not previously occurred to Ken that this could be a beautiful sight. Another uniform was bending over something blobby on the floor beyond the control panel. "I just came round to warn that it's site locking-up time, and... *Are* you all right?"

A pretty sodding silly question, Ken thought, considering the lumpy crimson outbreak that spread down his clothes and across the floor, making the green tiles one red. Who would have thought the old man ...? Enough quotations already.

"It's not mine," Ken articulated with great and spurious clarity. "It's his." Then he blacked out again.

"Do sit down," said Fortmayne next day. It was the same committee room.

"No thanks," Ken replied firmly. "I have injuries of a delicate nature." He had spent the night in a hospital bed on his stomach, and his jacket was blotchy and smelly beyond repair (all the perfumes of Araby were clearly not going to do a lot of good), but he looked forward to explaining everything to the remnants of the briefing group. His finest hour. "The first point that struck me in my investigation was a tiny one, but..."

"No need to cover most of what happened," Fortmayne said hastily. "Dr Croll was a good enough scientist to record yesterday's lab session. We played the tape."

"Lucky thing for you," Rossiter put in. "Otherwise you'd be nicked for assault by unknown means on the old loony. He's in intensive care, you know. But they couldn't find a mark on him."

"Never mind that. How precisely did you conclude there's no entropy ray? Was it a valid logical process? I want a sound explanation," said Fortmayne, poised for disbelief.

"Oh, good old Occam's razor, I suppose. I wandered round the site yesterday and sort of got the impression that, well, whenever I saw something driving out it purred along, and everything coming in was all clanking and wheezy. Greasy ... that is, a DPR associate I'm not at liberty to name ... once told me that for the car pool fiddle you need a rich stupid firm that doesn't audit its inventory too carefully. You take the company cars round to a bent garage, and swap the engines and tyres and things for clapped-out ones, and pocket a nice fee every time. Then the company pays to overhaul them or replaces them, a good bit sooner than it would have, and after a while you can do it again. Works best with a big motor pool, like in a place with nearly twelve thousand on the strength. Very profitable business, entropy."

There was an embarrassed little silence as everyone made a point of not looking at the chair where, today, Brownjohn was not sitting. Apparently he'd been psychic enough to detect something in the wind.

Theoretical Physics said: "How extremely uninteresting, though very much as one might have predicted. I must confess that I myself am more curious about what happened pertaining to Dr Croll."

"Ye-es," said Rossiter. "Security angles there too, mate. Not meaning any offence, we indented for a low-grade paranorm thick, not some kind of super voodoo killer."

"The DPR has its secrets," Ken said, preening a little and laying a finger alongside his nose. "I can just inform you that—very nearly too damn late—

I remembered Dr Croll had been sinking pints in the Mushroom Cloud at lunchtime, and therefore he'd still have alcoholic stuff trickling through his ducts. His veins. That left him at a disadvantage. There was a leak in his security."

Something seemed to be dawning on Fortmayne, who now looked distinctly unwell. "And you ...?"

"Some people," said Ken mysteriously, "will swallow anything."

He didn't feel it necessary to explain that all those shocks and horrors and suggestibility drugs had, overnight, jolted loose his talent in just the sort of small change Croll had wished. Well, almost.

After that last bloody awful drink—a sort of ultimate hangover cure—his subconscious seemed to have sworn off and shifted its attention to more practical desires than beer refills. Maybe down there in the basement of his mind there was an unexpected stratum of good taste, and this was taking no risks that he might now decide to emigrate and ponce around New York night-life in tuxedo and scarlet-lined cape, under some stupid name like Bloodfeast.

Small change, indeed. As he left the duct-infested committee room, with teeth clenched askew and one eye unobtrusively shut, he could feel his pockets growing heavier with a steady leakage of 20p and 50p and one-pound coins. They were all permanent civil servants. They could afford it.

So it wasn't too bad when Marcia haughtily red-pencilled all his most cherished expenses: replacement jacket, soothing Num-Tum indigestion salts, perfumes of Araby, etc. But he winced anyway, having failed to brace himself for her final, crushing remark: "And what's more, you *still* can't spell entopry."

1991

If Looks Could Kill

The law relating to the paranormal is almost incomprehensible, except to those who have studied it from their cradles, and even for them it is a labyrinth of uncertainties, of false clues, blind alleys, and unexplored passages.
A. P. Herbert, *More Misleading Cases*, 1930

"This is rather a curious kind of tower," observed Father Brown; "when it takes to killing people, it always kills people who are somewhere else."
G. K. Chesterton, *The Wisdom of Father Brown*, 1914

"Sir, I have no Talent. I have genius or I have nothing."

Caligula Foxe inhaled a firkin or two of air and glared across his desk at our visitor.

"I'm afraid, Mr Foxe, that you'll find that the question is for Committee B2 to decide."

"It is a confounded impertinence."

Certainly it was quite a job keeping my hands where they belonged, on the smaller desk and scribbling ostentatiously in the notebook. I kept wanting to hug myself.

When this Seyton Cream of the Department of Paranormal Resources had asked for an appointment, I'd booked him in on general principles since it was guaranteed to annoy Foxe. Half of my pay is for being a gadfly, after all: he signs the cheques and he said it himself. Also there was at present a certain coolness between Foxe and yours truly. Thank goodness my holiday break was a mere three days off.

Cream swivelled in the red leather chair we kept reserved for clients, and brought his bony face to bear on me. "I would greatly prefer this discussion to be private."

The corner of Foxe's mouth twitched invisibly. "Mr Goodman is privy to all my affairs." Anything that got on a pinstriped civil servant's nerves was

---

The second volume in the Temps *series (see note on "Leaks") was* Eurotemps, *taking a slightly more pan-European view of things. Structuralist critical analysis does not reveal why this impelled me to steal the world's biggest detective and establish him, thinly disguised, in London....*

okay with him. But then the world's biggest detective remembered his little dispute with me, shifted his one-seventh of a tonne irritably, and added: "Nevertheless, Charlie, on this occasion we shall dispense with the notes. Your transcriptions have been less than satisfactory of late."

I felt a hot flush just behind my ears. The fat old windbag. He knows damn well that I can outperform a cassette recorder for flawless playback, notes or no notes.

Cream said, "Very well. I would now like to come to the point."

"A truly astonishing declaration from a professed Eurocrat," murmured Foxe. "Sir, I believe I can approximate to your point without further aid. Your wretched Brussels committee has wallowed through eighteen months and more than a million words of legal verbiage, addressing the definition of paranormal Talent. You now intimate that deductive and inferential genius, such as I choose to hire out for pay, might soon be so classified. You imply that in the vilest governmental tradition of compulsory purchase, I myself could be placed on the DPR register..."

He shuddered involuntarily. He *never* left the old house in Westbourne Terrace if he could possibly help it. Talents have to report in at the DPR's lightest whim: I pictured Foxe edging his bulk sideways through the shabby door of their Praed Street office, and sternly suppressed a twinge of pity.

"I did not say..."

"Pfui. You unmistakably implied."

Cream fiddled with the regulation bowler hat on his lap. "Perhaps I have approached this matter in the wrong way."

"Indeed yes. The carrot is customarily dangled in plain view before any tactless allusion is made to the stick."

"I stand corrected. I've suffered through Committee B2 sessions for so long that I begin to forget how to deal with human beings. Sometimes it seems the thing will never end. You know how it is with the EC."

Foxe inclined his head politely.

With a visible effort, Cream started talking to the point about his outfit's problem, which had nothing to do with committees. It seemed there was this guy Xaos who might or might not be running a foolproof murder bureau. After a minute I let my attention slide a bit, thinking of a certain upcoming trip to Provence with Lila, a very good lady friend. Maybe when I got back Foxe would have seen sense about that antiquated typewriter that had caused all the coolness.

Clearly there was no chance at all of him accepting the DPR commission that was taking shape. A foregone conclusion. Foxe hates being a second choice, and part of the spiel was that the Yard's Odd Squad had already dead-ended on this one. He hates following orders, and Cream was issuing him a complete plan of action. He hates government work, and need I say more? Above all, he *really* loathes being coerced. No chance.

So it was a sudden cold shock when I heard him say distinctly, "Yes, I believe I shall be able to accept the case, at a fee to be determined by mutual agreement. Mr Goodman himself will be pleased to carry out the entrapment precisely as you suggest. I assure you that he is reliable, discreet and loyal ... indeed he will be giving up a long-planned holiday to work uncomplainingly on this very enquiry."

Cream was not visibly impressed. Me even less. As I said, a definite coolness.

This rift had started with the typewriter I use for all Foxe's reports and correspondence ... not to mention his damn plant records. Once upon a time an IBM Selectric 82c had been super-duper luxury; in 1992 it was a rattletrap and a pain.

"A great detective needs the best," I'd explained in courteous and reasonable tones, covering his desk with glossy brochures of word processors, laser printers. But Foxe decided to get on a hobby horse.

"Charlie," he'd declared, opening his fifth bottle of beer that morning, "there is a high dignity in words. You well know that I employ them with ceaseless care and respect. I consciously choose not to have my sentences agitated in some electronic cocktail shaker or capriciously rearranged at—as you remark—the merest touch of a key. Call it obstinacy, call it Luddism...."

I didn't call it anything, not out loud, but I'd privately opened up the Selectric and done things to the motor bearings. Now it made a noise like a two-stroke engine with asthma. I was planning to wear Foxe down.

After I'd showed Cream to the front door, I thought bitterly about the Provence trip and wondered if I'd worn him down too far. We discussed the case, very politely. I'll just pick out the highlights of the dossier.

Item: the corpse was a minor Parliamentary cog called Whittle, secretary to some Junior Minister's assistant.

Item: there was a villain, the man called Xaos who advertised a personal service for "removing obstacles" to a happy life, nudge nudge, know what I mean?

Item: there was a tearful confession, from Whittle's wife Diane, who had wanted a divorce, wanted it a whole lot. He hadn't. She closed out their joint account and went to pay a call on Xaos.

Item: there was no evidence. The Met had played pass-the-parcel with the affair. Forensic said flatly that there was nothing to show Whittle hadn't simply popped off from natural causes, immediate cause heart failure. Even the Odd Squad admitted that although the death was quote consistent with attack through psychic attrition unquote—the Evil Eye to you and me—the guy Xaos showed no sign of that Talent and anyway had apparently never got close enough to the victim. Maybe there was an accomplice, even if no one could trace one? But hey, this could well be something new and paranormal and therefore the DPR's pigeon. Pass the parcel. Exit Scotland Yard, chortling and washing their hands.

Item: I checked our file of current papers and found the *Eye* ad was still running. **OBSTACLES REMOVED.** *Clear the path to happiness. No satisfaction, no fee. Xaos, 071 022 3033.* Enough to set anyone thinking and wondering. Cream's dossier included the guy's address, a flat in Pimlico, but even this was no big secret. When I tapped in the number and made an appointment for 3pm, the chirpy voice at the other end told me just how to get there.

Foxe had further instructions. Our freelance colleague Paul Sanza, the best private operative outside Westbourne Terrace, was going to play the victim in this charade—the obstacle to be removed. "The bleating of the kid excites the tiger," Foxe murmured. And my part was to follow in the tracks of the embittered wife and consult Xaos.

"No doubt a circumstantial story will occur to you," said Foxe blandly. "For example, some attractive woman with whom you are besotted has chosen with the fickleness of all her sex to transfer her favours to Paul. Might this not constitute sufficient motivation?"

Paul is a skinny runt with an oversized nose and ears like satellite dishes. I have my own views of my personal attractions and was not best pleased.

"No," I said with feeling. "I thought I'd say he was a boss who'd stumbled into the kind of government work he never takes on, and totally screwed up my holiday with some attractive woman with whom I am besotted. And from whom I expect a sock in the eye tomorrow when I break it to her."

"Charlie. If I am to counter Mr Cream's grotesque implied threat of the temps register, I require leverage. It is necessary that we involve ourselves this once in their affairs."

I didn't believe a word of it and was composing a short, pointed speech, but then our chef Franz came in and announced lunch. His very own *beurre de cacahouettes avec confiture* is not a dish to keep waiting. Foxe demonstrated leverage and was out of the chair faster than you might think.

He allows no discussion of business at his table, and a week ago he'd decreed that all talk of typewriters and word processors counted as business. I wouldn't work for anyone else, but by God he could be trying. Today, between huge mouthfuls, it was language-lesson time. "Charlie, you will undoubtedly have recognized Xaos as a Greek name or pseudonym. The X is of course the letter *chi* and so the word corresponds to our term 'chaos'. A contemporary Greek translator would anglicize the name as Haos with an H, since..."

Talk about respect for the dignity of words. He's never happier than when he's slamming them against the ropes.

The weather was fine. I decided to walk through Hyde Park and stretch my legs on the way to the appointment. It also gave me more time to practise the story I planned to hand out to Xaos.

His place turned out to be nothing impressive, a dump above a seedy grocer's. "Mr Xaos?" I said as he peered over the door-chain. "I'm Bill Durkin." That was a safety measure. Charlie Goodman, brilliant assistant to Caligula Foxe, was occasionally mentioned in newspapers.

"Just Xaos, Mr Durkin. Can I offer you some coffee?"

I said no thanks, sat down and looked him over. You couldn't call him striking or sinister: chubby, light-haired, thirtyish, about five-six. But something in his very pale eyes made me wonder whether he needed any accomplice for whatever games he got up to.

He said cheerfully, "The usual thing is for you to tell me what you think is getting in the way of the life you want to lead. Then I tell you whether it's something my personal Dyno-Rod service can clear. I turn down a lot of people I can't help."

That had been in the dossier too. The Yard had located and interviewed some of his rejects. A man who wanted Lord Heseltine offed for political reasons. Another with a grudge against the Warden of All Souls for trying to change his sex via laser beams from UFOs. A woman whose husband had cut and run, she didn't know where but she wanted to know for sure he wouldn't come back. Foxe had pushed his lips in and out and eventually said, "Suggestive."

My avowed problem was of course Paul Sanza. It's best to cram as much truth as you can into a story like this, so I told Xaos several warranted facts, at length: that Paul was a private snoop but had otherwise been a pretty good pal, that I played poker with him and the gang three times a week, that he won too often for my liking, and that he knew all about my lady friend Lila.

"But now the bastard fancies her himself," I lied. "He's good at ferreting things out, and he's dug up stuff about me. Never mind what. Just let me say she wouldn't like it one bit. So I'm to lay off Lila or he'll leak things to her, maybe even to the police. I should never have trusted a guy in his slimy line of work."

For the duration I believed in it enough to produce a light sweat on my forehead. Give the man an Oscar.

"Yes," said Xaos. "I can see that you must really hate this Sanza now. Him and no one else?"

I thought of asking whether he offered a wholesale discount, but just nodded.

"Now you might be thinking, how does the Xaos service work and why did I pick this name? And I'll gladly tell you. There is absolutely nothing up my sleeve. I don't even ask a fee in advance. You pay only when fully satisfied. Of course, by then you'll also be satisfied about the measures I could take if you changed your mind ... but let's not go into that. Now: have you ever heard of chaos theory?"

"I read the colour supplements sometimes," I said cautiously.

"Then I expect you'll know the example they always give. The tiny beating of a butterfly's wing starts a chain of ripples which in the end affect the course of a hurricane on the far side of the world. A sensitive dependence on initial conditions. This is where I work, at a level that doesn't even register on instruments. A paranormal gift, you ask? No, I have no Talent in the usual sense...."

You and Foxe both, I thought. Me, I went and took the DPR tests like a good boy and was relieved when they classed me dead normal.

"But I do have an extraordinary sensitivity to the minute fluctuations of chaos. I see its patterns running through the world. Getting up in the morning, I might clearly sense that delaying one further instant in, say, pulling on a sock would set up a significant eddy in history. One that in the end could sway the political balance of Indo-China."

"What doesn't?" I said sourly. Was he just a common or garden loony after all? Were his successes just a few natural deaths that sort of happened by coincidence in a much longer roster of failures?

"I offered a deliberately far-out example, Mr Durkin. More to the point, if I choose to stay aware of some person's identity—someone such as your 'friend' Paul Sanza—then I can sense things about the flow of chaos as it relates to that person. By tiny choices I send out butterfly ripples. I turn the luck of the world against them. Perhaps it will be disease, perhaps accident. In all my waking hours when I'm on the job, I steer my actions with that in mind, and compel disaster. See, I twiddle this pencil *so*. Air currents move and propagate. Hours or days later it could mean the last straw for a particular party in Solihull or Dublin."

"Well, don't twiddle that thing at me." I usually manage a better class of repartee, but in his weird way Xaos was sort of impressive. His eyes got to you.

I offered him a Polaroid snap of Paul. He glanced at it and nodded. "Thanks. Since you've interacted with him so much in the past, my sensitivity has already picked up the feel of his pattern. It's important, by the way, that you don't deviate from your own routine. Keep going to those poker games with Sanza, and so on."

His casual attitude gave me a feeling of being somehow wrong-footed. Xaos didn't even seem specially interested in Paul's address. Foxe had been speculating after lunch about a repeat of the bluff someone had worked back in 1961, with witches and pentagrams and death spells as window-dressing to distract everyone from the strictly mundane planting of a lethal dose in the victim's larder. You needed an address for games like that. If there was any chance that he was on the level... Those eyes!

"Well, Mr Durkin," said Xaos, "I'd be pleased to make a small bet with you. If this obstruction to your happiness has not disappeared in, let's say, two weeks, I'll gladly pay you five thousand pounds. And, of course, vice versa."

Of course it was okay and perfectly in character to agree with a tremor in my voice, but I wished it had been one hundred percent an act. We shook on it.

"But don't you get a lot of unwelcome attention?" I asked, hoping to start a crack somewhere. "The ad could mean anything, of course, but the rumour I heard was pretty clear about what you offer."

A thin, knowing smile. "Believe me, I'm safely beyond the reach of the law. I cannot be prosecuted. Goodbye."

Back at street level I signalled unobtrusively to Terry Carver, our second-best freelance after Paul himself. His job was to keep watch and tail Xaos if he took it into his head to go visiting. Then I located a Mercury callbox and keyed in the Sanza home number. He sounded cheerful enough.

"The curse has come upon you," I warned. "Have you got Sally Cole babysitting you there?"

"All according to plan, Charlie. She sends her best."

Sally was a reliable witch-smeller on loan from the Bonner agency, hired to blow the whistle if there really was any weirdo attack. Anyway, the textbooks insisted that while evil-eye merchants didn't need actual eye contact, they could operate only at fairly close range. Our other regular operatives were watching Paul's flat in Haringey, around the clock. Nothing could get to him without being spotted. Surely.

As usual between four o'clock and six, Foxe was pottering in the plant rooms at the top of the house when I got back. I climbed three floors to report as instructed, but he was in a cantankerous mood, blowing hot and cold: "I am not altogether happy with this involvement. I might yet reject the commission. Bah. Please type a full transcript of your conversation with the man Xaos, making three carbons. They may be required."

I pronounced a word under my breath and left him alone with his babies. Why any grown man should want to cultivate paranormal saprophytes... They were no big thrill to look at, and you could spare only so much admiration for the way they rooted in weird surfaces. One grew on armourglass, another on Teflon, a third sucked its nourishment somehow from hard vacuum. Foxe's star item was a sport from Nevada that made out quite happily on a polished slab of depleted uranium, which would personally worry me if I lived in Nevada.

Six and a half pages into the transcript, Foxe moved majestically across the office, settled in the one chair in the world he really loves, and rang for beer. After a pause, he looked hard at me. His index finger moved in tiny circles on the desktop, which is usually a sign that he's bottling something up.

"Charlie. Am I correct in believing that the infernal clatter of that machine is worse than customary?"

"Pardon, sir?"

His eyes narrowed. He picked up one of the completed sheets I'd laid on his desk, and felt it between finger and thumb. "To the best of my knowledge, the system of embossing print on paper was made obsolete by the six-dot alphabet published by Louis Braille in 1829 and elaborated in 1837."

"Gosh, it must be the dedicated energy I put into it, sir, struggling with weakening fingers against antique machinery."

"Pfui. It is an electric typewriter. You have turned up the impact setting with intent to annoy."

He had me there. You can't fool a detective genius. But I was still mad about the holiday, and escalated things by typing on for another paragraph as though I hadn't heard.

"Mr Goodman!" This time it was a full-throated bellow. My eardrums twanged. "Let it be known that I have not the slightest intention of investing in the puerile gadgetry to which you are so attracted." He inhaled deeply, resenting the effort of bellowing, and went on in whiny, sarcastic tones: "But what is this? It was four carbon copies that I required, and not three. You must have misheard me, Mr Goodman. You will need to retype the six, no, the seven pages already completed. I do hope it does not make you late for your *important* appointment to play poker tonight."

I pronounced another inaudible word, with feeling.

Dinner was not a happy meal. It was *doigts de poisson "oeil d'oiseau"*, another of Franz Brunner's great specialities, but Foxe was distinctly off his food. In spite of its impressive size, any little thing could turn his stomach. I made bright conversation about chaos theory and butterflies. It didn't seem to help.

Afterwards, Foxe conscientiously endured the racket of the typewriter as he dipped into a book, *Chaos* by James Gleick. Conceivably he was working. From his bilious expression and the way he dog-eared the pages, I deduced that he wasn't enjoying the style. In all the time before I finished he only said one word. Looking to and fro between a page of my transcript and something in the book, he stated: "Untenable."

Nor was the poker game at Paul's a wild success. I was late after all that retyping and took some chaff about devotion to duty. So did Terry, ringing in hourly to report that he was half frozen and Xaos still hadn't budged from home. The rest of the hired help were mightily pleased to be getting paid for attending their regular card session, but they didn't have a genius to live with. Paul came out ahead by forty pounds, most of it mine. I passed certain remarks about how it was hard to play and bodyguard at the same time, and how I preferred to go easy on a doomed man, but my heart wasn't in it.

Next morning, Foxe evidently felt the same. He declared a relapse.

Relapses take him in various ways. Sometimes he shuts himself in the plant rooms for a week, fiddling with unlikely cross-pollinations. Other times he shoves Franz out of the kitchen and camps there obsessively, cooking *lapin pays de Galles* in fifty different styles. This one, though, was just plain malin-gering in bed.

What it always means is that his brain is going on strike. Here we were in this damn stupid case, for no better reason than Foxe wanting to needle me, and with nothing to do but sit on our bottoms waiting to see if Paul toppled over and died. No dangerous errands for intrepid Goodman. No spicy little facts for the genius to work on. The closest he'd got to actual thought was claiming that my dialogue with Xaos contained "interesting and suggestive points". I couldn't see them myself.

Foxe was laying it on with a trowel today. At nine he skipped his regular two hours with the plants, and stayed in bed wallowing in self-pity. At ten he called Dr Wolmer, and I groaned at the thought of the cheque I'd have to draw because Foxe never chose to walk three doors along the road to the surgery. At eleven Wolmer came down from the bedroom, looking non-committal.

"Tell me straight, Doc," I asked earnestly as I showed him out. "Are they baffling symptoms of a kind unknown to science?"

"You could say that," he said. Of course he was too polite to suggest the great man might be, ahem, imagining it all.

Towards noon my desk phone buzzed. "Come to my room at once," said Foxe. Maybe now he wanted a lawyer and a priest.

He is an awesome sight in bed, a vast expanse of yellow silk pyjamas like the endless prairies of wherever it is they have endless prairies. Doc told me once that a human being eats his own weight of food every fifty days, and seeing Foxe like that makes you wonder how he can ever find the time. I studied him critically. He looked more unhappy than ill.

"Charlie, I am entertaining a conjecture. The possibility is remote, yet... Since yesterday evening I have felt ... less and less well. I invariably distrust coincidence. Could the man Xaos have penetrated your deception in some fashion ... turned his weapon, whatever it might be, against not Paul but my-self?"

"Anything's possible," I said, humouring him. "With funny eyes like that, he might do all sorts of odd things."

"You will proceed ... no. I may require you here. You will telephone Terry and instruct him to break cover. He is to enter the flat and render Xaos uncon-scious. Paul or one of the others will go to him with a syringe and a supply of pentothal, to keep him so. If Xaos is to be ... taken at his own face value, he cannot maintain his influence while kept insensible. The conjecture will be tested."

I have omitted the distracting grunts and gasps. Foxe was really hamming it up. It was pathetic. My own professional pride wouldn't let me believe for a moment that Xaos had seen through the story—he'd have had to be a telepath *and* a damn good actor. All the same, I disliked him on principle and ap-proved of action, any action.

"I'm betting that you're wrong, sir, but here goes," I said, and sprinted downstairs, hoping Terry had remembered to pack his cellphone.

He had.

I cooled my heels for twenty-five minutes, flipping through much-thumbed brochures of Provence and once again growing increasingly irritated with Foxe. If I couldn't take my rightful holiday, why the hell couldn't it be me who burst in and socked Xaos on the jaw?

Then Terry called. He'd worked it better than that. "I just went up, told him a friend had recommended me to consult him, said yes to coffee and slipped him a Mickey Finn when his back was turned. Dead to the world. He was easy meat, Charlie."

"Right," I said. "Mr Foxe will tell me to say 'satisfactory' and so I do. Be seeing you."

I buzzed the sickroom and passed on Terry's message. "And do you feel a sudden surge of relief and well-being, sir?"

"No," said the theatrically feeble voice.

Which was exactly what I'd expected. Imaginary illnesses are real toughies to treat, I thought to myself.

By now, I dare say you've guessed the secret of how Xaos really worked his tricks. You're probably thinking I'm dumb not to have deduced it for myself. Let me just say that I'm not the genius in this household, only the legman ... and puzzles are a million times harder to solve when you're close to them, living through them.

I lunched off a glass of milk. That didn't bother Franz, but he came down almost in tears when Foxe refused the tray carrying a light, eleven-course invalid snack. I had begun to get the creepy feeling that something was going on right under my nose, that I was missing the obvious.

Around then, Ron Cohen of the *Eye* rang to remark that according to the whispers of little birds in his ear, our favourite fatso was now pulling chestnuts out of the fire for the Department of the Preternaturally Ridiculous, and what about an inside story? I bandied words with him, not referring to small ads.

Seconds after I'd hung up, Paul reported in. Xaos continued to sleep like a babe, he reckoned they could keep him that way for another 24 hours solid, and to pass the time our gang had made a fine-tooth search of the dump. No voodoo props, no death rays, no written records of the obstacle-removing business. No news: of course the Yard had done the same and drawn a blank, though their dossier kept sort of quiet about it.

Mid-afternoon, and I heard the whir of Foxe's private lift. His idea of exercise is to go up and down twice. I wondered if he'd pulled out of his goddam relapse and started making plans for the new problem of our court appearance when citizen Xaos gave evidence on charges of assault, conspiracy, actual bodily harm with a hypodermic....

Then I saw something I'd never seen before. Foxe was standing in the office doorway in his vast yellow pyjamas, swaying ponderously, looking shrunken, greenish and three-quarters dead. Great drops of sweat stood out all over his big face. It was a hell of an impressive performance.

"Charlie. An alternative conjecture. Please ... obey me without question. I instruct you to order the word processing equipment of your choice, for immediate delivery. Use the agency credit card. I ... also wish to apologize for the cancellation of your holiday ... shall make amends. I..." He closed his eyes and leaned hard against the door frame.

My God, I thought, he's actually delirious. He really was ill now, in such a state that I wouldn't have been surprised if he'd started splitting infinitives or using "contact" as a verb. It truly was sort of touching to think our little rift had been so much on his mind that he'd staggered down like this for a deathbed repentance scene.

"You should be in bed, sir," I said, and sincerely meant it.

"Mr Goodman. Kindly carry out my instructions at once." There was enough of the old snap in his voice that my hand dived straight for the telephone.

"Black Mountain Systems? I have an urgent order." I knew by heart what I wanted, of course. I mean, what the office wanted.

When I turned, Foxe was sitting behind the big desk in his pyjamas, mopping his face with the wrong handkerchief (it was a souvenir of the Ballard case and still had the original bloodstains) and breathing heavily. His colour was a little better now.

"Kindly fetch Mr Cream at once. I will instruct Paul to bring the man Xaos here. My alternative hypothesis has been fully confirmed. Thank heavens."

I have to confess I still hadn't the faintest idea what he meant.

By the time I'd hauled a strongly protesting Cream from his Ministry (lucky he wasn't off committeeing in Brussels again), Paul had arrived and decanted Xaos into one of the yellow leather chairs. He looked thoroughly groggy, and so would you. Foxe had dressed, shaved and—I'd bet—eaten his head off. I steered our client to the red chair.

Foxe looked at him with satisfaction. "Mr Cream, I would like to introduce you to Mr Xaos."

"Just Xaos. No Mr. And you won't believe the lawsuit I'm going to hit you with when I get clear of your goons."

"Be silent, sir. I shall be brief. As we agreed, Mr Cream, my operatives carried out a decoy manoeuvre. Mr Goodman approached the gentleman sitting there, who in effect undertook to ensure for a consideration that a certain man died within a fortnight. Several points about the reported conversation struck me, such as the nonsensical smokescreen of part-digested chaos theory, the seeming lack of interest in personal details of the proposed victim, and the emphatic remark that Mr Xaos himself was safe from prosecution. Indeed he is."

"If they can't prosecute, then you haven't earned your fee," said Cream sharply.

"We shall see. May I continue? Frankly, I know little of the pesky ways of paranormal Talent, but nevertheless I formed an interesting conjecture to account for this assurance of immunity. The Yard searched in vain for a murderous accomplice. What occurred to me was the notion of an unknowing accomplice."

Cream said: "That sounds like a contradiction in terms." Xaos chuckled uneasily.

"Mr Xaos, I speculated, is the possessor of an interesting Talent. He cannot himself wield, but can temporarily confer, a power of malignity akin to what is commonly known as the Evil Eye. To test this conjecture after visiting him," Foxe said through his teeth, "Mr Goodman undertook to act out spurious feelings of resentment and dislike towards myself, pretending for the purpose to be discommoded by an obsolete typewriter. A small and seemingly a childish pretext, but Mr Goodman's powers of theatrical self-deception are remarkable. The result..."

A cold shock like a bucket of ice-water had hit me in the stomach. If I'd been any madder with Foxe.... My eyes were popping with sheer rage at what Xaos had so goddam nearly made me do. The bastard, the absolute bastard. For a moment I couldn't speak, only glare.

"Charlie!"

Xaos had slumped sideways in the yellow chair. Paul Sanza was at his side straight away. "Heart, I think. My God, he's gone. No, he seems to be picking up again... That's odd. Pulse went and came back again. Yes, he should pull through now. I think."

"Which would tend to confirm my hypothesis," Foxe said silkily. "Have Franz bring brandy. Charlie, my apologies. I inadvertently goaded you into anger, forgetting the extent of your loyalty and devotion."

He takes a lot for granted, does Caligula Foxe. I fought for calm and worked away at swallowing the lump I'd never admit was in my throat.

Foxe's shoulders lifted a tenth of a millimetre, which for him was an expansive shrug. "You see, Mr Cream? Of course in the Whittle case it was the wife Diane after all. Following Mr Xaos's treatment, a period of serious hating at close range would have put paid to anyone. (One sees, does one not, why he refused customers who wished the deaths of people in remote or unknown locations?) You can't prosecute him: he didn't do it. You can't prosecute her: she acted unknowingly and the evil gift will have faded away, leaving no evidence. I deduce that it must fade because, otherwise, even the Yard would have detected her unwitting Talent."

No wonder Xaos had insisted I should carry on playing poker with Paul. Good grief. That, if only I'd had a real grudge, would have handed him the black spot for sure.

"H'mm," said Cream, scratching his jaw and pointedly ignoring the weak, catarrhal noises from the body in the yellow chair.

"I am pleased to release the man Xaos into your custody. In all justice the DPR should lock him away as a social disease, but no doubt you will prefer to place him on a meagre stipend and make some dubious use of his ability. Meanwhile, I shall ask no fee but require an assurance that your pestilent Committee B2 will in future regard deductive and intuitive genius as falling outside the scope of the paranormal."

"Nonsense. How the devil can I commit the Department to a stance like that?"

"Consider the alternative," said Foxe dreamily, wiggling a finger at him. "Mr Goodman occasionally publishes records of my cruder and more sensational cases. If the Xaos affair were made public, then so likewise would be the hitherto unremarked fact that temporary Talents can be induced. I rather imagine this would mean starting again, *de novo*, on Committee B2's legalistic definition of the paranormal. Eighteen months' work, do I recall your saying, and a million words of draft regulations?"

Cream had gone twice as pale as his name. "Jesus," he said. "I mean, how extremely inconvenient that would be. I... Very well. On behalf of the Department, I accept your terms."

"Satisfactory. Would you care for beer?" Foxe rang the bell.

"No, thank you." The civil servant issued a constipated little smile. "I suppose the DPR is getting off lightly. I've heard a great deal about your exorbitant fees and, frankly, am somewhat surprised that you don't want money as well."

"But I do," murmured Foxe, indicating the chair where, under Paul's and my tender care, Xaos was groaning and spluttering into his brandy. "A certain bet was made with an authorized representative of this agency. Assuming that Mr Sanza can contrive not to die before the end of the stipulated fortnight, Mr Xaos will owe me the sum of five thousand pounds. I intend to collect."

The ex-obstacle remover snarled feebly at Foxe. If looks could kill... But of course *his* couldn't.

Later, I struggled hard to master the new word processor as Foxe pretended to read his evening paper and gave me the occasional cynical look. It was a damn sight more complicated than the ads had claimed. Don't let him say anything, I thought as for the umpteenth time the machine beeped rudely and flashed *ERROR*. In five or six days, according to Xaos, the curse would wear off and I'd be able to risk getting mad at people again. For now, just don't let him *say* anything.

He said: "Tonight, at my request, Franz is preparing *crapaud dans le trou Anglais* in a sauce of his own invention. An excellent conclusion to the case."

It was a recipe he knew very well I could get along without. "I'll try my best to enjoy it, sir," I said with false eagerness, "but of course it could discommode me in some small and seemingly childish way. I might have to struggle to control my temper, you know, as brutal feelings of hatred rise up in me at each fresh mouthful...."

Foxe's eyes narrowed dangerously. I felt a huge, death-cold wave of sickening weakness crash through me and realized that Xaos had left him with a parting gift. By gum, for the next whole week we'd *both* have to be incredibly calm and polite. Somehow.

We discussed it.

1992

Lies, Damned Lies and *Ansible*

Obituary, 1979-1987

Ansible passed away peacefully somewhere in the war-torn aftermath of the 1987 Worldcon. In its best years, whenever they were, it was generally agreed that this fanzine had done great things for semicolons. Indeed, the entire cyberpunk movement is clearly influenced by the seminal production values of issue 2/3 (a testament to the artistic effect of runny duplicator ink on shiny paper). Later, though, there came a decline. After major bypass surgery to the colophon, the sadly self-indulgent *Ansible 666* concerned itself entirely with flatulent discussions about the protocol of stapling fanzines ("My teeth gritted, and the stapler went *spung.*"). The final, posthumous issues were so rambling, ill-written and ineptly edited that they earned the scorn of all true SF aficionados by becoming best-sellers, and there were angry scenes when one of these insults to science fiction was block-voted on to the 1987 Hugo shortlist by the sinister and hateful cult of "Britfanologists", already proven by Los Angeles researchers to have been collectively responsible for the Holocaust and the postal system. Although the special Conspiracy '87 *Ansible* was a large and imposing edifice, well suited to a Worldcon despite the poor state of repair, it cannot be denied that its manager was drunk and behaved appallingly. Let us pass over the later controversy and the sadness of *Ansible*'s lonely, alcoholic end ... and look back on the period of its greatness, believed to have appeared at the end of a sentence in issue 28.

The *Ansible* Review of the Year: 1992

Across countries, continents, galaxies, wherever science fiction is known, the merest mention of the scurrilous sf newsletter *Ansible* can produce an excited chorus of "What the hell's that?" Even more legendary is "The *Ansible*

My little sf newsletter Ansible *had a first series of 50 issues running from 1979 to 1987. Next came an obituary ... but, seduced by the ease of desktop publishing, I revived the thing on a strict monthly basis in 1991. Soon* Interzone *began to carry a bowdlerized (well, shorter anyway) version, the monthly "Ansible Link" column. As a completely unrepresentative sampler of* Ansible, *here are two annual news round-ups prepared for British convention programme books (Helicon in 1993, whose chairman was Tim Illingworth, and Confabulation in 1995, which mysteriously had a moose logo—bear these facts in mind), plus the special future-viewpoint edition of "Ansible Link" written for the* Interzone *guest-edited by Charles Platt. Oh yes, and that tear-stained death notice.*

231

Review of the Year", a once-traditional convention stopgap in which the editor read out bits from old issues of this rotten fanzine and laughed immoderately at his own jokes until, slowly but surely, the entire audience would find itself uplifted and transported as if by magic to the bar.

In the following lightning skim through the thirteen *Ansibles* published in 1992, the dates are generally those on the relevant issues. Any other system of dating would fatally prejudice the integrity of my historical approach (i.e., might involve actual work). Where accurate reprinting of an *Ansible* slur seems likely to mean an instant and massive lawsuit, I have changed the relevant name to an obviously fictitious one, "Tim Illingworth".

January

Garry Kilworth reported bemusedly that Methuen had made him change 19th-century yards and gallons (in his historical children's novel *The Drowners*) to metres and litres because "kids wouldn't understand". • The Simon & Schuster sales force suggested Brian Stableford's vampire novel title *Young Blood* wasn't thrusting enough—so he offered an Author's Note giving them full credit for inspiring the more "perfervid" substitute *The Hunger and Ecstasy of Vampires*. ("No, no, we love the original title really," they quavered.) • David Wingrove of *Chung Kuo* fame blitzed what seemed to be the entire membership of the BSFA with bitter complaints about a bad review of volume three. • That sf/horror TV series *Chimera* earned a memorable sneer in a science magazine: "As a piece of sf it was not exactly Isaac Asimov or Brian Heinlein." • The James Tiptree Jr memorial award for "gender-expanding sf" was announced and there was much speculation on which sf fans' genders could usefully be expanded. • Dave Langford denied all responsibility for the recent burning-down of Scientology's East Grinstead headquarters; no comment was received from the notorious cult founded by sinister pulp sf author and con-man Tim Illingworth.

February

Tanith Lee's expanded gender was revealed in the small print of *Kill the Dead*: "The right of Tanith Lee to be identified as the author of this work has been asserted by him...." • *Ansible* celebrated the tenth anniversary of Kingsley Amis's 1982 pronouncement (one of many) that sf was dead. • US fan Jeanne Bowman, famous for her toasted-afterbirth recipe (this is really true), won the TransAtlantic Fan Fund vote and bought her ticket for the 1992 British Eastercon. • An untrustworthy fan claimed that Larry Niven's correspondence with L. Ron Hubbard was to be published under the title *N-Grams*. • The SF Writers of America finally admitted the existence of that fantasy stuff and changed its name to SFFWA (much to the disgust of Frederik Pohl). • The death of Mirror Group megastar, international fraudster and pension-fund rifler Tim Illingworth had repercussions in sf publishing—a spate of bounced royalty cheques from Macdonald/Futura. • The Polytechnic of East London decided to evict the SF Foundation unless (which wasn't likely after ten years on a starvation budget) it became "self-financing".

March

John Clute wrote a sad obituary of Angela Carter. • Greg Benford was displeased by the announcement of a movie called *Timescape*, not based on his book (and Simon & Schuster's trademark) of the same name. • The fatally Maxwelled UK publisher Macdonald was bought by Little, Brown, thus saving the new edition of the *SF Encyclopaedia* from a death worse than fate. • The tenth anniversary of Philip K. Dick's death was remembered. • *Ansible*'s editor boasted interminably of his guest-of-honour trip to Boskone 29 in Massachusetts: "Gene Wolfe sneaked in halfway through my 'Insult Famous Authors' talk and asked later why I hadn't slagged his books. 'You're such a flagrant case,' I lied, 'that I dealt with you on page one.'" • Current fad spotted in New York editorial offices: inflatable Edvard Munch "Scream" dolls posed staring out of the windows.

April

Iain Banks, speaking at the Adelaide Writers' Week down under, said that he'd intended to smuggle in a machete with which to cut off the Prime Ministerial ocker hand that had dared to rest upon HM the Queen. • Arthur C. Clarke complained that his fax machine was swamped by crazed fans' birthday messages on HAL 9000's supposed creation date in 1992. • Gwyneth Jones won the first Tiptree award for her *White Queen*: the trophy was a chocolate typewriter. • Tom Shippey was gloatingly editing *The Oxford Book of SF Stories*, offering £500 a go for reprints and mortifying the countless authors who didn't get asked. • Brian Stableford informed a rapt convention audience that all sf ought to be sarcastic, just like him. "The reader should never be left feeling comfortable. The hero should never get the girl." • The demise was announced of the ill-starred bid to hold the 1994 Eastercon on the Isle of Man under the name "Con Tim Illingworth". • *Interzone*'s sister magazine *Million: the Magazine About Popular Fiction* thrilled its contributors with the news that editor David Pringle couldn't afford to pay them in money any more. (But all the free copies you can carry!) • Isaac Asimov died, with immense coverage in the non-sf media and even nasty critics saying, "Well, er, I liked his science fact articles...."

May

Ansible reported on Illumination, the 1992 Eastercon in Blackpool, as follows.... • Each registration pack came with a free fortune cookie containing a plug for *Chung Kuo—the epic*. Vicious cookie-fights followed when a large box of spares was hurled into a party room: we looked in vain for BSFA reviewers muttering, "As I thought, this sick and obscene work inevitably engenders violence." • Jim Burns foxed authors at a signing session by asking that they not just sign but add some "personal stain". For his pains he now owns a book containing "The Fractal Bogey of Benoit Mandelbrot". • As the firework display's titanic concussions rocked the Blackpool sea-front and triggered countless car-alarms, the small sad voice of James White was heard saying, "They're trying to make me feel at home." • Illumination's committee had some cute ideas: "Programme streams called Flopsy, Mopsy and Cottontail are bad enough," one writer puked gently, "but have I *got* to speak in a room called Peter Fan?" ("Shut up," the committee explained.) • The 1994 Eastercon was voted on: "Sou'Wester", to be held—despite widespread scepticism about the venue—in Bristol. • After cracking a joke about Storm Constantine in his talk, the *Ansible* editor was told sharply by her fan club: "You obviously know nothing about sex and have never experienced an orgasm." He was duly sobered.

June

More and more macho publishers boasted of pruning their sf lists of "unviables"—that is, books they'd signed a binding contract to publish but had now changed their minds about. Authors who dwelt on sordid details like the terms of the contract tended to be told, "So sue us." • Michael Swanwick's *Stations of the Tide* won the Nebula novel award and Ian McDonald's *King of Morning, Queen of Day* the Philip K. Dick award. • The new UK human-rights group Death Watch, which urged tourist boycotting of US states with the death penalty, struck a feeble blow against the coming World SF Convention with its first slogan: "Don't visit Florida—the Sunshine State that kills." • Gahan Wilson got the Horror Writers of America award for Life Achievement (announced long in advance to ensure it didn't surprise him at the presentation) ... a statuette crafted in the horrific shape of Tim Illingworth.

July

Edgar Rice Burroughs Inc. sued *Vogue* magazine for using trademark images without leave, i.e., pictures of "Tarzan" with underdressed Janes as part of some crummy fashion feature. $1 million damages were asked. • Jerry Pournelle terrified watchers of the BBC *Pandora's Box* by ranting on about the wonders of SDI and how he and Larry Niven had caused all by themselves the collapse of the Soviet Union: "We licked the evil empire," he belched, bent over a computer game and zapping simulated commie missiles. Larry Niven was featured, sitting at the great man's feet, *but he never moved nor spoke*. Some conjectured he was in fact a cardboard cut-out. • A memorial service at St-Martin-in-the-Fields featured readings from those devotional texts *Mort* and *Reaper Man* by Terry Pratchett. • The Society of Authors poll of how authors regard their publishers placed Headline clear favourite in the British sf/fantasy arena. Down near the bottom were Sphere, Macdonald and Simon & Schuster.

August

Pat Cadigan, who according to the late Robert Heinlein "has a very dirty mind", won the Arthur C. Clarke award for her *Synners*. • William Gibson's poem *Agrippa (A Book of the Dead)*—the one on disk that wipes itself as you display it—was reviewed at length in the *Ansible* Dumb Ideas Supplement (which went one better by self-destructing before anyone could read it). 1993 update: the bombproof copy protection on *Agrippa* was cracked within months of its release. • The film of Terry Pratchett's *Mort* hit a stumbling block when the film company broke it to him that Middle American consumer research indicated they'd have to lose the Death angle. • After the police seizure of and destruction order against Savoy Books' controversial novel *Lord Horror* and comic book *Meng & Ecker & Tim Illingworth*, sf writers Michael Moorcock and Brian Stableford gave evidence for the defence. The novel was let off, the comic was found obscene and despicable, and the defence witnesses were remaindered.... • Sou'Wester, the 1994 Eastercon, quarrelled with its Bristol hotel and was reduced to claiming that the South-West was actually going to be in Liverpool that year. • Ian Watson bragged of trading a story collection to Lithuania in exchange for amber beads. Unfortunately "a stall holder in Northampton market informed me that the market has really dropped out of amber beads since the Iron Curtain came down."

September

The London sf meeting (first Thursday every month) having suffered unspeakable privations as the Wellington pub venue began turning itself into "an upmarket wine bar", there was an exodus in various directions—in particular the Hamilton Hall bar on Liverpool Street Station.[1] • Fritz Leiber died and was mourned. • Patrick Nielsen Hayden of Tor Books announced a new anthology *Alternate Skiffy*, tales of universes where the history of sf itself was different: "*what if* H. P. Lovecraft had inherited the editorship of *Astounding?*" • Meanwhile the Midnight Rose shared-world-anthology team (*Temps*, etc.) fell out with Penguin over the latter's suggestion that following the surprisingly good sales, payments to authors should be cut by about a third. • The Café Munchen pub near Forbidden Planet, scene of a million book signings and launch piss-ups, confused the hell out of everyone by changing its name to Tim Illingworth. I'm sorry, I'll type that again: to The Conservatory. • Story too good to check: a young graduate newly employed by Radio 4 thought of a way to brighten it up and entirely on his own initiative wrote to Douglas Adams asking if he'd ever thought of adapting *The Hitch-Hiker's Guide to the Galaxy* for radio....

---

[1] Later it returned to the Wellington, but that's another story.

October

MagiCon, the 50th World SF Convention, in Orlando, Florida, was reported—our first news coming via a traditional drunken phone call from Martin Hoare: "Crackle buzz fizz 3:30am here glug belch British double!" "What, *Interzone* got a Hugo?" "No, don't be *silly*, you did and Glasgow won the 1995 Worldcon bid!" The sight of British fans bidding for Glasgow in kilts had apparently brought the opposition to its knees. (Our dirty tricks department also deployed haggis to sinister effect.) • Forbidden Planet bookshops and Titan publishers/distributors split, the latter being bought by US comics distributor Diamond—to immediate rumours about the phasing out of obsolete freight (books). • The Hugo-winning novel was *Barrayar* by Lois McMaster Bujold; the Campbell Memorial Award for best novel went to Bradley Denton's *Buddy Holly Is Alive and Well on Ganymede.* • J. G. Ballard claimed that his favourite reading was the Los Angeles Yellow Pages. • The SF Foundation decided to move with its library to the University of Liverpool, won over by totally unprecedented offers of academic support, staff, and even money. • Algis Budrys severed his links with "Tim Illingworth's Writers of the Future" to edit Pulphouse's new magazine *Tomorrow Speculative Fiction* (which he later bought from the ailing publisher).

November

Stephen Baxter nearly managed to go down in history by running over Stephen Hawking ("a motorized wheelchair came plummeting across the road in front of me....") but did not say whether he regretted the missed boost to his fame and sales. • John Brunner sent a glum letter about how antibiotics had given him diarrhoea for "months on end. I literally feel drained." • Fritz Leiber's funeral was reportedly a macabre affair, with the open-coffin ceremony giving Jay Sheckley the chance (after boring people to death with interminable readings) to swoop Dracula-like and kiss the corpse. Before the event was over, the late Leiber had a cigarette and a champagne glass in his hand for "his last party".... • Maxim Jakubowski gloated over having won a second world convention bid for Britain in 1995: the crime-fiction Bouchercon, to be held in sinister, grisly Nottingham. • Jonathan Carroll's *Outside the Dog Museum* got the British Fantasy Award. • Gollancz, after being owned for a while by Houghton Mifflin, was bought by Cassell and finally moved from its aged Covent Garden office with the wooden filing cabinets and all the famous places where George Orwell was told *Animal Farm* was unpublishable.

December

The second *SF Encyclopaedia* was finally delivered, to immense sighs of relief and groans about the coming treat of galley proofs for Christmas. • A Guy N. Smith fan club was announced, selling memorabilia such as terrifying, self-propelled clockwork crabs and illingworths. • World-bestriding editor Malcolm Edwards was the subject of a HarperCollins leak saying he'd moved to a "new role" giving him lots less time to spend with his sf authors. "Extrapolating from his availability in recent months," said an excited hard-sf writer, "this implies the concept of *negative time!*" • Paul Morley the *Guardian* hack had been sighted at a convention and followed up with an odd article about the demise of sf, all seemingly the fault of elves and Terry Pratchett. Knowing what conventions are like, fans wondered whether he'd research a piece on Anglican theology by visiting a church bazaar.... • Robert McCammon won the World Fantasy Award for his *Boy's Life.* • David Wingrove explained in the *Daily Telegraph* that poor reviews of his *Chung Kuo* were ascribable to the wicked spectre of Political Correctness and should thus be disregarded. • Games Workshop and their new co-publishers Boxtree sued Transworld over a coincidence of titles: GW once had a series of books tying in with their (defunct?) *Dark Future* game, and later Transworld published a young adult series by Laurence James called *Dark Future.* This would normally be nothing much, but GW had *(a)* trademarked the game title; *(b)* neglected to register the books with *Books in Print,* which is why L. James found no record when he checked for duplication.... To universal surprise, the first court hearing went against Transworld with £60,000 costs and an injunction to get their books off the stands. This one will run and run! • Inspired by this precedent, Helicon chairman Tim Illingworth obtained a court order forbidding Dave Langford to misappropriate his name *any more* in the Helicon programme book, on pain of having his Hugos crottled (a well-known sf euphemism). And so 1992 was hastily brought to an end.

1993

THE *ANSIBLE* MOOSE OF THE YEAR: 1994

Once again, the frosted and myopic lens of the infamous sf newsletter *Ansible* is blearily focused on the year just past. Once again, it emerges with blinding lack of clarity that, as usual, the year's central, unifying theme from the sf viewpoint was its dismal failure to come up with a central, unifying theme. So, just as in previous episodes, it's a quick skim through thirteen issues of *Ansible* in desperate search of sufficiently cheap and tasteless jokes— or even expensive ones, such as **The Scottish Convention.**

For fear of libel suits (and insufficient fear of wearing out old jokes), the null-signifying word "moose" has occasionally been substituted in scatological or legally dodgy phrases. For example, in place of the original, trenchant *Ansible* report you might find a sanitized version which runs: "Martin Moose, co-chairman of **The Scottish Moose**, has organized the moose with moose efficiency; his more determinedly moose Board members seem able to communicate only by e-moose. Greg Pickersgill's salty comment was: 'Moose moose moose the moose *moose!*'"

Here we go....

January

Christopher Priest was miffed to discover that DC Comics writer Jim Owsley had decided to adopt, henceforth, the more "spiritual" name Christopher Priest—without apparently being aware that having this name greatly increases one's chances of a death threat from Harlan Ellison. • Ellison himself was reported as announcing in public that William Shatner "would screw a sheep in the window of Bloomingdale's if you gave him the chance", while "Gene Roddenberry was a lying sack of shit ... a scum bag." • Douglas Adams's fan club revealed its name for the great man himself, based on close study of his signature: "Bop Ad". • Scientologists announced plans to preserve L. Ron Hubbard's writings forever on millions of indestructible stainless steel plates from which civilization could be rebuilt after its collapse: quite apart from the terrifying implications for the future of remaindering, imagine science being reborn from study of *Battlefield Earth*, whose physics, chemistry and mathematics are widely regarded as a load of moose.

February

Carl Sagan complained bitterly about Apple's use of "Sagan" as their private, internal nickname for a new computer project; at once the machine was renamed the BHA, widely leaked as standing for "Butt-Head Astronomer". • The Women's Press enthusiastically explained to John Clute that they were reissuing Joanna Russ's *The Female Man* without "that awful downmarket sci-fi cover" ... painted, as it happened, by his good lady Judith Clute. • Sf casualties of the Los Angeles earthquake were confined to one cat and Harlan Ellison's nose (he fell downstairs in the dark)—"Moose moose moose!" commiserated Chris Priest uncontrollably. • An interestingly endowed lady was unearthed in an sf novel by George Turner: "For answer she drew her hands right and left across her full breasts and raised them above her head...."

March

Cecelia Holland finally got around to reading William James's **Sunfall** trilogy, published here by Orbit and noted by *Ansible* in mid-1993 as bearing a Curious Resemblance to her 1969 historical novel *Until the Sun Falls* (a book about Mongol hordes, the James books being about colonists on a distant planet who behave *uncannily like* Mongol hordes): "I ... am convinced this guy sat there with my books open next to him on the table while he 'wrote' his." • John Holm, Harry Harrison's collaborator on *The Hammer and the Cross*, was discovered to be our very own Tom Shippey: "It's 90% Shippey," said a Birmingham pundit, yet Holm isn't even credited on the jacket of the US edition *The Hammer and the Moose*. • Meanwhile Carl Sagan's litigious rumblings caused that Apple computer project to be renamed the LAW ("Lawyers Are Wimps").

April

Pat Cadigan confided her affliction of Progressive Syllable Loss, meaning that following *Mindplayers*, *Synners* and *Fools* her next novel must of necessity be called *S*. ("You dog, Langford," she added traditionally.) • Gene Wolfe gloated over stealing Harlan Ellison's World Fantasy Convention Grand Master trophy and appearing with it in all the award photographs, having explained to H. E. that "I was older and a better writer. (Both true.)" • The real name of William James was revealed to be James William Bell; Robert Jordan, we learned, began life as Jim Rigney; and gossip columnist Eva D. Fanglord was exposed as a pseudonym of Dave Moose. • Good lines were found in Connie Willis's *Doomsday Book* ("She knew how to embroider and milk a cow.") and Peter Hamilton's *Mindstar Rising* ("He lifted her tee-shirt over her head. Her silk panties followed."). • The Catholic magazine *The Tablet* came up with a *Star Trek* K/S headline: "KIRK SPLIT ON HOMOSEXUALITY".

May

Christopher Priest, learning that Jim Owsley had now legally changed his name to Christopher Priest, protested to DC Comics: "If Jim must use a pseudonym, why doesn't he pick a really silly one, like, say, 'Harlan Ellison'?" • In a fit of butt-headedness Carl Sagan sued Apple on the grounds that the term "Butt-Head Astronomer" had brought him "hatred, contempt, ridicule and obloquy". • Colin Greenland discovered that the anonymous loon who plagues him (and Brian Stableford, and me, and John Gribbin) with daft pseudo-scientific plot ideas had taken things a step further by writing to the BBC posing as Colin Greenland. • William Gibson, working on the *Johnny Mnemonic* film, met his first producer and reported, ashen-faced, that he now knew exactly how a virus felt when it met its own specific antibody. • Brian Stableford was delighted to find himself listed as dead in *The Writers' Directory* and insisted on providing his own obituary: "Would he really have wanted so-called friends crawling out of the woodwork to proclaim that he had always been underappreciated, and to declare that his abysmal failure as a writer and as a human being had been at least a trifle unfortunate?" • Jeff Noon received the Arthur C. Moose award for *Vurt*.

June

Mexicon self-destructed with Mexicon 6, where Greg Pickersgill's charismatic rhetoric caused the convention not only to vote itself unanimously out of existence but to hand all the money to a brand-new Worthy Cause, the Mexicon Moose. • Paul McAuley's lawyers successfully shut up "the lunatic wannabe from Canterbury" who laid claim to much of the McAuley sf *oeuvre*— which this person was trying to resell to publishers—and who also insisted

that "Paul McCartney stole the lyrics and music of 'Yesterday' from him." •
GUFF candidate Kim Huett was also worried: "Either you exaggerate Greg
Pickersgill's pronouncements beyond all belief or he is a Rasputin-like figure
with long greasy hair and filthy shapeless clothing...."

July

Everyone seemed to be referring to Iain Banks's new novel as *Stewpidde
Tyettul*. • Harlan Ellison, champion of free speech, boasted that by adroit legal
threats he'd halted distribution and sale of Chris Priest's *The Book on the Edge
of Forever* (the trade edition of his exposé *The Last Deadloss Visions*, telling the
story of an anthology still unpublished after nearly a quarter-century of promises); but somehow copies seemed to sell briskly. • In Australia, Terry Pratchett
was required to sign a can of Fosters that had been sanctified by the touch of
his godlike lips. • Anne McCaffrey declined to introduce even the most tasteful hint of romance between *male* moose in her novels: "I have a lot of younger
readers and I must be careful what I write." (See *Dragonflight*: "She felt his
body rock-firm against hers, his hard arms lifting her up, his mouth fastening
mercilessly on hers as she drowned deep in another unexpected flood of desire" ... this is just fine for the tots, but to change the pronouns would result in
filth incarnate.) • **The Scottish Convention** hinted that its hotel booking forms
would be released at the Canadian Worldcon in August, a prediction which
proved accurate to within six months.

August

Algis Budrys couldn't make it to the Wincon convention because the US
State Department, after several months' hard thought about this suspicious
foreigner who'd lived there for only 58 years, found itself unable to issue a re-
entry permit until too late. • During Wincon itself, Jack Cohen's enthusiastic
account of animal sperm collection techniques was heard with riveted attention in a McDonald's full of fans drinking thick milk-shakes. • Philip G.
Williamson lashed out at an insensitive reviewer (me) who called one of his
books routine fantasy fare: "I may well don the outer garments of generic
fantasy," he said memorably, "but my underwear is full of surprises...." • The
Fantasy & SF Book Club claimed the *SF Encyclopaedia* contained OVER ONE
MILLION PAGES, and John Brunner insisted that once, in a week and a day,
he'd written a complete 71,000 word moose.

September

The ever-inventive book dealer Barry R. Levin of California tempted
fans with THE MOST HORRIFYING COPY OF ANY VAMPIRE NOVEL
... Poppy Z. Brite's *Drawing Blood*, which, thanks to the helpful chap who
committed suicide by setting himself on fire with a Molotov cocktail right
next to a mailbox containing copies of the book's limited edition, could now

be offered in the rare state "Odor of burning human flesh otherwise fine in slipcase". Only $600.00! Though filled with a strange inability to comment, *Ansible* did wonder about marketing the Barry R. Levin Horror Novel Price Enhancement Kit, comprising a jar of petrol and a pork chop. • Harlan Ellison turned his tactful attention to Mensa: "A vast group of defectives who don't get laid regularly." • The Rev. Lionel Fanthorpe clobbered Guy N. Smith's March "world record" for bashing out words in 24 hours: "I'm the new world Champion with a total of 22,871 words against Guy's previous record of 16,000. I'd have done a lot more if the moose hadn't crashed four times ... I think that cost me at least three hours' production time during which I should have done another 4-5,000 words." He wuz robbed.

October

Arthur C. Clarke was nominated for the Nobel Peace Prize on the basis that geosynchronous satellites have helped get world leaders talking to each other: "Hi, Fidel, this is Bill." He didn't win.... • Carl Sagan may safely be called a BHA or Butt-Head Astronomer, ruled the US District Court for Central California as its judge threw out Sagan's libel suit against Apple: "One does not seriously attack the expertise of a scientist using the undefined phrase 'butt-head'." • Cecelia Holland grew angry at lack of response from Orbit and William James to her plagiarism complaint, and decided to file a lawsuit. • The annual American Booksellers' Association event was prefaced by a Writers of the Future celebration at the "Scientology Celebrity Center" in Hollywood, where sf people became grumpy about the organized, compulsory "three cheers for L. Ron Moose—hip, hip, hooray!" • *Ansible* researchers found a fascinating bit of geography in Brian Aldiss's *Remembrance Day*: "She wore large bronze earrings made in an obscure country which rattled when she laughed."

November

Jerry Pournelle's secret career in sports writing was revealed on the blurb page of a Poul Anderson novel, which named Pournelle as co-author of *Football ... Ansible* has yet to trace his collaborative venture on off-track betting, *The Tote in God's Eye*. • L. Ron Hubbard's posthumous career climaxed with the Ig Nobel Prize, presented by *Annals of Improbable Research* magazine to those whose achievements "cannot or should not be reproduced": the Literature trophy inevitably went to L. Ron "for his crackling Good Book, *Dianetics*, which is highly profitable to mankind or to a portion thereof." • Bridget Wilkinson of Fans Across The World returned from her Worldcon trip and groaned: "I spent some time at the World SF Society business meeting. Ouch! What a bunch of rules fetishists! I thought the Trotskyites were bad 'til I met that lot." • HarperCollins's publicity for *Green Mars* by Kim Stanley Moose— Hugo winner for Best Novel—revealed that this wasn't hard sf at all but a spiritualist work in which, to reach Mars, you "Cross the astral belt...."

December

Cecelia Holland finally triumphed: Orbit stated that they were recalling the William James **Sunfall** books and ceasing distribution—a move made with lightning speed only a year and a half after the strong resemblances were first pointed out.... • Ian Watson was boggled to learn that his Games Workshop tie-in novel *Warhammer 40,000: Harlequin* had been too successful and was therefore banned from sale in Games Workshop outlets in case the spotty customers should buy it instead of a game. • Jules Verne's *Paris in the 20th Century* reached print at last after a typical publishing delay ("Your cheque is in the post") lasting 131 years, and became a French bestseller. • Harlan Ellison, horrified to discover cyberspace full of people speaking with the frank openness normally reserved for Harlan Ellison, denounced the entire Internet as "a breeding ground for bullies ... who would not dare to practice their hooligan ways were it not for an environment devoid of civility, courtesy and the common proprieties which govern how human beings should behave toward one another."

Xmas Special Issue

The Poet McGonagall (assisted by *Ansible*'s editor and Abigail Frost) brought all his famous talents to a tear-jerkingly lyrical *Ode to The Scottish Moose*, beginning with how the Worldcon bidding was won partly through inspired costume-work:

... the hardened voting residue of doubters and laggers
Were taken quietly outside and intimidated with a haggis.
But some terrified fans fled south of the nearest available border
At the sight of Martin Hoare dressed up as Harry Lauder:
'Tis true the sense of wonder most proverbially wilts,
With fear of finding what's worn under such unconvincing kilts,
Whose wearers oft had one bloodstained sock (although they didn't
     mean to),
After ineptly thrusting there the traditional dirk or *skean-dhu*.
Our TAFF administrator still declares, to anyone who meets her,
"'Twas about as authentically Scottish as a chicken tikka pizza."

And on this inspirational note, accompanied by a faint aroma of burning moose, 1994 came to its long-awaited end.

1995

ANSIBLE HYPERLINK, 2010

Complaints about this page should be sent to me at the venerable ansible@cix.compulink.co.uk address, *please*. This applies #!$!%(@@ to those who didn't like our light-hearted January squib about ~!#^*&<>@ and the Royal !!??#$%¢£¡÷° , and tried to ≠~•∞£¢¬æ by infecting the *Interzone* node with a viroid that HA HA HA SMEG AVENGER SAYS EAT ENCRYPTED DEATH LANGFORD. This isn't fair §¶∞•ªºᵈ› readers of

The Ministry of Truth

Pat Cadigan plans a radical publishing route for her thirteenth novel, to be coded as DNA introns in a harmless but contagious strain of colonic bacteria—"green" biological distribution that conserves Earth's dwindling resources of net bandwidth. "This one will hit you right in the gut," she promises.

Robert P. Holdstock cancelled his contract to rework the early Holdstock fiction *Mythago Wood* (hitherto available only in non-hypertext form) as a republishable novel. He claims technical inability: "I can't even program my new bathroom, let alone this hard stuff." Instead, the transliteration will be done by in-house wetware at HarperCollinsGollanczHodderHeadlinePanPenguinTransworld.

L. Ron Hubbard remains locked in a legal death struggle with the Reformed Church of Scientology following his AI re-creation in Church neuralnet cores. "Hubbard" has written what is claimed to be our field's first-ever hektology (a story extending over 100 book units), but the Church feels its high reputation in sf circles could be diminished by the appearance of the work. A netsurfer spy claims that the sequence caters to still-falling literacy standards by being written wholly in monosyllables, 80-85% of them violent.

Harry Adam Knight's recent death in several parts of London was followed by eulogies. "He was the true Dean of Horror," said Ramsey Campbell. "He and Guy N. Smith taught me all I know." The horrific freak accident with a mutated (or tailored?) fungal growth is still under investigation, and author John Brosnan—said to be "very close" to the deceased—is helping the police with their enquiries.

Larry Niven impersonators continue to infest US conventions; there have been nasty scenes with as many as five pseudo-Nivens of various sexes claiming precedence. This follows a security breach in the Known Space Library project ... the engineered RNA secretor enabling subsidiary collaborators to "think like Larry" has been widely bootlegged to aspiring authors, carrying its notorious side effect of personality confusion. From his cyberwheelchair in California the grand old man himself wisecracked, "America can count itself lucky—it might have been Jerry."

Rog Peyton, the Birmingham arcana dealer whose Andromeda "Book Shop" closed for the last time this month, was resigned but cheerful. "We knew it was a doomed enterprise and one day there wouldn't be enough paper books to stock a shop—but it's bloody good to see we outlasted W. H. Smith's, Foyle's, Blackwell's and BCA! Don't quote me, Langford you bastard."

Sir Christopher Priest, in the wake of editing Harlan Ellison's 75th birthday *Festschrift* last year, has sold a story to that eagerly awaited anthology *The Last Dangerous Visions*.

Claude Scrote, star of world-famous children's fantasy series *Pringle & Scrote*, contracted his unwritten first novel to ArrowOrbitMillennium: this is expected to top UK best-seller lists next year. Since Scrote is a non-aware 3D animation, there's hot speculation as to which genre author will be commissioned for the typing role. Outline and title remain undecided, but the target genre is humorous fantasy ... news which led to narrowed eyes in the vast Legal Division of Discworld PLC.

Infinitely Improbable

BSFA Sticks Neck Out. Despite the risk of proscription, the British Science Fiction Association is spearheading a protest against our country's latest Criminal Justice Bill proposals—which BSFA hotheads argue will further reduce the legal maximum membership of sf conventions from 250 to 100. This may be a good cause (though fans have learned to love smaller, cosier events), but some proposed tactics have been illicit in Britain since 1998 ... in particular, harassing MPs with mail and discussing politics on the net.

SFFHWPPMOA ... controversy continues over the "too narrow and elitist" admissions policy of the SF, Fantasy and Horror Writers, Poets, Programmers and Miscellaneous Originators of America.

Hugo Nominations. Following the recent introduction of Hugo awards for Best Digital Video Interactive, Best Nanoware, Best Hypertext, Best VR Presentation, Best Braided Giganovel, Best Netzine (professional and amateur) and new parallel fiction and nonfiction categories for freeware, shareware, machine-generated, guided-aleatory and PierreMenarded works, this column is not afraid to say it has no room to list the nominees.

15 Years Ago, in April 1995, Charles Platt himself guest-edited a paper issue of this very magazine. Hard to believe—but that was before the lonely years of prison and exile, the assassination attempt, the surprise DNA rescripting, and his astonishing elevation. Remember he was once one of us...

1995

What the Black Holes Foretell

Aries: 22 March to 20 April

The special and general theories of relativity will continue to operate normally for you, especially on Tuesday. Your lucky publishing word is "Remainder". Being intelligent as well as remarkably handsome, you never take horoscope columns seriously but sometimes read through them and are mildly surprised by the intermittent accuracy of their remarks—such as that you often work too hard, take over-much trouble for others, ought once in a while to be more decisive, sometimes like to pamper yourself, etc. How do the astrologers know all these things, making only an occasional small error by putting your distinctive qualities under the wrong signs?

Taurus: 21 April to 21 May

Watch out for planetary influences: specifically, look for trouble with Newton's Law of Universal Gravitation should you feel in a mood to jump out of any fourth-storey windows. Your lucky anthology is the new spinoff shared-world concept based on *Trivial Pursuit*, in which motley bands of fantasy adventurers ask each other amusing conundrums as they travel to confront the Black Quizmaster in his Tower of Doom (who holds all the cards with hard questions about quantum chromodynamics). Being insightful as well as sensitive, you can readily see that magazine horoscopes are self-evident nonsense: how can any observation apply uniformly to one-twelfth of the world's population? This objection is indeed shared by a number of "serious" astrologers who have denounced the inanities of newspaper-style horoscopes, only to be reproved by their fellows on the important scientific grounds that dog should not eat dog, that media splashes are lots more important than astrological accuracy, and that breaking ranks is bad for the balance sheet.

Gemini: 22 May to 22 June

Lucky you—you have nothing to fear this week from causality violation or temporal paradoxes! This week a major sf publisher will take over another, or be taken over, or narrowly avert being taken over, or not. A number of important future remainders will be published. But being meditative as well as slightly overweight, you have thought a little bit about horoscopes and wondered whether, say, the gravitational disposition of the Solar System at

---

To explain one esoteric allusion: this was written for Paul Brazier's Nexus, *the other sf magazine from Brighton, England.*

your birth moment *might* possibly have had some slight effect? It's possible. Somewhere at the back of your mind there might even be hazy ideas about the Moon's legendary influence not only on the sea but on madmen and etymology: "lunacy", "lunatic".... [1]

Cancer: 23 June to 23 July

In and around your place of work this week, entropy will continue on the whole to increase, particularly on Monday and Thursday. Your lucky sf anthology is *The Worst Stories Of All Time* ed. Greenberg and Waugh ("A terrific strain on my computerized anthology generation system!" said Martin Greenberg: "We'd never included a story-quality criterion before."). Being mathematically gifted as well as compassionate, you can easily calculate the relative gravitational effects of various bodies at your moment of birth. Your mother's, for example, exerted some 20 times the pull of Mars at its closest approach; the figure for a nearby doctor or midwife is about 6, for a likely hospital building about 500. Suddenly it seems that astrologers should far be more interested in precise 3-D maps of birth surroundings than in the positions of celestial trivia like Neptune (0.03), Uranus (0.1), Mercury (0.38), Saturn (3.3), Venus (27) or even Jupiter (46).[2] Einstein himself rejected the whole parapsychology package because he could swallow many things but not a heady indifference to the inverse-square law. Do you prefer to consider not direct pull but the weirder tidal forces we learned about at Larry Niven's knee? Sorry: the planetary influences now fade even more dramatically in comparison to mothers and midwives, since tidal force drops off very much faster with distance (inverse *cube*).

Leo: 24 July to 23 August

If you feel like a desperate gamble today, why not put your shirt on the outside chance that the law of conservation of energy will be upheld all year—even in the House of Lords? Your lucky sf magazine is published in Brighton. *[Please be more specific—Ed.]* Being just as well as generous, you may listen with sympathy to the professional astrologers' reply that factors other than gravity are involved, that the situation is immensely complex, and that a true astrological chart requires vast calculation based on precise knowledge of each birth's date, time, latitude and longitude.

---

[1] The legendary influence tends to fade in the face of impartial statistical examination of whether murder, suicide and violence in general *do* actually correlate with the phases of the moon. See for example "The Moon Was Full and Nothing Happened", *Skeptical Inquirer*, Winter 1985-86.

[2] Being mathematically adequate but dead lazy, I have lifted these figures from *Astrology: True or False?* by Culver and Ianna, 1988. Maximum effects from the very closest planetary approaches are assumed throughout.

Virgo: 24 August to 23 September

Throughout this month you can rest assured that Fermat's Last Theorem (that there is no solution in whole numbers to $a^n + b^n = c^n$ if n is greater than 2) will *not* be proved to be one of Kurt Gödel's "undecidable" propositions.[3] Isn't that cheering? Your lucky sf series is the new "Nostalgia" line of reprint anthologies: *Great Stories of Mesmerism and Animal Magnetism, The Radium Years, Death Rays and Force Screens of the Golden Age, Forgotten Tales of Cyberpunk*, etc. Being awkward as well as compassionate, you pause to wonder how a precise birth instant can ever be calculated for anyone: babies don't exactly quantum-tunnel from the womb, after all. In addition, there has been—for a long, long time, since before the days of Ptolemy—a desultory debate as to whether the time of *conception* mightn't be the important one ... which is likely to make some slight difference but could be even harder to record with stopwatch accuracy.

Libra: 24 September to 23 October

You will continue on a long and tortuous journey whose instantaneous velocity vector is compounded from Earth's rotation, Earth's motion around the Sun, the Sun's own career through space.... Several remaindered volumes of an L. Ron Hubbard dekalogy are likely to cross your path: this need not be a sign of bad luck and gross stupidity unless you buy them. Being intellectually tenacious as well as morally upstanding, you wonder now how the principles of astrology were first deduced. Much of it is supposed to go back to antiquity (with late extras like the planet Pluto bolted on to the system when pointed out by mere astronomers, having mysteriously failed to appear as bias factors in astrologers' calculations). How on Earth did ancient folk manage the necessary *precise* measurements of date, time, latitude and longitude? And with this handicap, in eras before high populations, birth registries or worldwide communication, how did they ever pile up enough observations to deduce not merely the complex effect of each planet in each of twelve (28 for the Chinese) astrological houses, but of all their possible combinations and permutations: conjunction, opposition, square, trine, sextile ...?

Being knowledgeable though modest, you may or may not ponder that even in the present day (however assisted by the scorned efforts of astronomers) astrologers are heavily split over the issue of when the rather important "Age of Aquarius" actually begins, or began. An impressive and authoritative variety of dates has been published, from 1781 to 2740 AD, with intermediate stops at 1962, 1983 and 2000—among others. Meanwhile, the most popular current systems of astrological houses make it impossible to cast horoscopes for anyone born within the Arctic or Antarctic circles. Out there, it seems, people are just devoid of destiny.

---

[3] Oh, all right. If it's undecidable, there can be no solution—since a solution would rather tend to decide the issue. If there's no solution the theorem must after all be true and not undecidable.... *(Mere seconds after this article appeared, or about a year after it was written, a proof of Fermat's Last Theorem was claimed. Oh well.)*

Scorpio: 24 October to 22 November

You will be particularly subject in the coming weeks to the direct influence of the Sun itself, which will personally irradiate you with huge numbers of neutrinos. Be wary as ever of yuppieback books. Being pragmatic as well as sexually magnetic, you muse that besides the constant problem of systematic errors in statistics, there are non-celestial factors that may produce slight correlations of the sort that get touted as Scientific Proof of Astrology—Gauquelin's "Mars Effect" and the like. In Britain, your birth date determines when you slot into the educational system, perhaps months sooner or later than you "should". Do winter babies (kept carefully indoors, heating turned up) start off a little differently from summer ones who get more fresh air and a different class of outdoor bacteria? Most interestingly of all, if our culture is littered with horoscopes based on the crude stereotypes of sun-sign astrology, could there be a tiny effect of self-fulfilling prophecy? "You will get on particularly well with partners born under Aries and enjoy fantastic orgasms." Enough to make any red-blooded half-believer at least try to check it out.

Sagittarius: 23 November to 22 December

Sad to say, a first- or second-order perpetual motion machine is not about to be invented; you find consolation elsewhere. One fringe scientist, however, claims to have observed perpetual motion in the output of Terry Pratchett. Being open-minded as well as kind-hearted, you give due consideration to the astrologers' dictum that "the stars incline; they do not compel". That is, astrology merely indicates what *ought* to happen to you, but you might do something else. That is, although an astrological prediction which comes off ("I see the recession continuing, or ending some time") is a plus point for astrologers, one which fails can never, ever cast any doubt on the eternal truth of astrology. Karl Popper's lyrical phrasing "The criterion of the scientific status of a theory is its falsifiability, or refutability, or testability"[4] can in this context be roughly translated as, "Pull the other one, mate, it's got bells on."

Capricorn: 23 December to 19 January

When a friend offers to show you a means of constructing a square equal in area to a given circle using a compass and straight-edge alone, hit him in the mouth. You have an idea for a shared concept anthology in which *all the authors will use exactly the same plot*, but dismiss this as too absurd.[5] Being unusually far-seeing as well as staggeringly patient, you remember the astrologers' fall-back claim of being able to give you useful vocational and psychological guidance by casting your natal horoscope and talking to you. The latter is important; trials by so-called investigators have shown astrologers singularly

---

[4] *Conjectures and Refutations*, 1963, revised 1972.

[5] Besides, it's been done—in that deeply bizarre volume *The Fothergill Omnibus*, 1931. G. K. Chesterton was one of the contributors.

bad at matching people's birth charts to their psychological profiles without meeting them. You consider the possibility that anyone with a bit of empathy could do as much and that astrology is simply another of those pseudoscientific systems which—like the Tarot, the I Ching, the Kabbalah, the appendices of *The Lord of the Rings*—are sufficiently big and full of symbols to get lost in, with the capacity to provide something vaguely relevant-sounding for any situation whatever. Any map of the universe is a comfort, however distorted or plain daft. You note, of course, that this is not the same as calling every astrologer a charlatan. Merely those who churn out those instant, freeze-dried newspaper and magazine efforts.

Pisces: 20 February to 21 March
    Your horoscope today will contain a prediction whose truth or falsity you are completely unable to determine. (It is the previous sentence.) Your lucky sf collection is in the recent tradition of alternate-world anthologies—*Alternate Presidents, Alternate Wars*, etc.—and is called *Alternate Stories*, edited by Douglas Hofstadter with each contribution based on the science-fictional premise "*What if* every story in this anthology had been completely different?" Being a little weary of reading and exceedingly weary of sentences starting like this, you put down the magazine with the thought that maybe your own skewed map of the cosmos might be a better one to steer by than the mouldy legacy of the constellations ... or even that there may after all be no magic in this complicated universe that we don't read into it ourselves. Which, after all, is plenty.

1993

Our Lady Of Pain

It was one of Huxley the Mad Mathematician's parties. Perhaps the one when the fire extinguisher was placed in his bed and embarrassingly proved to leak. Perhaps the one after which they played indoor croquet in Martin Hoare's room: it wasn't the hour of 5am he objected to, but that they were so noisy about hammering the hoops through his carpet. An Oxford bed-sit the size of a young cathedral (since redeveloped into four spacious student flats and a dining hall), it was crammed sardine-fashion with people, cheap wine, Warren and me.

"I don't see a lot of talent here," said my research partner in crime, physics practicals and H. P. Lovecraft. Warren had lately been studying women with the abstract intensity of Ahab swotting up whales, and with rather scantier success.

As Brownian motion forced us back on to a passing sofa, I found I'd sat by a dim figure with promisingly long hair. Any social risk was better than hearing, once again, Warren's General Theory of Where the Talent Was. In a conversational gambit of great daring I said, "Hello."

"Hello," she said. "I'm glad somebody's sitting down."

"You're well in there, Dave," said a plaintive voice on my deaf side.

She was called (let us say) Dolores, she was studying English, and she recoiled slightly on discovering I was a low-caste physicist. "Oh, I speak English too," I said confidently. "I mean, I read it. Once upon a midnight dreary, while I pondered, weak and weary, over many a quaint and curious volume of forgotten lore..."

I'd recently memorized the entirety of "The Raven" for a bet. God, we were wild and reckless youths in those days.

"You're not handling this the right way," whispered Warren.

"Can you remember it all?" said unattainable womanhood, curiously.

I could. I did. We giggled over the sillier bits while Warren appeared to be taking notes. (*Tuesday. Learn "Rime of the Ancient Mariner". Find woman.*) One thing led to another, until I barely heard the thin complaint of "Isn't that a bit *public*, Dave?" This being a seething Huxley party, nobody else even noticed.

It is obligatory, once in any writing career, to record in sombre prose the red-hot secrets of one's early love life. This enables friends to reel and stagger at the uninhibited revelations and to gasp, "I don't believe a word of it!" O ye of little faith.

Dolores, it proved, was an enthusiastic kisser of the Vampirella persuasion. Her face crashed into mine like an iceberg impacting the *Titanic*. Bits of tooth enamel flew wide. After the first wave of oral cavalry charges had begun to subside, I selflessly fetched drinks and took the opportunity to lick all my wounds except the most disturbing one, which appeared to be on my tongue. This was ... well, different. (My last brush with passion had been when I escorted a lady to the college ball and, as I took her hand for a dance, she confided a deep-seated phobia about being so much as touched by anyone. It was a long, chaste night.)

As I lurched back, juggling leaky paper cups, I realized why Dolores had been so cheered when someone sat by her, and why Warren's infallible whispered strategy for Getting Her Back to Your Room would be as useless as it was unconvincing (etchings, etc.). Her leg was in plaster, up to the thigh.

After driving her home to Lady Margaret Hall college I passed a sleepless night. The throbbing pangs of lust were, unusually, centred on my upper lip.

"... Charnel," said Warren in the Nuclear Physics lab. "You have to have a charnel stench."

I consulted the notes. "We've got two. Including 'Ah! Ah! The smell! The smell! The charnel stench!'"

We were conducting a serious scientific experiment, to make the university computer write H. P. Lovecraft stories. There was a rich vein of phrases to be quarried.

"'Lumbered on its eldritch course.' That's a good one. Your lip looks funny, Dave."

"Pardon?" I said unconvincingly. "And 'a writhing mass of blood-red serpent forms'."

"I said your lip looks funny.... Which story has got the writhing mass of blood-red serpent forms?"

"None of them. It's a brilliant pastiche based on the spaghetti bolognese we had for lunch."

Warren became very serious, and paused in his thumbing through *The Lurking Fear*. "That's not *right*. It won't be *authentic* if you put in things like that." He stared at my swollen upper lip. I began to suspect the canker of jealousy in his soul when he also rudely blue-pencilled the snappy line "I am the public health inspector, what about this charnel stench?"

Though for weeks I visited her and drove her to parties, Dolores and I never actually succeeded in having a conversation. "I'm very fond of John Donne," she would say dreamily, and I would reply, "Something sings in my soul when I contemplate the second law of thermodynamics." Once I tenderly wrote Rutherford's equation for the scattering of alpha-particles on that enplastered leg. The mutual blank stare would be hastily interrupted by a demonstration of how all Dolores's pent-up, immobile energy could be directed into a single white-hot focus—a transcendent frenzy in which her rather attractive mouth became a pitiless machine for converting male faces to hamburger meat.

My dentist, listening to an evasive account of how a front tooth had become chipped, fell about in unsubtle hysterics.

Warren, though he dutifully typed in raw data for the mighty computer program ("Long, greenish-grey tentacles with red sucking mouths!"), remained distant and reproachful.

"I love the seventeenth-century poets," said Dolores to the ceiling as she lay on her bed. "Come and sit here."

"I like the nineteenth-century poets," I offered, drinking her sherry and failing again to build intellectual bridges. Nineteenth-century poets, it transpired, were the pits. My massive 40p investment in Swinburne was to be of no avail. Trying again for common literary ground, I described the awesome Lovecraft Program. Dolores, strangely enough, had never read Lovecraft: I quoted with fervour. "Shrieking, slithering, torrential shadows of red viscous madness chasing one another through endless, ensanguined corridors of purple fulgurous sky ... formless phantasms and kaleidoscopic mutations of a ghoulish, remembered scene; forests of monstrous overnourished oaks with serpent roots twisting and sucking unnameable juices from an earth verminous with millions of cannibal devils; mound-like tentacles groping from underground nuclei of polypous perversion..."

"Only a computer could churn out rubbish like that," she sniffed.

"No, that's the real stuff, from 'The Lurking Fear'."

"My God. Come here and kiss me."

As was becoming usual, I didn't sleep well that night. Large tracts of my face seemed afflicted with terminal radiation burns and about (unlike the rest of me) to drop off. In the small hours I gloomily browsed through the 40p Swinburne....

> By the ravenous teeth that have smitten
> Through the kisses that blossom and bud;
> By the lips intertwisted and bitten
> Till the foam has a savour of blood;
> By the pulse as it rises and falters,
> By the hands as they slacken and strain,
> I adjure thee, respond from thine altars,
> Our Lady of Pain.

These very Lovecraftian cadences were thought so exciting *circa* 1866 that they were banned, and defiant Oxford undergraduates marched through the cloisters chanting such extracts from "Dolores", and as I tossed on my bed of strange agonies it occurred to me that those young gentlemen of yore knew bugger all about the subject.

"You look terrible," my fellow-physicists told me. I weakly laughed it off, with the same reflex that makes one convey that last night's eighteen pints were nothing to one's iron digestion, any pallor and trembling being ascribable to cholera picked up from a draughty toilet seat. "No, you look *really* terrible," they said, and Warren delivered the clincher.

"Your lip," he paraphrased, "is oozing a foetid greenish-yellow ichor. A blasphemous ichor. Honest. Frothing in primal slime, it is."

I dubiously located a mirror, and fainted. Could one catch lip cancer from inadequately sterilized English students? The college doctor, persuaded at length to issue antibiotics, fell about even more painfully than had the dentist.

For a week I lay low, sipping rum and reading the complete works of James Branch Cabell. Dolores failed to reply to an agonized deathbed letter: my unexpected grin of relief was properly punished by eldritch cracking sensations and a dribble of unnameable juices. Presumably she escaped from the plaster ("The heavy white limbs, and the cruel Red mouth like a venomous flower"—SF reputations have been founded on lesser prescience), reverting to a healthy life of hockey and tennis. I didn't see her again, and vindictively cannibalized the poem which called her to mind. While I convalesced, Warren sat at a teletype and dutifully transcribed "barren delights and unclean", "things monstrous and fruitless", "the lips of the foam and the fangs", etc., without ever noticing their dubious parentage.

The Lovecraft-writing program was a great success, but I'll spare you its actual deathless output. Term ended; the long summer passed; autumn was a new Oxford year, and I was induced to feed all the latest SF group members' names into the computer (programmed this time with an SF generator which combined the literary pretensions of E. E. Smith with the tight continuity of A. E. van Vogt). Several yards of rubbish ensued, and soon I was accosted by a bespectacled lady who said in pained tones: "I am not frigid!"

This is not a usual form of introduction.

Sure enough, random factors had thrown up the immortal SF line, "The frigid Hazel Salter was reloading his ultimate weapon."

"Er," I said, falling back on the vacation's literary feat (141 stanzas memorized after an even rasher bet with Huxley the Mad Mathematician). "'Just the place for a Snark!' the Bellman cried, As he landed his crew with care, Supporting each man on the top of the tide By a finger entwined in his hair. 'Just the place for a Snark!' I have said it twice, That alone should encourage the crew. 'Just the place for a Snark!' I have said it thrice...."

"Can you remember it all?" said Hazel, curiously.

"What I tell you three times is true."

A few months later, despite the misgivings of my mother ("She's not black, is she?"), we were engaged. I owe it all to the nineteenth-century poets.... The wretched Swinburne, though weird, wrong and anyway preferring the attentions of strict governesses, will doubtless insist on the last word:

> Time turns the old days to derision,
> Our loves into corpses or wives;
> And marriage and death and division
> Make barren our lives.

Goodness knows how H. P. Lovecraft would have put it.

1986

art by Dave Mooring

Highballs!

Respectable SF criticism has this habit of focussing on good writers, well-known writers, historically important writers—no two of which categories wholly overlap. Ask Mummy to draw the pretty Venn diagram for you. I sometimes take a perverse interest in what's left in the vast and shoddy obscurity beyond the diagram ... for three reasons.

First: unlimited quantities of rotten SF exist out there in the sludge reservoirs, influencing the image of the genre; and most of us have read all too much of it. What questing spirit raised on hard SF can resist a journey into extraliterary space?

Second: it's horribly true that the compulsiveness of SF can (for most readers when they're young, for too many throughout their whole lives) exist independent of your actual literary virtues.

Third: just as physicists begin by examining "simple" systems, so perhaps (I rationalized to myself, having decided to write this piece anyway) critics can make useful generalizations from books whose crude fantasies and formulae are nakedly visible.

My choice of obscure writer for an experimental once-over was the erstwhile bus driver Philip E. High. He was British (chauvinism), I had most of his stuff either from my indiscriminate SF-buying days or as review copies (opportunism), one or two fans had made enthusiastic, completist noises and deplored High's lack of fame (optimism), and I vaguely remembered having once been tempted to sweeping generalizations about him (lack of controlled laboratory procedure).

From 1964 to 1979, High's fourteen novels were published in the grottier literary circles: Ace Doubles, Robert Hale, Dobson. (Apart from Ace, all publishing imprints mentioned here are British. Most are defunct.) This is at once a bit of a handicap for any author. For example, my dim recollection that our man's *Prodigal Sun* (1965) was better than most turned out to be, in part, what scientists call an artifactual datum—i.e., that book, the only one to be published in the almost respectable Compact SF paperback line, was also virtually the only one to be copy-edited.

In the rest, High's preference for commas where colons, semicolons, dashes, new sentences or no punctuation at all, are required, often results in text like this, it is peculiarly irritating to read, the only SF author nearly as bad is Harry Harrison and he at least usually confines it to speech in quotation marks, possibly on the theory that people don't make true sentences in conversation. Also, far too many "significant" lines are delivered ... portentously, in ... *italics*!

Let us be scientific. Pausing to refresh my memories of 13 out of High's 14 novels (the omission is *Butterfly Planet*, 1971, which I've never come across), I made a chart to see whether good, strong formulae and instructive trends would emerge. You bet they did. Many of them, I predict, will remind you of other books before and since.

High's peculiar charm lies in his patent spring-loaded plotline, which invariably starts from a position of rock-bottom despair and then *keeps on getting more cheerful.* Thus in 87% of my sample, the opening scenario is shittily dystopian and/or post-holocaust; in 100%, we get a happy ending of global and often galactic proportions. One side effect of the exponential rate of improvement is that flashbacks are always to not-so-good times and are thus invariably downers. Another is that High's plots tend to suffer from premature ejaculation. We've barely taken in the fact that the ravening Vegan mind-hordes are giving the hero a stiff time before, rather too soon, he's gone off and overcome them.

As a result, the shorter novels like *Invader on My Back* (1968, possibly the best of the lot) read better. When carried too far on High's roller-coaster of new technologies and victories multiplying at compound interest, the book tends to peter out in cosmic flatulence, like the dully schematic interstellar-war finale of *The Time Mercenaries* (also, oddly enough, 1968).

Whence the initial unpleasantness? Although humanity always contains nasty specimens, chiefly power-mad demagogues, the basic threat of a High book tends to be external: aliens in 54% of our sample, rising to 92% in the light of later revelations about how perceived human baddies are in fact being manipulated by the aforesaid Vegan mind-hordes.

By way of non-rigorous confirmation: three of the novels were indeed reprinted in Arrow's "Venture SF" space-opera series, which loudly claimed to hark back to those golden days when "the only good alien was a dead one". In justice to High and the Vegan embassy I should mention that in 77% of cases, including all the Venture trio, the balance is redressed by wise old alien mentors who Help Out when the happy ending starts looking difficult to achieve. Some sort of record is set in *Fugitive from Time* (1978), where the extraterrestrial foe is so superior, despicable and innumerable that no fewer than three—or, depending how you count them, five—independent alien mentors are required to push the wheezing plot to its triumphant finale.

Ah, but you'll identify with the human hero (100%) or heroine (0%), who is ever ready with such sophisticated gallantries as, "I'm sorry, it was reflex. In my culture it is incumbent upon the male to protect the female" (*No Truce with Terra*, 1964). If not an officer of the British Navy (8%) he is invariably some other species of physical or mental superman (92%), though his mindboggling abilities will characteristically be clouded at first by amnesia or deceptive stupidity (62%). "Intelligence Quota, conscious mind, 110; Intelligence Quota, potential, 612..." (*Double Illusion* aka *The Mad Metropolis*, 1966).

Frequently he will have self-doubts or weaknesses, and accuse himself of being too easy-going, or over-fond the ladies (46%), a form of randiness whose chief discernible symptoms are holding oneself rigidly in check and taking many cold baths. In only one book, *Twin Planets* (1967), does this uncontrollably guilt-making erethism actually result in pregnancies. This is also the only book where such an astonishing if demurely offstage consequence is actually required by the plot.

However, the High Hero is cultured and will often quote a bit of randomly appropriate Literature to demonstrate this (62%—the sample here is a mite inadequate, but one gleans that the all-time top bard is Swinburne). At the end of his long toil he naturally gets the girl (100%), often under the terms of that social contract which is High's favourite utopian vision: predestined telepathic sex with the One Right Person (69%), a boon frequently extended to all or most of the human race (54%).

Speaking of races, ethnic minorities quite often receive a determined mention (38%). As in early Doc Smith before the Rigellians got integrated, equal opportunities consist of a cameo part showing how splendid and staunch your minority is, after which chore the WASP heroes return to the actual business of the plot. There is a sort of ghastly, bumbling well-meaningness about the mould-breaking way in which High's whites demonstrate their total lack of prejudice by "jokingly" addressing black walk-ons as "Black Boy" (*Sold—for a Spaceship*, 1973) or "Old blubber lips" (*Blindfold from the Stars*, 1979). Actual, systematic racism is however practised only against artificial or cyborgized races (23%), who when they've shaken off their insidious Vegan mind control are later allowed to use the same toilets as everyone else.

The High trademark most favoured by his fans is an inventive gift for devising boys' toys in the form of exotic weaponry (100%) ... over a wide range from solar bombs via flesh-rotting handguns, pencil-sized personalized cruise missiles and automatic repeating crossbows to tiny hunter-killer submarines which cruise the bloodstream, electrocuting bacteria. High-tech small arms will often have deeply silly names, usually made sillier by italics. From a single book's extensive armoury one may at leisure select an italicized Prengos, Vildustuck, Zu, Zine, Narth, Zac, Bute, Spond, or even Garrett (all from *Come, Hunt an Earthman*, 1973). An interesting sub-obsession involves subjective, hypnotic weapons (31%): the psychosomatic whip, the hysteria bomb. This comes to a head in *Reality Forbidden* (1967), whose culminating arms race happens entirely in the mind: force screens may be physically impossible, but the villains are dismayed to realize that "*Our* illusion of an H-bomb won't penetrate *their* illusion of a force screen...."

Horrid infections and tumours are also rife (54%), many of them preying exclusively on bad guys who are not in tune with the Force. Oddly enough, the nasties aren't related with particularly gory relish, and the genocide count is remarkably low for such heavily armed SF (only 8%).

Much more familiar is the gung-ho enthusiasm with which the hero and/ or human race tends to have whole new technologies developed to production-line point within about a week of getting a new idea or taking apart an advanced alien gadget. Pretty remarkable, when phenomena as simple as animal pelts move them to gems of scientific insight like "This fur, I concluded, had evolved as some sort of protection against the ever-present radiation" (*Fugitive*, and yes, he does mean hard radiation) or, "There was a wide band of silver fur on the animal's back which absorbed sunlight. This energy was converted into food"—to sustain a doggoid the size of a pony (*Blindfold*).

On the high-tech front I also admired the miniature race which developed miniature nukes: "In all probability the 'mushrooms' of these devices seldom rose higher than a normal mushroom" (*These Savage Futurians*, 1967). Only the brave should dare High's version of genetics (*Speaking of Dinosaurs*, 1974), involving such concepts as "blank genes" ripe for recording your favourite TV programmes, and the notion of a genetic racial memory which will one day make us sit up and realize with much smiting of brows that we call ourselves what we do owing to dim recollections of being descended from the Yewmen Race of planet Terth.

Enough of cheap jokes. Despite obvious enthusiasm and a surprising measure of "good bad book" readability, High is a dire and unimportant writer, displaying in his works a classic sloppiness and stereotyping which detract from the books' legitimate escapist fun and cheerily nasty invention. In that sense he's a bad example, rotten with fantasies of power and wish-fulfilment. Yet it's rather touching that his heroes are never particularly interested in conquering the universe, merely in achieving a little peace to sit down and, when the opportunity presents itself (38%), to enter into total symbiosis with the ecosphere. Meanwhile, any remaining baddies are merely chastened/reformed (38%) or rot quietly away on exposure to the light of sweet reason (31%).

Contrasting this with, say, the equally ill-written but wildly successful Skylark and Lensman books, wherein a series of multiple genocides purges the cosmos of every single member of every non-cuddly race ... and you can't help wondering whether High's obscurity is largely because his weapon-toting, universe-shaking supermen, far from embodying fascist ideals, are merely too Britishly unpretentious, and wishy-washy, and nice.

This intensely litcrit analysis is dedicated to all those other enthusiastic writers like High who thought SF was jolly wonderful, who scraped together an idea or two and tried without any huge talent to make their names immortal—and who (99.8%) didn't succeed even to the extent that he did. Remember them. They perished that our remainder shelves might live.

1989

When The New York Review of SF *printed a version of this piece, the title was thought too raunchy and outspoken; cautious hands changed it to "On High".*

Inside Outside

It is well known in certain circles that all science fiction is trash, since it's always possible for an "outside" critic to give it the quick once-over and discover a book which doesn't meet selected literary standards. Like travel journalists summing up an entire country's unmistakable state of decline after the close experience of a 24-hour stopover and two conversations with taxi drivers, such visitors unerringly find what they expect.

The converse argument that the bad non-genre books X and Y and Z condemn all "real" fiction by their mere existence is never seriously advanced, but is worth keeping in mind as a parable or thought experiment.

Now there are a number of well-worn debating points to be made here about the dread walls of the sf genre ghetto, but this logomachy seems outdated. Sf these days is a fuzzy circle on an imaginary Venn diagram of literature. Some writers play around in its broad, ill-defined borders and are called "slipstream": Christopher Priest's *The Affirmation* (1981) is an excellent example. Some stand just within the border zone, but with much still depending on which way they happen to face: Robert Harris in *Fatherland* (1992) uses the traditional sf device of an alternative history but aims his story more into the overlapping Venn circle of thriller/detective fiction.

And certain writers wander deep into sf while resolutely keeping their eyes shut and claiming that they are doing no such thing. Whitley Strieber, for example, writes about literal flying saucers and presumed aliens in his partly original novel *Majestic* (1989) but has been heard to argue that this novel is by no means nasty old sf because, being based on the "true" story of the ever-controversial 1947 Roswell UFO incident, it's *set in the past*. P. D. James once insisted on TV that her *The Children of Men* (1992), despite inhabiting a recognizable and indeed well-worn niche of bleak near-future speculation, is not sf since it contains neither spaceships nor robots. One rather assumes that the late great Anthony Burgess might have had his own sf excursions slightly in mind when he praised Brian Aldiss's 1978 *Enemies of the System* (set 1.09 million years hence and featuring faster-than-light interstellar spaceships) as "... rich, allusive, full of real people and unfailingly interesting. It is not, then, real SF."

Slightly more serious in tone, this: an essay which appeared in the Gollancz trade-paperback incarnation of New Worlds, *and was so influential that* New Worlds *was immediately cancelled by the publisher. Thus it's solid litcrit from here onward; if at any moment you feel a sense of submarginal colloquy or disjunctive haecceity you will know I've been reading too much John Clute.*

Turnabout is fair play. Critical tourists in sf reasonably insist on applying literary standards. Literary visitors to the genre can hardly complain if we apply the related sf standards, those rules of thumb which codify gut feelings about what makes sf work. Some of the pitfalls, in no particular order:

• *Information feed.* Writers accustomed to telling the reader highly subtle things about characters' relations, through natural-seeming nuances of narrative or dialogue, can go bananas when confronted with the task of conveying a new chunk of history, a new society, a new world. They may not descend to lines like: "Er, Professor, tell me again how the present war came about, as though I knew nothing of it" ... but some come fearfully close.

Robert Harris in *Fatherland* has a relatively easy task in this area; the alternative history where Hitler won is all too imaginable. Harris handles the mechanics well, neatly allowing a tourist guide to describe the ghastly architecture of Albert Speer's planned post-war Berlin—including a genuine sf *frisson* concerning the Great Hall of the Reich, largest building in this world, which when crammed with a rally of 180,000 Nazis develops its own internal rainfall. After which the book heads off into bog-standard thriller territory and the sf critic says farewell.

• *Consistency with natural law.* This largely means internal consistency rather than slavish adherence to physicists' current snapshots of how things are. A faster-than-light spaceship is a legitimate plot device—this *is* fiction, and General Relativity may not be the last word on the cosmos. Writing about a spacecraft that lands on the surface of the sun or Jupiter (both of which are a bit lacking in surface) is harder to justify.

The tediously familiar example here is that of Piggy's glasses in William Golding's remotely science-fictional *Lord of the Flies* (1954). Piggy is shortsighted; his spectacles thus have concave lenses which will spread rather than concentrate sunlight, and can't be used to start a fire. This is a peripheral blemish, a small solecism which by no means destroys the book as some sf pedants have claimed. Oddly enough, the problem was solved better on another fantasy island which Golding surely knew: that of J. M. Barrie's play *The Admirable Crichton* (1902), where resourceful Crichton plausibly contrives a lens from two watch-glasses with some water between them.

• *Consistency with the present.* This could also be called common sense. Much writing about tomorrow seems instantly archaic because the author hasn't assimilated the "givens" imposed on the story by today. It isn't necessary to take this as far as those cryonics enthusiasts who are so keen on their plans for frozen immortality that they will rubbish any imagined future which fails to centre on an ever-growing reserve of corpses in liquid nitrogen.

But today's proliferation of personal computers and the Internet *does* strongly imply a data-riddled millennium where virtually every literate person with an income will be linked into the global web. (As I write, a million new users are joining the net each month.) Near-future sf can't afford to leave this out of the reckoning—unless, as in *The Children of Men*, a convenient disaster or social collapse can help sidestep the issue. So many writers have devastated half the world in order to produce a future sufficiently crippled to be easily imaginable. I've done it myself. We are all guilty.

Another author praised outside sf is Kathy Page, whose *Island Paradise* (1989) comes with a warm plug from Malcolm Bradbury. It's quite well written; the low-key dystopian scenario (of which more below) is convincing enough; and then we learn that this over-governed world has a secret nuclear arms dump into which large, informal parties can wander at will to carry off the conveniently miniaturized doomsday weapons, in backpacks. The only thing missing is a sign saying "Please Take One". To the innocent eye of the sf reader, this is plotting which simply will not do.

• *Futurespeak.* Jargon—especially scientific or pseudoscientific jargon—must be worked over and subjected to plausibility tests until something reasonably credible emerges. Slang is folk poetry: perhaps the real thing can be created only by poets (later on we'll remember that Marge Piercy is a poet of some note). The real-life tendency of capital letters to fade into the lower-case undergrowth should also be noted: we just don't write words like LASER and RADAR in caps any more.

Here's a fine novel studded with micro-lapses of invariably capitalized terminology: *The Handmaid's Tale* (1985) by Margaret Atwood, of whom the *SF Encyclopaedia* remarks that her "attempts at the language of genre sf are not unembarrassing". There are religious outbreaks called Prayvaganzas, the poorer chaps' women are Econowives and the democratic tearing-apart of a victim by a mob is Particicution. People don't phone but use the Compuphone, not to mention banking at the Compubank and sticking their credit cards into a Compubite—all reminiscent of those pseudo-futuristic prefixes in pulp sf, like "space-rations" and "plasti-boots", or the omnipresent "synthi-" in Judge Dredd comics: "synthinylon".

Island Paradise, already mentioned, has a humane voluntary-euthanasia program whereby they don't cart older folk off to lethal chambers, but instead a social worker closely resembling Margaret Thatcher comes round and nags you to do the decent thing. This is portrayed in terms of Timely and Untimely Deaths, the former being the Price of utopia—awkward capitals again, as though today we went on about Pensions and Bus Passes. This book also speaks of power (that is, Power) being imported from somewhere called "Planet Three". Ignoring the impossible economics of shipping power across interplanetary space, the suspicion here is that Kathy Page somehow got the idea that mentioning Venus or Mars would be *too sci-fi*—and so she substituted this colourless yet deeply unbelievable name.

• *Unrepeatability.* If an sf story depends on an event or discovery which is billed as unique and never to be repeated, there had better be a good reason why. "The secret of the deadly Wibble Ray, that could so easily have ended all life on Earth, died with Professor Jones. It was a thing with which Man was not meant to meddle. Now the horror is over forever." No, it isn't: some other damned researcher in some other country is busy inventing the thing all over again. Scientific genies are not so easily coaxed back into the bottle. Examples will follow.

• *Uniformity*. Sf often deals with the actions of large numbers of people: a whole population responds to global threat or the apparition of Elvis in the sky. The point here is that people are very diverse and won't all react the same way. Only lazy writers give us stuff like, "The entire world was convinced at once by President Spong's call for universal overtime without pay in order to defeat the Vegan economic assault."

Our remaining specimens deserve examination at greater length. The following selections were made by a computer randomization process not wholly uninfluenced by what I actually had available.

The Children of Men by P. D. James was a UK paperback best-seller in Spring 1994. Essentially this is the standard sf novel of sterility, strongly reminiscent (to genre readers) of Brian Aldiss's 1964 *Greybeard*. The book is well written—perhaps too much so in places; as John Grant observes, some of the more mannered passages would definitely have rated three stars if included in *Cold Comfort Farm*.

Strangely, there is a terminological glitch on the first page. After a striking enough opening about the death of the last-ever man to be born, the narrator mentions hearing this on the "State Radio Service". Later we meet the "State Security Police". But this is Britain—Britain under a dictatorship, admittedly, but even a very stupid dictator (and this one is reputedly a genius) won't go around changing institutions' names merely to make them more science-fictionally sinister. Of course the State Radio Service and the S.S.P.—note that S.S.!—would be soothingly called the BBC and the police.

Next comes a whopping information dump. The protagonist begins a painstakingly literate diary and records in merciless detail the history of the world from now to his present day of 2021. Not for posterity, because there won't be any—and just in case, he announces his firm intention of burning the diary. Meanwhile, he shows an uncanny ability to give just the background information which might be required by a reader situated in the early 1990s, almost as though his hand were being guided by some omnipotent Author....

The story he tells is pretty odd, too. All human sperm ceased quite suddenly to be fertile by 1995, now subtly renamed "Year Omega". It's a possible premise, though such absolutes in biology are to be distrusted. The cutoff has to be absolute for James's plot, which requires a Last Generation and no distracting kids around for the big event subtly hinted by the fact that while Part 1 of the book is called "Omega", Part 2 is called "Alpha". Therefore, testing our credulity to the limit and beyond, it is stated that even artificial insemination or *in vitro* fertilization using frozen sperm from the potent days won't work. One fights to resist the image of an offstage fleet of alien spaceships manned by robots and broadcasting infertility rays.

We also have a touch of what I've called the fallacy of uniformity when it comes to the Omegas, as those born in Year Omega are subtly named. Every member of this Last/Lost Generation was, it seems, thoroughly pampered (unbelievable uniformity of parents world-wide), and now in their maturity they are without exception unusually beautiful (no explanation for this) and menacing, the epitome of the Youth Problem. Credibility would be much enhanced by permitting a reasonable percentage to be overweight; have acne; prefer rock-climbing, tiddlywinks or reading detective stories to the bouts of orgiastic violence so necessary for a further kink in the plot of *The Children of Men*.

"Unrepeatability" is another of the sf touchstones listed above. Warning bells ring under this heading when we hear of the one remaining secretly fertile man in the world: what, just one? And gosh, he's dead now, so we have to hope the one pregnant woman's baby is a boy. But after the abrupt way human reproduction was halted, there's a broader implication that the displeasure of God has now ceased or the aliens have turned off their sterility rays, and that if one chap is functional then lots more probably are. This detracts somewhat from the tension of the final chapters—though there's a wonderful pulp-sf bit where the dictator himself, who personally controls the entire security forces of Britain, turns up alone to shoot it out with the protagonist.

The book is often well written; there are nice character touches and poignant images of Oxford in decay ("just like *Greybeard*," mutters the unregenerate sf fan); but there is also this nonsense cluttering up the plot. Nonsense, too, which one would expect an sf editor to sort out before publication. Is it significant that *The Children of Men* was first published by Faber ("just like *Greybeard*"), which no longer has an official sf list or editor?

Martin Amis avoids the difficulties of dealing with the future in *Time's Arrow* (1991), by running his story backwards from the present day into the past. This is not a cop-out (Amis knows his sf) but an attempted *tour de force*, the telling of an entire life from a time-reversed viewpoint.

Time running backwards is hardly a new sf idea. Brian Aldiss—that man again—toyed with it in *An Age* alias *Cryptozoic!* (1967) but cannily avoided taking the actual narrative into reverse; Roger Zelazny, J. G. Ballard and others wrote short stories on the theme; Philip K. Dick's unusually eccentric and flawed *Counter-Clock World* (1967) revolves around life-spotters rescuing the awakening dead from their graves and librarians erasing texts to expunge knowledge forever. There was even a 1989 episode of *Red Dwarf* called "Backwards".

The familiarity of the idea is no obstacle here: Amis is gifted enough to get away with a great deal, and it's good to see him come to grips with the technical challenge of time-reversal ... for a while. What he sinks into might be called the pitfall of the prolonged conceit—as with those early sf writers who so much loved the ingenuity of their One Big Idea that, to them, the story seemed to require only that this notion be laid out at length on the page and admired from every angle.

Thus whole chapters of hyperkinetic Amis prose and clever postmodern bits come to seem a desperate waltz of distraction, smoke and mirrors to obscure the fact that uneventful decades told backwards are not really more interesting than their forwards version. Successive shocks of reversed bodily function have a diminishing effect (and we are spared nothing, not even the preliminary to a good backwards puke as the protagonist pulls the toilet handle and "The bowl filled with its terrible surprises."). The sf reader begins to shuffle slightly, remembering perhaps that *Counter-Clock World* also had a plot going before the end of chapter one.

The identity of the narrative voice who inhabits the protagonist is a dodgy philosophical problem. Like all those convenient amnesiacs in sf, this personality's memory (none) and abilities are determined solely by the storyline. He is not the protagonist retracing his own timeline, since it is required that he should not know the appalling past that is his future. Equally, he's not a brand-new soul whose reversed experiences begin with the protagonist's death, since like a computer he comes prepackaged with useful functions: English, general knowledge, the sense that things are going backwards, and a tiresomely constant capacity to be surprised by this. Well into the narrative he's still referring to post-coital languor as foreplay (which is quite witty) and mentioning that the protagonist has "jumped the queue" (which seems dumb: joining the queue at its head is the norm in retrograde time and the narrator should by then be entirely used to it). An important nightmare of the protagonist's, foreshadowing or postshadowing that nasty area of the past, is played in forwards time for no apparent reason than to give the reader a better chance at understanding. There are other small niggles. Backward ran dialogue until reeled the mind....

At the heart of the book, when time has rewound to 1944, comes the short story for which the rest of *Time's Arrow* is an elaborate frame and apparatus of translation. It is the reversed story of Auschwitz, made hideously lyrical by its presentation as a sort of joyous creation myth. Men of infinite compassion and power cause a whole race to be born from flame, etc.

I truly don't know whether all the rest of the laborious backward narrative is justified by this segment of ironic distancing taken to a point beyond irony. The Holocaust is one of the major arcana of the twentieth-century cultural pack, a card which may be devalued by playing it too often—at risk of spreading a further blur of familiarity over the reports of people like Primo Levi who were actually there.

(Yes, this card is also played in *Fatherland*, but very nervously and discreetly; not, as it were, face up.)

Nietzsche said: "If you gaze for long into the abyss, the abyss gazes also into you," although I believe he said it in German. Perhaps my worry is that if you gaze for long into the abyss, the abyss begins to look ordinary or even boring.

The winner of the 1993 Arthur C. Clarke award amid some slight controversy, Marge Piercy's *Body of Glass* (1991) comes from an author already known in sf for *Woman on the Edge of Time* (1976)—though most of her work lies outside the genre and, for many, the sf bits of *Woman ...* were the least convincing.

Most of *Body of Glass* works rather well, with its free rendition of the story of Rabbi Loew's golem in 17th-century Prague linking nicely with the exploits of the 2059 cyborg Yod to whom the old tale is being told, and who like the Golem is created to defend a threatened Jewish community. The historical resonance is effective enough to quell carping critics who might suggest that Yod, being primarily designed as a self-acting AI weapon to be deployed in cyberspace, hardly needs a perfect humanoid body at all—let alone one capable of tireless yet tasteful sex. John Sladek's argument is also valid here: that we *will* create anthropomorphic robots when we can, because the idea is so fascinating.

Similarly, Yod's final sacrifice to save the community has been criticized as unnecessary since (being an artificial intelligence) he could be multiply copied, downloadable into other cyborg bodies. Yes indeed, but he explicitly chooses suicide and also takes pains to bump off his maker and destroy the manufacturing records, because Yod himself has come to disapprove of having been created as a weapon. There is a hint of the uniqueness pitfall discussed above, in that now it's known that Yods are possible more will surely be built, very probably by the nasty conglomerates against whose depredations Yod was made as a counterweapon ... but that's the future, after the book ends.

What is a little dissatisfying about Piercy's novel is that her whole picture of state-of-the-art 2059 cyberspace comes straight from the work of our very own sf visionary and technological know-nothing William Gibson. This is implicit in the text ("She called up the time on her cornea") and explicitly acknowledged: "I have freely borrowed ... I figure it's all one playground." Which is fine, except that the real world of the net has already read Gibson and moved on.

The threat against the lovable Jewish commune of Tikva, where people embroider folksy computer software better than anyone else in the world, consists of information pirates who lethally invade Tikva's local cyberspace work-zone through the net. Such a mode of attack is not yet with us, but we already have the defence—you pull the plug and disconnect your local computer system from the net. Or, with more sophistication, you work behind "firewall" systems which allow data in and out without surrendering program control to any outside source.

I suspect that Piercy is one of the many people who haven't quite got the hang of the difference between data and programs. When Yod and friends electronically invade the cyberspace of the wicked conglomerate Yakamura-Stichen, they do so "along the com-con channels, to pass in with messages. There was no way a base could distinguish between legitimate entering data and folks along for the ride." Right. They have transmitted computer simulacra of themselves as data, like a multi-gigabyte electronic mail message. The next step is presumably for this data to be run as an executable program within the Y-S system—otherwise it just lies there, inert. Who is going to run it for them? "Hey, that's interesting, an anonymous friend has sent me this 15 gigabyte program file—I wonder what it does? Let's try it and find out...."

For the rest: the street slang is pretty good, although I couldn't swallow the Glop—would you? This is the name for an extended urban blight closely resembling Gibson's Sprawl, based on the term apparently on all street folk's lips until shortened by usage: "megalopolis". H'mm. Least ept future scene-setting: I imagine one must need a good eye for fashion to spot that a silk robe is "from the mutated worms that were the rage".

Body of Glass is an enjoyable read but its second-hand cyberpunkery ex-udes a vague aura of staleness.

There is another oft-told tale lurking in Paul Theroux's *O-Zone* (1986): the thuddingly familiar sf yarn of the very bad place, the feared land beyond the pale, which when confronted at ground level turns out less awful than ex-pected—indeed rather a good thing, whose noble savagery makes a man of you. O-Zone is this place, a chunk of midwest America (Ozarks) closed off "for over fifteen years" after an escape of radioactive wastes. Wastes with short half-lives, presumably; their impact on the plot is zero.

Theroux is never less than literate, but his narrative has strange dips and lurches, with dense pockets of exclamation marks. O-Zone! Think of that! They were here, here in O-Zone! In forbidden O-Zone itself!—like that. It may be a sign of not wholly thought-out sf that the first official party to be issued an Access Pass and allowed to land in O-Zone after its long seclusion are not official explorers, nor investigators checking whether the land is com-mercially reclaimable, but tourists out for fun.

Besides O-Zone the USA comprises sealed, fortified cities of the decadent rich, who evince decadence by things like walking around naked except for masks. There is also "Godseye", a semi-official organization of futuristically armed psychopath vigilantes whose hobby is to blast, stun or incinerate any-one seen behaving suspiciously on the street—e.g., running in terror, looking like a member of the underclasses, or standing too close to such a suspect person. (It seems a distinct flaw that these weapons freaks never, ever compare their beloved killing tools in terms of brand names, but go on *and on* about generic burp guns, particle beams, stunners or lasers.) Later we visit a community echoing the wonderfully banal American Good Place of a thousand ungood sf novels, a town where people go to church, eat nice home-made pies, wear decent, old-fashioned guns with real moving parts....

The story is burdened with one of the most tiresome characters in recent sf—Fisher "Fizzy" Allbright, teenage physics genius and brat, whose neurotic inability to cope with human relations goes beyond parody. Naturally he's soon dumped in O-Zone and forced to get along with some of its native hunter-gatherers over the course of a lengthy trek, maturing slightly in the process. One marvels at the good nature of Zone dwellers, who put up with Fizzy calling them aliens (city jargon), monkeys, herberts, dongs, tools, whackos, jigs, dipshits, shit-wits, etc, and at no time drop him down a deep hole. There is a complementary strand about the O-Zone girl called Bligh who is taken off to the joys of city life, but she seems almost devoid of personality and barely reacts.

O-Zone's science is quite remarkably unconvincing, conveying the impression that Theroux regards lasers, particle beams and fibre optics as all very much the same thing. Fizzy's deep knowledge of particle physics seems to be based on study of E. E. Smith or Hugo Gernsback: "It's fibre-optics, fuck-wit. [...] This weapon can do it. We just program it to fire a continuous exode full of antigons." When someone who knows a little physics complains (as did I) that he's never heard of antigons, the reply is, "I only discovered antigons last year, wang-face!" What the weapon, a particle-beam handgun with a ludicrous seven megawatt output, is being programmed to do is to bend the lethal laser beam which runs near ground level around the O-Zone perimeter, so the party can slip under it and escape. Why they can't jump over it is unclear, but using a particle stream to bend a laser ray makes as much sense as trying to deflect light with a magnet. And it would have taken very little research to ascertain that, far from being silent and invisible, the mooted laser and particle beams have power densities that would violently ionize the air in something like a continuous, noisy lightning bolt.

O-Zone has a worthy stance, a general worrying about dependence on technology and the resultant depersonalization. Its tiresome length and its over-familiarity to any sf reader must count against it, though, and the technobabble smells of that dangerous attitude, "I can put down any old rubbish—this is only sf."

Nicholson Baker's *The Fermata* (1994) uses yet another premise with deep sf roots. H. G. Wells started this particular hare in "The New Accelerator", his account of a potion that temporarily speeds one's biological clock by a factor of thousands. Like a conjuror Wells distracts you from the absurdities by keeping the story short, thrusting one surprise consequence under your nose (the accelerated experimenters' trousers begin to smoulder as they whiz around) and concluding with a spectacular diversion in the form of a practical joke. Much practical joking also features in the best and funniest treatment of the notion,

John D. MacDonald's sf thriller *The Girl, the Gold Watch and Everything* (1962). Here the speed-up is wisely rooted in physics rather than biology, with some though not too much thought given to its effects: the super-accelerated hero finds the slowed outer world dull and red, while objects seem to have huge inertia and speedy things like bullets do visibly move even from the fast-lane perspective.

Baker's endlessly prattling hero Arno Strine does not merely slow external time but stops it completely, through a mere effort of will and belief. He calls his private time-zone the Fold or Fermata, in which he lives and moves while the universe outside is static. There are periods when he can't enter it and needs to find a new focus of belief (ranging from simple gestures through gadgets—transformer, switch, fingernail clippers—to odd or fetishistic acts like stitching thread through his skin). One sees the dramatic opportunities: Strine will be unable to enter the Fold when he urgently needs to; will exit into real time at an inconvenient, embarrassing or downright dangerous moment through failure of concentration....

No, *not one* of these possibilities is followed up. For a man with super powers, Strine lives a life oddly short on drama—perhaps because his moral sense won't let him use the Fold to steal, and he even feels intensely guilty after dealing with armed muggers by halting time and lashing them by their goolies to a nearby signpost. However, Strine's otherwise rigid code does let him use stopped time to remove women's clothing; also to fondle them all over, explore their orifices from "ane" to "vadge", spy on them in the bath, attach electric sexual stimulators to them as they ride on public transport, cause subliminal flashes of rude photographs in their field of vision, scrawl dirty comments in the margins of books they're reading (although not books written by women, which would be going too far), ejaculate all over them, affix exotic "nipple nooses" to them during bookshop signings (you'll have to believe me when I tell you that the person singled out for this fate is, of all people, Anne Rice) ... the list goes on.

Not much drama, but a great deal of fuzzy embarrassment for the reader; one hardly knows whether it's the narrator's or the author's painful transparency which is so uncomfortable, most especially in the dildo-infested porn fiction—included in full—which Strine writes to excite women whom he can then watch masturbating. How different, how very different, from the home life of our own dear Queen.

Best coinage, all too appropriate and evidently loved by the author since it's repeated several times: "chronanism". Worst euphemism, by a hair, out of an enormous selection: "my triune crotch-lump". (When I quoted that one to John Clute he sat down very suddenly and said, "I used to be interested in sex until a minute ago!")

Excuse me, I was talking about the sf content. Of course *The Fermata* is pure fantasy, but there is the occasional rationalizing mention of physics. Baker is savvy enough to consider that if all time-flow ceases outside Strine's body, he'll be trapped in a form-fitting bubble of frozen air. So our chronanizer's immediate vicinity is not quite halted: women aren't rigid statues but conveniently warm and soft, while equally conveniently failing to be conscious. Far enough from Strine himself, the stasis is total. There is some babble about Polaroid photos taken in the Fold not developing properly. Taps merely trickle because "water pressure is never good in the Fold"—nonexistent, surely, cut off at the time-frozen main? Electrical supplies are similarly fudged when Strine wants to use his word processor.

Thought experiment: Strine halts time out in bright sunlight. An infinitesimal fraction of a second later, total darkness must surround him (the Sun is not in his immediate vicinity) and the only illumination is infra-red blackbody radiation from Strine himself and any women unfortunate enough to be adjacent. Blackout.

Thought experiment: safe in the Fold, Strine strips a woman and gropes her for an hour. All this time she is warm but not breathing; it is uncertain whether her heart beats. Are the inner chemical furnaces at work, burning sugars to generate warmth? If the answer is no, she ends up probably dead from hypothermia; if yes, definitely dead from anoxia. You choose.

All this shows the superiority of Wells's and MacDonald's device of slowing down exterior timeflow (or speeding interior time) by a large amount, rather than introducing the awkward factor of infinity.

But what's the use? *The Fermata* genuinely is about sexual fantasy and nothing else, and even there refuses to explore any dangerous edge (compare Alasdair Gray's harrowing "slipstream" *1982, Janine*). Its shallowness really does run deep. Even one's growing hope that Strine will eventually meet a sharp come-uppance is frustrated—in fact he postmodernly gloats over this fact. That's the joke: a practical joke on the reader.

Now would be the time for some lofty generalization about these sf or sf-like works written by—let's not say outsiders, but writers other than the usual genre suspects. The exercise is pretty futile, though: even this small sample is too diverse for facile summary. Just like science fiction, really.

1994

Bio-Bibliography

Born 10 April 1953 in South Wales. Brasenose College, Oxford, 1971. BA in physics 1974. Weapons physicist at Atomic Weapons Research Establishment, Aldermaston, 1975 to 1980. Freelance ever since, writing sf, fantasy, horror, reviews, popular science, futurology, humour and tedious computer stuff. Married since June 1976 to Hazel Langford. 1980 TAFF winner. Sideline as tiny software house Ansible Information (with Christopher Priest) since 1985. Rarely used pseudonyms: Roy Tappen, William Robert Loosley. BSFA Award, 1986, for story "Cube Root". Hobbies include real beer, antique hearing aids and the destruction of civilization as we know it today. Pleased but baffled by nine Fanwriter Hugo awards, 1985 to 1995 (plus 1987/1995 Fanzine Hugos for *Ansible*).

Books and Chapbooks

The Necronomicon with George Hay, Robert Turner and Colin Wilson— 1978 "non-fact" reconstruction and critique of this "lost occult book". (Jersey, Neville Spearman, and Corgi pb, UK.)

War in 2080: The Future of Military Technology—popular non-fiction, 1979. (Newton Abbot, Devon, David & Charles/Westbridge; and Sphere pb, Military Book Club, UK; Morrow USA.)

An Account of a Meeting with Denizens of Another World, 1871—"non-fact" UFO book, 1979. (Newton Abbot, Devon, David & Charles UK; St Martin's USA.)

Facts and Fallacies: A Book of Definitive Mistakes and Misguided Predictions with Chris Morgan—non-fiction, 1981. (Exeter, Devon, Webb & Bower, and Corgi pb, UK; St Martin's USA.)

The Space Eater—science fiction novel, 1982. (London, Hutchinson/Arrow, UK; Pocket USA; Baen Books USA.)

The Science in Science Fiction with Peter Nicholls and Brian Stableford— popular non-fiction, 1982. (London, Michael Joseph, and Mermaid pb, UK; Knopf USA.) European SF Award, 1984.

Micromania: The Whole Truth about Home Computers with Charles Platt— popular non-fiction, 1984. (London, Gollancz, and revised Sphere pb, UK; US edition as by Platt alone.)

The Leaky Establishment—satirical novel of British nuclear research, 1984. (London, Frederick Muller, and Sphere pb, UK.)

The Third Millennium (A History of the World: AD 2000-3000) with Brian Stableford—futurological non-fiction, August 1985. (London, Sidgwick & Jackson, and Paladin pb, UK; Knopf USA.)

The Transatlantic Hearing Aid—report on TAFF (TransAtlantic Fan Fund)trip to the 1980 World SF Convention, 1985. (Reading, UK, Ansible Information.)

Earthdoom with John Grant—world-shattering spoof disaster novel, May 1987. (London, Grafton.)

Platen Stories, collection of fanwriting and criticism published by the World SF Convention, 1987.

Critical Assembly, indexed collection of first 50 "Critical Mass" sf/fantasy review columns, 1987, revised and reset December 1992. (Reading, UK, Ansible Information.)

The Dragonhiker's Guide to Battlefield Covenant at Dune's Edge: Odyssey Two—SF/fantasy parody collection, October 1988. (Birmingham, UK, Drunken Dragon Press.) CONTENTS: Introductions, "Xanthopsia", "Tales of the Black Scriveners", "Look at It This Way", "The Distressing Damsel", "Duel of Words", "The Thing in the Bedroom", "The Gutting", "The Mad Gods' Omelette", "Jellyfish", "Lost Event Horizon", "The Spawn of Non-Q", "Outbreak".

Let's Hear It for the Deaf Man, a further collection along *Platen Stories* lines, ed. Ben Yalow, 1992. (NESFA Press, USA; 1993 Non-fiction Hugo nominee, yay yay.)

Critical Assembly II, revised and indexed collection of "Critical Mass" sf/fantasy review columns 51-101, 1992. (Reading, UK, Ansible Information.)

Irrational Numbers, "Lovecraftian" story chapbook, May 1994. (Rhode Island, Necronomicon Press.) CONTENTS: "Deepnet", "Serpent Eggs", "The Lions in the Desert".

The Unseen University Challenge, a quiz book based on Terry Pratchett's Discworld fantasies. With an introduction by Pratchett, May 1996 (London, Gollancz/Vista pb.)

SHORT STORIES

"Heatwave": SF in *New Writings in SF 27* ed. Ken Bulmer, 1975.

"Takeover": SF/supernatural in *8th Armada Ghost Book* ed. Mary Danby, 1976,

"Accretion": SF/fantasy in *Andromeda 2* ed. Peter Weston, 1977.

"At the Corner of the Eye": horror in *10th Fontana Book of Great Horror Stories* ed. Mary Danby, 1977.

"Connections": SF in *Andromeda 3* ed. Peter Weston, 1978.

"Sex Pirates of the Blood Asteroid": SF/humour in *Aries 1* ed. John Grant, 1979. Series character Mac Malsenn.

"Training": SF in *Thor's Hammer* ed. Fred Saberhagen, 1979. Later revised and incorporated into *The Space Eater.*

"Imbalance": SF in *Ad Astra 4*, June 1979.

"Understudy": SF in *Practical Computing*, October 1979

"The Chess Set": supernatural in *12th Armada Ghost Book* ed. Mary Danby, 1980.

"Cold Spell": horror in *13th Fontana Book of Great Horror Stories* ed. Mary Danby, 1980.

"Turing Test": SF in *Practical Computing*, April 1980.

"Law of Conservation": SF/fantasy in *Ad Astra 10*, June 1980.

"The Final Days": SF in *Destinies 3:1* ed. James Baen, 1981.

"Sacrifice": SF in *Destinies 3:2* ed. James Baen, 1981.

"Transcends All Wit": SF/fantasy in *Pictures at an Exhibition* ed. Ian Watson, 1981.

"Semolina": SF/fantasy in *Peter Davison's Book of Alien Monsters* ed. anon, 1982.

"Friendly Reflections": SF in *Practical Computing*, February 1982; changed from own title "Answering Machine".

"Lukewarm": SF in *Alien Encounters* ed. Jan Howard Finder, 1982.

"Under the Bedclothes": supernatural in *14th Armada Ghost Book* ed. Mary Danby, 1982.

"Hearing Aid": SF in *Practical Computing*, October 1982 (in badly mutilated form); full version in *Knave*, 1984.

"Too Good to Be": fantasy in *Imagine 3*, June 1983.

"Lost Event Horizon": SF/humour in *Imagine 12*, March 1984. Series character Mac Malsenn.

"In the Place of Power": fantasy in *Beyond Lands of Never* ed. Maxim Jakubowski, 1984.

"3.47 AM": horror in *The Gruesome Book* ed. Ramsey Campbell, 1983.

"Statement of a Minor Offender": SF in *Knave*, June 1984.

"The Distressing Damsel": fantasy/humour in *Amazing SF*, July 1984.

"Sidetrack": SF in *Knave*, August 1984).

"The Thing in the Bedroom": horror/humour in *Knave*, November 1984.

"The Mad Gods' Omelette": fantasy/parody in *White Dwarf 59*, November 1984.

"Wetware": SF in *What Micro?*, November 1984.

"Cube Root": SF in *Interzone 11*, Spring 1985.

"Jellyfish": SF in *Knave*, May 1985.

"Notes for a Newer Testament": SF in *Afterwar* ed. Janet Morris, 1985.

"The Power of the Frog": SF in *White Dwarf 74*, February 1986.

"In a Land of Sand and Ruin and Gold": SF in *Other Edens* ed. Christopher Evans and Robert Holdstock, 1987.

"Blit": SF in *Interzone 25*, September/October 1988.

"Xanthopsia", "Tales of the Black Scriveners", "Duel of Words", "The Gutting", "The Spawn of Non-Q" and "Outbreak": all parodies with first commercial appearance in collection *The Dragonhiker's Guide ...*, 1988.

"The Facts in the Case of Micky Valdon": horror/satire in *Dark Fantasies* ed. Chris Morgan, 1989.

"The Motivation": SF in *Arrows of Eros* ed. Alex Stewart, 1989.

"A Surprisingly Common Omission": SF in *Drabble II: Double Century* ed. Rob Meades & David B. Wake, 1990.

"Ellipses": SF in *More Tales from the Forbidden Planet* ed. Roz Kaveney, 1990.

"What Happened at Cambridge IV": SF in *Digital Dreams* ed. David V. Barrett, 1990.

"A Snapshot Album": SF in *Interzone 43*, January 1991.

"Waiting for the Iron Age": SF in *Tales of the Wandering Jew* ed. Brian Stableford, 1991.

"Leaks": SF in *Temps* ed. Neil Gaiman and Alex Stewart, 1991.

"Encounter of Another Kind" in *Interzone 54*, December 1991.

"Blossoms that Coil and Decay": SF in *Interzone 57*, March 1992.

"The Arts of the Enemy": fantasy in *Villains!* ed. Mary Gentle and Roz Kaveney, March 1992.

"If Looks Could Kill": SF in *Eurotemps* ed. Alex Stewart, November 1992.

"The Lions in the Desert": SF/horror in *The Weerde II: The Book of the Ancients* ed. Neil Gaiman and Roz Kaveney, 1993.

"Christmas Games": SF in *Christmas Forever* ed. David G. Hartwell, 1993.

"Deepnet": SF/horror in *Irrational Numbers* as above, 1994, and *Shadows Over Innsmouth* ed. Stephen Jones, 1994.

"Serpent Eggs": SF in *Irrational Numbers* as above.

"The Net of Babel" in *Interzone 92*, February 1995.

"Blood and Silence" in *100 Vicious Little Vampire Stories* ed. Stefan Dziemianowicz, Robert Weinberg and Martin H. Greenberg (Barnes & Noble, USA, 1995).

REGULAR COLUMNS AND MISCELLANEOUS

Fission Fragments: sf/fantasy news and comment column in *Ad Astra* magazine, 1979-1981.

Critical Mass: monthly sf/fantasy review column in *White Dwarf* magazine, 68 columns 1983-1988.

Disinformation: irregular column of computer tips and invective in *Apricot File* magazine, 1985-1988.

Langford's Printout (later just *Langford*): monthly column on computers and writing in *8000 Plus* magazine (later *PCW Plus*), since 1986; bimonthly from 1991, with one long gap.

Critical Hits: monthly SF/fantasy review and gossip column in *GM* magazine, 17 columns from late 1988 to the final issue dated March 1990.

Critical Mass: third incarnation of "Critical" review columns for *Games-Master International*, 15 columns 1990-1991.

Slightly Foxed: column on popular fiction in *Million* magazine, 1991-1993.

Ansible Link: monthly news/gossip column in *Interzone* magazine, from issue 62 dated August 1992.

[Untitled] paperback sf/fantasy reviews in *The Guardian* newspaper, 1994-1995.

[Untitled] monthly column of sf opinion/comment in *SFX* magazine, from its June 1995 launch.

Also contributions to ... *University Desk Encyclopaedia*, 1977. *Macmillan Encyclopaedia*, 1981. *The Directory of Possibilities* ed. John Grant and Colin Wilson, 1981. *The Complete Book of SF and Fantasy Lists* ed. Malcolm Edwards and Maxim Jakubowski, 1983. *The Complete Commodore 64* ed. Allan Scott, 1984. *Anthony Boucher*: Zomba Books "Black Box" omnibus of his novels (introduction), 1984. *Sex Secrets of Ancient Atlantis* by John Grant—weapon-physics consultant, 1985. *Chelsea House Library of Literary Criticism: Twentieth-Century American Literature* ed. Harold Bloom, 1986 (on Robert A. Heinlein). *Magic* by G. K. Chesterton (play), introduction to English Language Society reprint, 1987. *Frontier Crossings* published by Conspiracy '87. *The Drabble Project* ed. Rob Meades and David B. Wake, 1988. *Horror: 100 Best Novels* ed. Steve Jones and Kim Newman, 1988 (on G. K. Chesterton). *100 Great Detectives* ed. Maxim Jakubowski, Xanadu, 1991 (on John Dickson Carr's Dr Fell). *The Encyclopaedia of Science Fiction* (2nd ed) ed. John Clute and Peter Nicholls, Orbit, 1993. *The St James Guide to Fantasy Writers* ed. David Pringle, Gale Research International, 1996. *Hollywood: the 100 Best Novels* ed. David Pringle, forthcoming. Contributing editor of *The Encyclopedia of Fantasy* ed. John Clute and John Grant, forthcoming.

SELECTED FANZINES

Ansible: informal SF newsletter. ISSN 0265-9816. Hugo winner. 50 issues 1979-1987. *Second series* ... monthly since October 1991. Sometimes contains news.

Cloud Chamber: generic Langford APAzine since 1976. Distributed through OMPA (1-2), WOOF (3), FEAPA (4-5), FAPA (6-7, 10, 13, 17),

FLAP (8, 10-13, 15-16, 19-21, 23), APA-SF&F (9, 13-14), Europa (13, 17), Frank's APA (21-22, 24-35), one without any apparent name (38-9) and Acnestis (40-67).

Drilkjis: sf genzine co-edited with Kevin Smith. 6 issues, 1976-1982.

Sglodion: personalzine 1989-1992. Three-and-two-halves issues only (numbered 1, 1-1/2, 2, 3 and 3-1/2); there may be more, but probably not while *Ansible* continues.

Twll-Ddu: personalzine of expressed existential horror at conventions, parties, cars, life, etc. Regarded as humorous except by critics. Hugo nominee. 20 issues since April 1976, but thought to be in suspended animation since March 1983. Issue 17 alias *Taff-Ddu* was a TAFF promotional special with Jim Barker as guest co-editor.

June 1996

UPDATES AT THE SECOND PRINTING

Two further fanwriter Hugo awards, 1996 and 1997.

A third Fanzine Hugo for *Ansible* in 1996.

The Encyclopedia of Fantasy ed. John Clute and John Grant, published 1997, with David Langford a contributing editor who wrote 80,000 words of entries.

The *PCW Plus* column ended with the magazine's demise, 1996.

Cloud Chamber continues in the Acnestis APA and reached issue 77 in September 1997.

September 1997